Video Encoding by the Numbers

By Jan Ozer

Doceo
Publishing, Inc.

Video Encoding by the Numbers

Eliminate the Guesswork From Your Streaming Video

Jan Ozer

Doceo Publishing
412 West Stuart Drive
Galax, VA 24333

www.streaminglearningcenter.com

ISBN 978-0-9984530-0-2

Printed in the United States of America

For Jack and Lillian

Proof that age is just a number
and that love isn't wasted on the young.

Acknowledgments

As with my previous books, I couldn't have written this one without the backing of the Streaming Media team—the seminars they've sponsored, the contacts they've fostered, and the various writing assignments that helped me become familiar with the products and technologies discussed herein. So to Eric Schumacher-Rasmussen, Steve Nathans-Kelly, Troy Dreier, Dan Rayburn, Dick Kaser, and Tom Hogan Jr. and Sr., thank you, thank you, thank you.

I also want to express my appreciation to the vendors that have provided hardware, software and bountiful technical assistance. These include Adobe, Beamr, Bitmovin, Capella Systems, Elemental Technologies, Google, HP, Hybrik, JW Player, Livestream, MainConcept, Microsoft, Moscow State University, MulticoreWare, NVIDIA, RealEyes Media, Sorenson Media, SSIMWave, Streamroot, Telestream, Wowza Media Systems, and I'm sure some that I've forgotten.

This book is the eighth published by my company, Doceo Publishing. As always, budgets are tight, time is short, and the topics are fast moving, so I apologize in advance for any rough edges. Any polish that you see is wholly attributable to my editor/proofreader Lucy Sutton, with the glitzy cover produced by Becky White.

As always, thanks to Pat Tracy for technical and marketing assistance.

Contents

Contents

Introduction

Figure 1. The old way of comparing compression technologies.

I have been encoding and comparing compression technologies and configurations for longer than I care to remember. For most of those years, I would compress using the various alternatives, play the compressed files side by side, and draw some conclusions regarding comparative quality. More recently, I began inserting the compressed files into a sequence in Adobe Premiere Pro that enabled the type of frame-by-frame comparison shown in Figure 1. In retrospect, it looks pretty primitive, but among reviewers in computer magazines and websites, I was doing more than the average bear.

I was aware of objective quality metrics like the peak signal-to-noise ratio (PSNR) and structural similarity (SSIM) index, but often the results of studies based on those metrics differed from my objective results. For example, the famous Moscow State University (MSU) H.264 codec comparison always found the x264 codec miles ahead of MainConcept, but the two were always much closer in my subjective comparisons. It's tough to believe a number when your eyeballs are telling you something different.

Then, in the summer of 2014, I began a consulting engagement that compared three compression technologies using 16 test clips in 10 different configurations of HEVC and H.264. If you run the numbers, that's more than 480 different comparisons. That's a lot of sequences to create in Premiere Pro, particularly because Premiere Pro couldn't import HEVC files at the time. It's also a lot of time spent poring over different sequences looking for differences that may or may not exist. Clearly, I needed to rethink my technique for comparing the technologies.

Earlier that summer, I had worked with the trial version of the MSU Video Quality Measurement Tool (VQMT) when comparing high-end encoders from Elemental Technologies and Telestream, and found results helpful. Since VQMT was the only reasonably priced ($995) objective quality analysis tool, I took a chance and bought the full retail version. From an analysis perspective, it's the best move I've ever made.

Not only were the results easier and faster to produce, they were much more credible (and dare I say impressive) for the client. As you'll see, using the Video Quality Metric (VQM) algorithm, the MSU tool was able to identify true differences between the various technologies, while providing an interface that let me see and verify them, and even show them to the client. You'll learn more about this shortly, and in Chapter 5 all about VQMT. Before I go too much further, however, let's explore what objective benchmarks actually are and what they do.

About Objective Quality Benchmarks

Without question, the gold standard in codec evaluations are comparison studies by actual human viewers. The problem with these kinds of studies are that they are expensive and cumbersome to administer. Objective benchmarks attempt to predict the results of these subjective comparisons, and they are rated on their ability to predict how subjective viewers will actually rate the videos they are comparing. This is shown in Figure 2, which is a math geek's dream. It looks intimidating, but only takes a second to explain and understand.

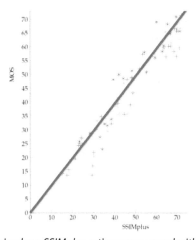

Figure 2. A scatter graph showing how SSIMplus ratings correspond with subjective MOS evaluations.

As you'll learn about later in the book, the SSIMplus algorithm is produced by the SSIMWave Video Quality-of-Experience Monitor (SQM). In Figure 2, the left axis shows the mean opinion score (MOS) of actual viewers on a scale from 0 to 100, while the bottom shows the SSIMplus rating, also on a scale from 0 to 100. Each plot in the scatter graph comprises two values: the

MOS score and the SSIMplus rating. The graph shows various ratings from tests performed with multiple files at multiple data rates.

Take a second and think. If the SSIMplus algorithm were perfect, the MOS score would exactly equal the SSIMplus rating at every point in the graph, which is represented by the blue line that I've added to the chart. While the plots aren't totally together, there is clearly a strong correspondence between the MOS score and the SSIMplus score.

This is particularly true when you compare SSIMplus with other metrics, like PSNR shown in Figure 3. Since the cluster around the line is much less distinct, it means less of a relationship between the objective quality metric and the actual subjective rating. Obviously, the more accurately an objective quality algorithm predicts subjective ratings, the more useful it is.

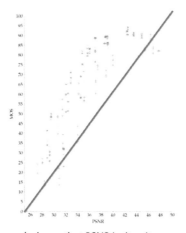

Figure 3. A scatter graph shows that PSNR isn't quite as accurate as SSIMplus.

Still, I used PSNR to influence or guide many decisions in this book. Why? Because as you'll read in the next section, in the admittedly limited test case I used to test all metrics, PSNR performed well. Also, as you'll see, Netflix still uses PSNR. And if it's good enough for Netflix, it's good enough for me.

Overview of Objective Benchmarks and Tools

All video quality metrics are used to predict how subjective viewers will rate the quality of the video being tested. As you'll read in this section, however, not all video quality metrics are created equal, and all aren't equally effective. However, at least in the one test detailed below, there may be less difference between the results than you might think.

Figure 4 is from a Tektronix White Paper titled "Understanding PQR, DMOS, and PSNR Measurements" (bit.ly/Tek_WP). It defines the key differentiators between simple math-based metrics like PSNR and SSIM, and more advanced metrics like Tektronix's Picture Quality Rating (PQR) and Difference Mean Opinion Score (DMOS) metrics.

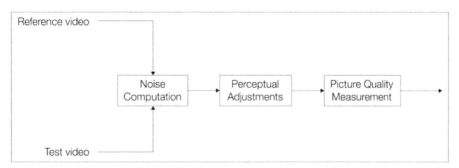

Figure 4. Differentiating simple and more advanced metrics.

According to the white paper, simple metrics like PSNR and SSIM are noise-based measurements that "compute the noise, or error, in the test video relative to the reference video." They measure the error in the test video, but in no way attempt to gauge how much an actual viewer would notice the error.

In contrast, more advanced metrics factor in perception adjustments that "use human vision system models to determine the perceptual contrast of the reference and test videos."

Table 1 details this and other differentiating features of several of the various metrics available to video developers. Across the top, the metrics are PSNR, VQM, the Multi-scale Structural Similarity Index (MS SSIM), SSIMplus, and the PQR and DMOS ratings from Tektronix. The table also lists features provided by the tool, rather than the metric.

	PSNR	VQM	MS SSIM	SSIMplus	PQR	DMOS
Basis	Error	Some Perceptual	Some Perceptual	More perceptual	More perceptual	More perceptual
Predictive Value	Fair	Good	Good	Very Good	Very Good	Very Good
Score Correlation	Ad hoc	No	No	Yes	Yes	Kind of
Tool Specific Features	Tek PQA	VQMT	VQMT	SQM	Tek PQA	Tek PQA
- Device Specific	in PQA	No	No	Yes	Yes	Yes
- Attention Weighting	in PQA	No	No	Yes - CLI	Yes	Yes
Cost	Free/$999	Free/$999	$999	~$4K	$19K	$19K

Table 1. Metric and tool features.

Let's briefly discuss the line items in the table and then we'll examine how each tool evaluated the single test case that I ran through all the metrics.

- **Basis.** This refers to the basis for the test. The simpler tests are primarily measure the raw error in the compressed file, while more advanced tests purport to measure perceptual differences as well.

- **Predictive value.** This is my perception of how well the tool predicts subjective ratings, which is impacted by tests presented by SSIMWave and Tektronix, as well as Netflix.

- **Score correlation.** By score correlation, I mean that the score correlates with presumed subjective ratings. For example, with SSIMplus, a score between 80 and 100 predicts that the viewer will subjectively rate the video as excellent. In contrast, while comparative VQM scores tell you which video looks better or worse, they don't predict how a viewer would subjectively rate the video. You can draw some inferences from the score, of course, but there's no designed correlation built into the metric.

- **Device specific.** Tools with this capability customize the score by the viewing device—for example rating videos differently depending upon whether they're viewed on a smartphone or 4K TV set. Obviously, this makes perfect sense, since a 640x360 video that looks great on a 4-inch smartphone screen would look pretty awful stretched to full screen on an 84-inch 4K TV set.

- **Attention weighted.** Tools with this capability rate the video based upon the region that the viewer is most likely to pay attention to. For example, if a talking-head video looked great in the face but a bit sketchy around the edges, an attention-weighted score would take this into account.

Our Test Case

To test all the tools, I encoded three files used throughout the book—Sintel, Talking Head, and Haunted—to 720p resolution at 1.5 Mbps using the Baseline, Main, and High profiles. I tested each file with the metrics listed in the table.

Peak Signal-to-Noise Ratio (PSNR)

PSNR is a simple metric that's based upon mean squared error (MSE), which measures the raw differences between the original and compressed frame in decibels (dB). I find the predictive value to be good, although generally it's considered to be among the least effective metrics in predicting subjective ratings. Most tools that compute PSNR don't enable device-specific sores or attention weighting, although the Tektronix PQA tool enables both. I used VQMT to compute PSNR.

While there's no direct correlation between score and subjective ratings, Netflix has said that scores under 35 dB will show encoding artifacts, while scores over 45 dB produce no perceptible quality improvements (bit.ly/nf_pt2).

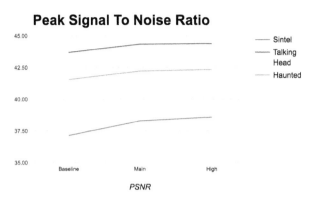

Figure 5. PSNR ratings for the three test videos. Higher scores are better.

Figure 5 shows PSNR scores for our test videos. Looking at these, I would be concerned that the Sintel video might show some artifacts in all profiles, and might boost the data rate if artifacts were present. The other two videos should be fine quality-wise. In terms of the quality difference between the profiles, PSNR found the most significant difference between the Baseline and Main profile, with only minor differences between the Main and High profiles.

Video Quality Metric (VQM)

VQM uses error calculations along with some perceptual adjustments, which you can read about at bit.ly/vqm_paper. Lower scores are better.

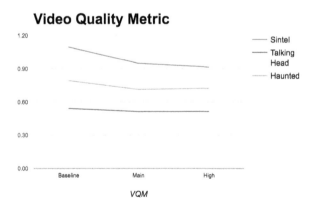

Figure 6. VQM ratings for the test videos. Lower scores are better.

I find VQM the most sensitive metric for differentiating the quality of two videos—although the lack of any correlation with actual subjective ratings limits its applicability to this book. That is, if comparative VQM scores showed a 50 percent difference in rating, but the comparative PSNR scores are 41 dB and 42 dB, VQM feels like much ado about nothing. As implemented in VQMT, VQM has neither device-specific capabilities nor attention weighting.

Looking at our test case, VQM found that the Sintel clip had the lowest overall quality. It also found a more significant qualitative difference between the Baseline and Main profiles than between the Main and High profiles. In short, very similar to PSNR.

Multi-scale Structural Similarity Metric (MS SSIM)

MS SSIM adds perceptual weighting to the heavily math-based SSIM metric, making it a better predictor of subjective ratings than purely math-based ratings. As implemented in VQMT, there is no device-specific capability, attention weighting, or direct correlation with subjective ratings. Higher scores indicate higher quality.

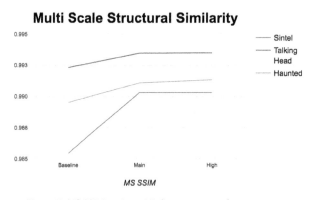

Figure 7. MS SSIM ratings. Higher scores are better.

How did MS SSIM rate our test videos? More of the same. Like the other two ratings, MS SSIM rated Sintel the lowest, and found the most significant difference between the Baseline and Main profile, with much less difference between Main and High. Once again, it's hard to draw any conclusions about subjective ratings or artifacts from these results.

SSIMplus

SSIMplus is another advancement of the basic SSIM metric with even more perceptual advancements which make it a very good predictor of subjective MOS evaluations (see Figure 2). In addition, SSIMplus is the first metric where the score correlates with predicted subjective ratings. That is, scores from 80 to 100 predict an excellent rating, 60 to 80 a good rating, 40 to 60 a poor rating, and so on down the line. This correlation obviously makes it simple to apply the metric since you know exactly the quality level it predicts.

Beyond correlation, the SSIMplus algorithm, as produced by SSIMWave Video Quality-of-Experience Monitor (SQM), offers two new features. First is a device-specific rating that you'll read more about in Chapter 6. This means a video will get different ratings for a smartphone than a 4K big-screen TV set, which obviously makes perfect sense.

In addition, in the command-line version of SQM, you can also access attention weighting features that allow you to minimize lower quality in certain regions in the video. Again this makes perfect sense, as we don't notice poor quality at the edges of the video as much as we do in the middle.

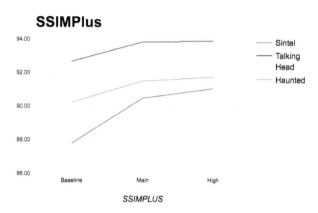

Figure 8. SSIMplus scores for our three test videos. Higher scores are better.

What does SSIMplus tell us about our three videos? Higher scores are better, and as you can see in Figure 8, again Sintel is the lowest-quality video. Once again, we see the largest quality disparity between Baseline and Main Profiles, with much less differential between Main and High profiles. If you overlaid SSIMplus with MS SSIM, the difference wouldn't be that great at all.

On the other hand, since any score over 80 predicts an excellent rating, all of these videos should be fine from a quality perspective. From this, we can conclude that most viewers wouldn't notice any improvement from using the High profile over the Baseline.

Picture Quality Rating

The Picture Quality Rating was introduced by Tektronix in its PQA analysis tool. Like the next metric, it enjoys attention weighting and device-specific scores. Conceptually, the PQR metric centers around the concept of a just noticeable difference. Scores range from 0 to 100, with lower scores being better. According to the rating system, however, each PQR score is one Just Noticeable Difference (JND) apart. When interpreting comparative scores, Tektronix tells us in the aforementioned white paper (bit.ly/Tek_WP) that one JND is very hard to distinguish, but that 90 percent of viewers will discern differences in videos if they are two JND apart. At three JND, 100 percent of the viewers will tell them apart.

Figure 9. PQR ratings. Lower scores are better.

What does Figure 9 tell us? At a high level, Sintel has the worst quality and Talking Head the best. The difference in scores are greater between Baseline and Main than between Main and High, but no differential comes close to even one JND, much less the two necessary for 90 percent recognition. In short, not much of a difference between any of the settings in any of the videos.

Attention Weighted Difference Mean Opinion Score (AW DMOS)

AW DMOS is designed to directly predict the results of subjective evaluations by human eyes. That is, during subjective tests, subjects rank video quality on a scale from 0 to 100, with lower scores being better. So the excellent region is 0 to 20, while the bad region is between 80 and 100.

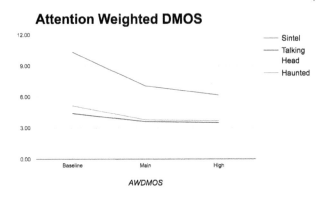

Figure 10. AW DMOS ratings. Lower scores are better.

What does Figure 10 tell us about our three videos and nine test cases? Again, lower scores are better, so Sintel has the worst quality—although all test cases fall comfortably in the excellent range. And again, the difference in quality between the Baseline and Main profiles was less than that between Main and High profiles.

Overall, while there are clearly minor differences between the relative scores of the metrics, the most important findings are consistent. Sintel has the worst quality of the three videos, and the qualitative difference between the Baseline and Main profile is more significant than that of Main and High profiles.

Netflix VMAF

In June 2016, Netflix introduced its own quality metric called the Video Multimethod Assessment Fusion (VMAF) (bit.ly/nf_vmaf), which replaced PSNR in the per-title encoding scheme you'll read about in Chapter 16. Of course, the fact that Netflix replaced PSNR in June 2016 didn't automatically convert it from useful to useless; before then, Netflix had made literally millions of encoding decisions based upon PSNR.

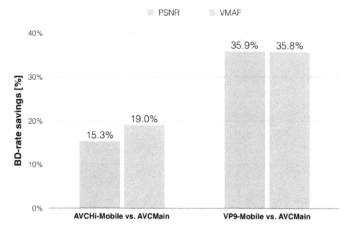

Figure 11. Data rate savings produced by Netflix's new mobile encoding techniques as measured by PSNR and VMAF.

As you can see in Figure 11, as late as December 2016 (and probably later), Netflix continues to present qualitative results in both VMAP and PSNR (bit.ly/mo_eff_mobile). Here, Netflix researchers showed the bitrate savings realized by their new mobile-oriented encoding techniques (AVCHi-Mobile/VP9-Mobile) against how they formerly encoded mobile videos (AVCMain). On the left, according to PSNR, AVCHi-Mobile saved 15.3 percent versus AVCMain, compared with 19 percent according to VMAF. On the right in the figure, VP9-Mobile saved 35.9 percent versus AVCMain according to PSNR, compared with 35.8 percent for VMAF. Not much of a difference in either case.

The bottom line is that while PSNR isn't technically the "best" metric out there, it is the most accessible, including via FFmpeg, which is a big focus of this book. In the land of the blind, the one-eyed man is king. It makes little sense not to use a benchmark at all just because it's not the most technically sophisticated. In addition, as we saw in the limited testing above, PSNR seems perfectly well suited for the simple, "Which technique is best?" discussion that dominates this book. Even by Netflix's numbers, it remains pretty accurate.

What about my earlier caveat about objective quality metrics sometime disagreeing with my subjective conclusions? What I love about the MSU tool is that it identifies where the problem areas are and lets me visually confirm the tool's objective findings. You'll learn all about that in Chapter 5, but if you want a quick demonstration, take a look at the YouTube video at bit.ly/VQMT2_5v6_5. What makes the MSU tool so useful is that it gives me the numbers, and the ability to verify them. The key to successfully using objective metrics is like the old Ronald Reagan truism to trust but verify.

The bottom line is that in this book, I use PSNR, VQM and SSIMplus early, but transition almost exclusively to PSNR towards the end. SSIMplus still figures heavily in my consulting work, but I wanted to use the metrics most relevant to the largest number of readers.

How to Use Objective Metrics

How can a compressionist use objective quality benchmarks? Perhaps a more accurate question is how could we ever live without them?

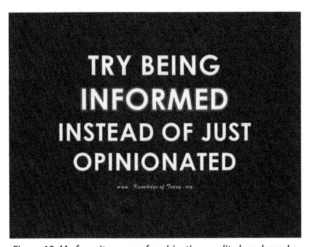

Figure 12. My favorite meme for objective quality benchmarks.

Each encoding professional makes dozens if not hundreds of compression-related decisions every time he or she encodes a file. Absent the application of objective quality benchmarks, these decisions are largely based upon opinion. Opinion is great, but when I'm advising clients, or evaluating a product or technique for publication, I want facts. In keeping with a meme (Figure 12), objective quality benchmarks let me be informed, rather than just opinionated.

How to Use this Book

I wrote this book to serve three classes of readers. The first class wants to learn how to use objective quality measurement tools and apply them in their own practices. For this class of reader, I include detailed descriptions of how to use to objective quality measurement programs, as well as detailed procedures for the tests performed throughout this book.

The second class of reader will simply apply the results shown in this book to their own compression practices. For example, if you're looking for the optimal data rate for 1080p mezzanine files to upload to an online video platform, the best key frame interval for animated files, or which x264 preset to use, you'll find the answers herein. The answers will be based upon fact, not opinion, and you'll find the test procedures useful in determining how to apply the results.

Because different types of clips encode differently and may need different encoding parameters, I used eight different videos for most tests performed herein. You can see their names and descriptions in Table 2, which is also Table 7-1. As you can see, these videos included simple and complex animations, movies, concerts, talking heads, and videos from screencam capture and converted PowerPoint presentations. So whether you're encoding for Hollywood or for the corporate training room, you should find useful guidance throughout the book.

CRF23	Frame Rate	Description	Data Rate	SQM	Overall PSNR	Low PSNR
Tears of Steel	24	Movie	4,485	94.28	41.71	36.96
Sintel	24	Complex animation	5,002	94.45	41.53	34.36
Big Buck Bunny	30	Simpler animation	3,375	95.91	43.64	32.62
Screencam	30	Camtasia	1,200	98.83	46.85	36.06
Tutorial	30	PowerPoint and talking head	690	97.93	47.28	41.49
Talking Head	30	Simple talking head	2,638	93.24	44.09	40.58
Freedom	30	Concert	5,467	91.56	41.87	38.63
Haunted	30	DSLR movie-like production	6,064	92.05	42.23	36.74

Table 2. Most tests considered eight different videos.

My one caveat is that different encoding tools and different codecs encoding different test clips may produce results different from those shown in the book. While I think the results shown herein are very useful for general-purpose guidance, if you want to seriously fine-tune your own settings, the best approach is to use your own test clips in your own encoding tool.

The third group of readers are those who want to use FFmpeg for their encoding. You really can't use objective quality metrics without FFmpeg for the conversions and scalings that are often necessary. Once you get to know FFmpeg, you learn that it's the ideal tool for many applications, and the x264 codec that it deploys is clearly the world's best. Rather than rely upon an application for my test encodes, I decided to use the encoder deployed by Netflix, YouTube, and most other large video distributors that encode their own video. Once I decided to use FFmpeg, it was a short step to decide to include what I learned about the tool in this book.

What's in this Book?

Let's run through the chapters to give you a feel for what's available and where.

Section I: Introduction

Chapter 1: Technology Fundamentals. While the book is targeted towards intermediate to advanced compressionists, I cover encoding basics like codecs and container formats for newbies, or for a quick refresher for advanced users.

Chapter 2: Basic File Parameters. Sounds silly, but I logically couldn't start talking about how to use objective quality metrics without describing file parameters like data rate, resolution, frame rate, and bits per-pixel. Here I define them at a high level, in later chapters you'll learn how to customize them with information gleaned from your objective quality metrics.

Chapter 3: Essential Tools. Beyond the objective metrics themselves, there are several tools that deliver file information that you simply can't live without, like MediaInfo, Bitrate Viewer, and Telestream Switch. In this chapter you'll learn what these tools do and where to get them.

Chapter 4: Testing Overview. Like video compression itself, objective testing is a garbage-in/garbage-out medium. If you start with bad inputs, you'll end up with worthless results. This chapter covers a range of testing procedures, from choosing a test clip to verifying your encodes before applying the metric.

Chapter 5: Working with MSU VQMT. This tool has quickly become absolutely essential to me and my encoding practice and in this chapter you'll learn why, and how to use it most efficiently.

Chapter 6: Working with SQM. SQM has several features that VQMT doesn't offer, including the ability to rate quality by playback device. It's an expensive tool at over $3,000, but I've found it very valuable in my encoding practice.

Section II: General Application

Chapter 7: Choosing Data Rate. Now that you know how to use multiple objective benchmarks, we'll start to apply that knowledge to learn how to choose file data rates. You'll also learn how to use constant rate factor (CRF) encoding, a mode in the x264 codec (and VP9/x265) to assist your data rate decisions.

Chapter 8: Bitrate Control. You choose between constant bitrate encoding (CBR) and variable bitrate encoding (VBR) based upon three factors; overall file quality, transient quality, and file deliverability. In this chapter you'll learn the impact of your bitrate control technique on all three. If you have only one chapter to read in this book, this should be it.

Chapter 9: I-, B-, P-, and Reference Frames. Rules for choosing key frame and B-frame interval, and the number of reference frames, by video type and by type of deployment (single file or adaptive).

Section III: Codec-specific Application

Chapter 10: Encoding H.264. This chapter covers H.264 specific instruction like royalties, entropy encoding, and how quality varies among the various H.264 codecs.

Chapter 11: Encoding HEVC. This chapter covers the HEVC royalty situation; where you can consider using HEVC and where you shouldn't; how the various HEVC codecs compare quality-wise; and how to encode with x265, a high-quality, open-source HEVC codec.

Chapter 12: Encoding VP9. This chapter details where VP9 plays (everywhere), how quality compares with that of HEVC and H.264, and how to encode VP9 with FFmpeg. You'll also learn that VP9 will soon be replaced by a codec called AV1, from the Alliance for Open Media—a response to the slow, muddled, and overly expensive royalty policies proffered by HEVC patent owners.

Section IV: Multiple-screen Adaptive Bitrate Delivery

Chapter 13: Choosing an ABR Technology. This chapter identifies the technologies you'll need to deliver to computers, mobile devices, OTT devices like Roku and Apple TV, and smart TVs, like HTTP Live Streaming (HLS), Dynamic Adaptive Streaming over HTTP (DASH), and others. In particular, you'll learn about the transition from Flash to HTML5 on computers, and the various components of HTML5, including Media Source Extensions and Encrypted Media Extensions.

Chapter 14: Configuring Your Encoding Ladder. This chapter walks you through how to choose the rungs on your adaptive bitrate ladder, and issues like whether to use one ladder for all targets, or a different ladder for each target.

Chapter 15: Encoding and Packaging ABR Streams. So you've chosen your ABR technology and created your encoding ladder; now it's time to encode. In this chapter, you'll learn how to use FFmpeg to create your encoding ladder, and create media and master playlists for your HLS streams. You'll also get an extensive look at the Apple tools for HLS creation, Media File Segmenter, Variant Playlist Creator, and Media Stream Validator. For DASH, you'll learn how to use open-source tool MP4Box to do the same. You'll also learn when to consider workflows like dynamic packaging that can save big bucks in high-volume encoding operations.

Chapter 16: Per-title Encoding. You'll learn early on that every video is different and really requires a unique encoding ladder. In December 2015, Netflix introduced its per-title encoding algorithm, which does just that. YouTube followed soon thereafter, as did one commercial application, Capella Systems Cambria. You'll learn what per-title encoding is, how it works, and several techniques for applying it yourself—including capped CRF.

However you attempt to apply the knowledge learned from this book, welcome. I hope you find it truly useful.

Chapter 1: Technology Fundamentals

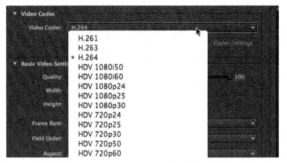

Figure 1-1. Choosing a video codec in Adobe Media Encoder.

This book is generally targeted towards intermediate to advanced compressionists, but I didn't want to exclude precocious beginners so I'm including this and the next chapter to discuss technology fundamentals and basic file parameters. Many readers will be able to skip over these and jump in with Chapter 3 on Essential Tools.

In this chapter, I'll define streaming-related terms and concepts so you can follow the more technical conversations to follow. Specifically, you will learn:

- about compression and codecs

- how to choose the right codec

- what a container format is and why you care

- the difference between progressive download, streaming, and adaptive streaming.

Since the concept of compression is absolutely pervasive to all streaming media, we'll start with a quick look at the definition of codecs and compression. We're not going deep here, just providing a high-level view so you can understand the basics and the strengths and weaknesses of the technology alternatives we'll be considering throughout the rest of the chapter.

Compression and Codecs

As you probably know, video files are very bulky, which is why full-length HD Hollywood movies are delivered on Blu-ray discs that can store 25 to 50 GB of information. Compression is a technology that shrinks your audio/video streams down to sizes that you can deliver to desktop and mobile viewers. Compression is also the technology that can make your video ugly when you apply too much of it—as Figure 1-2, a frame from a video of my eldest daughter, shows.

Figure 1-2. Too much compression makes your videos look ugly.

That's because all video compression technologies are lossy, which means they throw away information during compression. Upon decompression, lossy technologies create only an approximation of the original frame, not an exact replica. The more you compress, the more information gets thrown away and the worse the approximation looks. Obviously, we threw away too much data in the frame shown on the right in Figure 1-2.

What's a Codec?

If you've messed around with compression in the past, you've probably heard the term "codec." Simply stated, codecs are compression technologies with two components: an enCOder to compress the file in your studio or office and a DECoder to decode the file when played by the remote viewer. As the nifty capitalization in the previous sentence suggests, the term codec is a contraction of the terms "encoder" and "decoder."

There are lot of video codecs—like H.264, H.265, MPEG-4, VP8, VP9, MPEG-2 and MPEG-1—and lots of audio codecs—like MP3 and Advanced Audio Coding (AAC). What are the primary video codes today? Let's run through them very quickly, with Table 1-1 as a summary.

Codec	H.264/ AVC	H.265/ HEVC	VP8	VP9	MPEG-4	MPEG-2
Date first available	2003	2013	2010	2013	1995	1998
Originator	ISO/MPEG	IOS/MPEG	Google	Google	MPEG	MPEG
Compression efficiency	The baseline reference	2x H.264	Same as H.264	2x H.264	.75x H.264	.5x H.264
Typical resolution	Up to 1080p	Up to 4K	Up to 1080p	Up to 4K	SD	SD, but up to 1080p
Typical use	Everywhere	SmartTVs and 4K	Browser/ YouTube	Browser/ YouTube	Very old phones	DVD, broadcast
Royalty status	Encumbered	Encumbered	Open source	Open source	Encumbered	Encumbered

Table 1-1. The most commonly used video codecs.

This discussion uses terms like "resolution" and "data rate," which we'll define in the next chapter.

H.264/AVC (Advanced Video Coding). Today's "it codec," H.264 plays almost everywhere (in Flash, Silverlight, in most browsers, virtually all mobile and TV-related platforms), so is as close to a universal video codec as is available today. H.264 is a joint standard formulated by two standards bodies, the International Organization for Standardization (ISO) and Moving Picture Experts Group (MPEG). That's why it has two names: H.264 and Advanced Video Coding (AVC). H.264 is typically used at up to 1080p resolution, although it can extend beyond 1080p. As you'll learn more about in Chapter 10, it is encumbered by patents so royalties apply for some uses.

H.265/HEVC (High Efficiency Video Coding). H.265/HEVC is the standards-based successor to H.264/AVC that plays primarily on 4K TVs—although Android 5 includes a software decoder and the iPhone 5+ uses HEVC for FaceTime video. Usage is very restricted for general-purpose streaming (at least in 2016) because of the lack of a generally available decoder. This is primarily because the royalty picture is cloudy but potentially quite expensive. H.265 is roughly twice as efficient as H.264, which means the same video quality at about 50 percent the data rate of H.264. You'll learn about HEVC in Chapter 11.

VP8. Google's open-source competitor to H.264, which delivers about the same quality. VP8 came from technology purchased from a company called On2 Technologies. It was used almost exclusively by YouTube until it was replaced by VP9 in 2014.

VP9. Google's open-source competitor to H.265, which delivers about the same quality. The successor to VP8 that was almost exclusively used by YouTube until mid 2016, when several other companies started to leverage the bandwidth savings the technology affords over H.264. You'll learn about VP9 in Chapter 12.

MPEG-4. A standards-based video codec about 25 percent less efficient than H.264 that has been supplanted by H.264 except for very old devices.

MPEG-2. An older standards-based codec created for broadcast and DVD. It's still very widely used in broadcast applications, but hardly ever for streaming. MPEG-2 is about half as efficient as H.264, which means that to achieve the same quality you would need to encode at double the data rate.

A couple of other codecs are worth mentioning for completeness's sake. On2's VP6 was the codec that powered Adobe Flash until it was supplanted by H.264 in 2006. Ogg Theora was the codec that powered HTML5 video until Google launched VP8, which made Ogg disappear overnight like a magic trick (never did like Ogg). Looking ahead, the AV1 codec from the Alliance for Open Media should debut in early 2017, and it will slowly replace VP9 in many applications. You'll learn about AV1 in Chapter 12.

I place only minimal attention on audio in this book, but you should know the following:

Advanced Audio Coding (AAC). AAC audio codecs are used with the H.264, H.265, and MPEG-4 video codecs.

Opus codec. Opus is the audio codec used with VP8 and VP9.

MPEG-1, Layer II Audio Coding. This is the audio compression typically used with MPEG-2 video compression. Not to be confused with MPEG-1, Layer III Audio Coding, which is more commonly referred to as MP3.

As you can see in Figure 1-1, choosing a codec is the first choice you make when compressing a file. Of course, you can't compress a file without choosing the compression technology. How do you choose a video codec? Well, there are multiple factors.

Choosing a Codec

First, when you target a particular distribution platform like computers or mobile, you have to make sure that platform includes the ability to decode the files you're about to send them. For example, iPhones play H.264 video, but not MPEG-2 or H.265 (at least not in early 2016). If you want video to play on an iPhone, encode it using the H.264 codec. In fact, H.264 is as close to a universal codec as we have in this world. It plays in Flash, in Silverlight, in most browsers, on all mobile and over the top (OTT) platforms like Roku, on Apple TV, and on all smart TVs.

Beyond compatibility, you have to consider suitability for a particular purpose. For example, most smart TVs can play H.264 and H.265, but H.265 is more efficient for 4K video than H.264. So Netflix, Hulu, Amazon, and other companies targeting these TV sets use H.265. Most of these sets also play VP9. I would expect many of these services to cut over to VP9 in 2017 and beyond.

What about environments that play back multiple codecs? For example, Google Chrome plays H.264, VP8, and VP9—and probably Ogg for that matter. Which should you use? Since it costs money to encode your video into different codecs, you should start with H.264, which plays everywhere, and then deploy VP9 or H.265 when the bandwidth savings more than cover the extra cost of encoding.

For example, in 2016, JW Player started deploying VP9-encoded video in their online video platform, in addition to H.264. That's because VP9 was able to cut their data rate by about 50 percent, reducing costs and allowing them to send higher-resolution videos to viewers on lower-bandwidth connections. You can read about this in my Streaming Media article titled "VP9 Finally Comes of Age, But Is it Right for Everyone?," at bit.ly/JWP_VP9.

Choosing the Container Format

Another fundamental decision you make when encoding a file is the container format, which is likely a concept you know, but may not know you know (not to go all Donald Rumsfeld on you). Let's start with an easy one. When you see a file with a .docx extension, you think Microsoft Word. Although a .docx file can contain exactly the same content as a .txt or .rtf file, it's stored a bit differently in each. So you may not be able to open a .docx file in a simple text editor, and if you can, the text might look a bit strange. In a .docx file, the content is the text, and how the data is stored within the file is the container format.

If you see a file with a .mov extension, you probably think QuickTime file, which means that the data within the file is stored in a way that the QuickTime Player, and products built around the QuickTime standard, understand. In these cases, the video in the file is the content, and QuickTime is the container format.

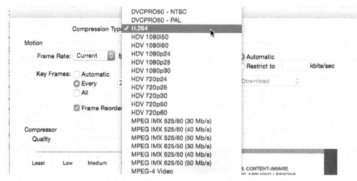

Figure 1-3. You can output multiple different codecs in a QuickTime file with a .mov extension.

What's critical to understand is that a container format is separate from the codec. You can see this in Figure 1-3, the standard video compression settings screen from QuickTime Pro. While you can create the file with all the compression technologies shown, each file would have a .mov extension. The codec is how the video is compressed, while the container format controls how that compressed data is stored within the file.

Wikipedia defines a contained format as a "meta-file format whose specification describes how data and metadata are stored." Fortunately, you don't need to know the technical details of each container format you use, you just need to know which container format to use when delivering a file to your different targets. With most encoding tools, you don't even need to know what that container format is; you just need to choose the right target.

You can see this in Figure 1-4, a screenshot from Sorenson Squeeze. Here I've selected output for HTTP Live Streaming (HLS), which as you may know is the adaptive streaming technology used to deliver video to iPhones, iPads, and other Apple devices. HLS uses MPEG-2 transport streams for delivery, which have a .ts extension. Squeeze knows this, so when I choose the HLS preset, it outputs files in the proper container format (MPEG TS Adaptive Streaming).

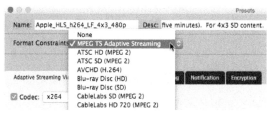

Figure 1-4. When I choose HLS, Squeeze knows to output MPEG Transport Streams.

We discuss the container formats necessary to deliver to different platforms in Chapters 13 and 15. What you need to know now is that container formats are different than codecs, and that different container formats can contain video encoded using the same codecs. So, the MPEG-2 Transport Stream used in HLS can (actually, must) contain H.264-encoded video, and so can fragmented MP4 files used in the Dynamic Adaptive Streaming over HTTP (DASH) standard. In fact, both can use the same compressed H.264 video, which makes it simple to switch from one container to the other.

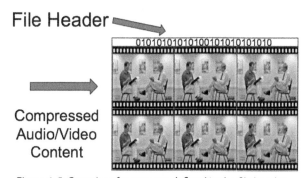

Figure 1-5. Container formats are defined in the file header.

This is shown in Figure 1-5, which represents the container format as the zeros and ones in the file header, and the H.264 encoded video as the cute frames below, which comprises the vast bulk of the video file. The fact that the file header controls the container format makes it very simple to convert from one container format to another because you simply have to manipulate zeros and ones in the file header; you don't touch the compressed audio and video at all. This concept is called transmuxing (or dynamic packaging) and we'll talk about it more in Chapter 15.

While we're in definition mode, let's cover a few additional concepts.

Distribution Alternatives

When deploying web video technologies, it's important to recognize that they offer varying delivery options, including progressive download, streaming, and adaptive streaming. Since these techniques are critical to streaming operation, let's describe how they work.

Progressive Download

Video delivered via progressive download is delivered by a regular HTTP web server rather than a streaming server. Since the video is delivered just like any other file on the website—be it a large graphic or a large PDF file—it's delivered as quickly as possible, as opposed to metering out the video as it's being watched.

This is shown in Figure 1-6. On the left is Firefox, showing a video playing back from the user-generated-content (UGC) website Vimeo. On the upper right is a streaming video capture tool called Jaksta. On the bottom right is the file location where Jaksta is storing the files.

Figure 1-6. Although I'm just 59 seconds into this 8:29 video, the download is complete.

In the player window in the browser on the left, you can see that I'm only 59 seconds into the file, but Jaksta shows that the download is complete and the video file is stored on my local hard drive—a total of about 52 MB. If I stopped watching 59 seconds in, about 89 percent of that transfer, or 46 MB, would be wasted. This boosts Vimeo's bandwidth costs and can degrade quality of service, because while Vimeo was busy delivering the video to me as quickly as possible, it may not have had the capacity to deliver video to others.

In most instances, video delivered via progressive download is stored on the viewer's hard drive as it's received, and then it's played from the hard drive. Since the video is in a standard MP4 format, this makes it very easy to copy.

Streaming

The technical definition of "streaming" is video delivered as it's needed. Traditionally, this was accomplished via streaming servers like the Adobe Media Server (formerly Adobe Flash Media Server), Wowza Media Server and other similar products. More recently, this has been enabled for videos distributed without a streaming server, as you'll learn about in Chapter 14 when we detail how adaptive streaming works.

You can see this concept in Figure 1-7, which shows the same three windows as the previous figure, but a file streamed from Bloomberg.com rather than Vimeo. At the time I captured this screen, Bloomberg delivered its videos via a streaming server that used the RTMP delivery protocol, which is falling out of favor with Flash—although the specific protocol isn't important to this discussion.

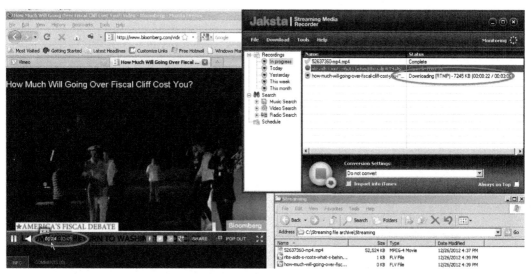

Figure 1-7. The Bloomberg media server is doling out the video as the viewer is watching it.

What is important is that the server doles out the video in chunks as necessary to support the viewer's continued watching. On the lower left of the figure, you see that video playback is at 24 seconds, while the upper right shows Jaksta has finished downloading a chunk starting 22 seconds in. If the viewer stopped watching at this point, very little extra bandwidth would have been wasted. In addition, this metered delivery schema is much more efficient for maintaining a high quality of service to large numbers of viewers than the progressive download approach.

> **Note:** *You can see a video tutorial showing both distribution techniques at bit.ly/prog_rtmp. This video is also the source of the two preceding figures, so it should look immediately familiar.*

Adaptive Bitrate (ABR) Streaming

Both progressive download and traditional streaming use a single encoded file. In contrast, adaptive bitrate (ABR) streaming technologies encode a single live or on-demand file into multiple streams with varying configurations and switches them adaptively based upon changing line conditions and other variables. When the connection is good, the viewer gets a high-quality, high-data-rate stream. But if connection speed drops, the server will send a lower-data-rate file to ensure a continuous connection—albeit at lower quality. Adaptive streaming provides the best of all possible worlds: great-quality video for those with the connection speed to retrieve it (and the CPU required to play it back) and a passable-quality stream for those with Wi-Fi, mobile or other slow connections or those watching on lower-power devices.

Figure 1-8, a slide from a presentation by Akamai's Will Law, shows why ABR streaming is superior to single bitrate (SBR) streaming. Basically, if you choose a single stream, it will be perfect for the users who can retrieve at exactly that bandwidth. But 99.9 percent of other users will either have too little bandwidth, resulting in buffering, or sufficient bandwidth to download a higher-quality version, so their experience is suboptimal. Not surprisingly, nearly all premium content delivered over the Internet today is delivered via ABR streaming.

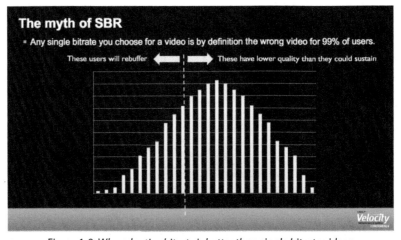

Figure 1-8. Why adaptive bitrate is better than single bitrate videos.

Interestingly, most ABR technologies use progressive download to deliver a streaming-like experience from an efficiency perspective. That is, these technologies break each file into segments between 2 and 6 seconds long, and then upload them to a website. Using techniques described in Chapter 14, the player is in charge of locating and downloading the right chunks. If the viewer stops watching after 30 seconds or so, the player won't download any additional chunks, so very little download bandwidth is wasted.

As you'll learn about in Chapter 13, there are multiple adaptive streaming alternatives today, including the aforementioned HLS and DASH, as well as Adobe's Dynamic Streaming (either RTMP or HTTP), and Microsoft's Smooth Streaming. However, supporting multiple adaptive streaming technologies is not as complex as it sounds. That's because many products, like Wowza Streaming Engine, can convert a set of files from one adaptive format to another. Specifically, as described above in the section on container formats, these products simply change the container format as necessary for the respective formats, and create any required metadata files.

OK, that's enough background for one chapter. In the next, we'll cover basic file details like resolution, frame rate, and data rate.

Chapter 2: Basic File Parameters

Figure 2-1. The A, B, and C of file encoding.

Whenever you encode a file, you first have to choose your audio and video codecs, which I covered last chapter. Next, as suggested in Figure 2-1 from Sorenson Squeeze, you have to choose resolution (or frame size), frame rate, and data rate—the A, B, and C of file encoding.

Most readers know these parameters, so I'll only cover them briefly, but I want to focus on their interplay. Basically, you can't set any one of these parameters without knowing the setting for the other two. One of the most useful concepts in streaming production is bits per pixel, a single number based upon the relationship between resolution, frame rate, and data rate.

In this chapter, you will learn:

- the definitions and applicability of the terms resolution, frame rate and data rate

- what bits per pixel is and why you care

- how to set resolution, frame rate, and data rate (or bitrate) in FFmpeg—a complete, cross-platform solution to record, convert, and stream audio and video.

Note that I'll introduce you to these parameters in this chapter. Once you get through the next four chapters on creating test files, objective quality measurement tools, and analysis tools, we'll take a closer look at these same parameters. Let's get started.

Overview

Last chapter, you learned about adaptive streaming and met Apple's HTTP Live Streaming (HLS), an adaptive streaming scheme that dominates mobile and over-the-top (OTT) platforms. Apple provides specific encoding recommendations for HLS in a document titled "HLS Authoring Specification for Apple Devices" which you can find at bit.ly/A_Devices_Spec. For your convenience, I've copied a snippet from the 16:9 recommendations into Table 2-1, below.

Video average bit rate (kb/s)	Resolution	Frame rate
145	416 x 234	≤ 30 fps
365	480 x 270	≤ 30 fps
730	640 x 360	≤ 30 fps
1100	768 x 432	≤ 30 fps
2000	960 x 540	same as source
3000	1280 x 720	same as source
4500	same as source	same as source
6000	same as source	same as source
7800	same as source	same as source

Table 2-1. Encoding recommendations from Apple.

As you would expect, the Apple spec details file parameters like resolution, frame rate, and bitrate (also called data rate). That's because these three parameters are absolutely essential to video quality. Mess up any one of these, and quality will be irreparably compromised. Get them right, and you have a foundation for excellent quality.

So these are the foundational building blocks of video quality. As compressionists, we identify the optimal resolution, frame rate, and video bitrate for each standalone file, or stream within an adaptive group, and plug them into an encoding program to produce our files. While all encoding programs look different, they all let you configure these same basic options.

Understanding what these configuration options are and how they interrelate will allow you to make better, more informed decisions, and avoid some potholes. So let's start with the first configuration item in the Apple document: dimensions, or more commonly called resolution.

A couple of thoughts before we move on. First, regarding the Apple spec, very few producers follow the recommendations completely as is. Most adjust them one way or the other, usually because the bitrates are quite high, and more than necessary for acceptable quality.

Finally, the concept of a single encoding "ladder" for all videos has been eclipsed by per-title or per-category encoding, at least in theory. Basically, there are multiple types of videos—like cartoons or more complex animations, talk shows, action movies, screencams, etc—and they all encode differently. To get the most efficient results, this means that you should encode them using different parameters. Although it's nascent at this point, per-title encoding is the clear wave of the future. You'll learn how to dip your toe in the water in Chapter 16.

Video Resolution

Resolution is the height and width of the video in pixels (Figure 2-2). Most video is originally captured at 720x480 (NTSC Standard Definition) or 720x576 (PAL standard definition); 1280x720 or 1920x1080 (high-definition); or 2820x2160 or higher (ultra-high definition).

Figure 2-2. Resolution is the width and height of pixels in the file.

However, often these high-resolution files get scaled to smaller resolutions for streaming. This scaling reduces the number of pixels being encoded, making the file easier to compress while retaining good quality. For example, a 640x360 video has 230,400 pixels in each frame, while a 1280x720 video file has 921,600 pixels—or four times as many, as shown in Figure 2-3.

Referring back to Table 2-1, this is why Apple recommends dropping to lower resolutions as bitrates decrease. While you're losing resolution and some detail, you're avoiding the kind of gross blockiness and other artifacts that mar overly compressed video files, like that shown on the right in Figure 1-2 last chapter.

Figure 2-3. Scaling a file to lower resolution reduces the number of pixels.

A Brief Word About Mod-16

Many compressionists recommend using what's called a mod-16 resolution, where both the width and height parameters for each stream are divisible by 16. Why? Because most codecs, including H.264, encode in 16x16 blocks. If the height and width aren't divisible by 16, the codec will create the full block anyway, adding more pixels to the file. This adds data that needs to be compressed to the file.

For example, a 16x16 video file would require one 16x16 block to encode. But an 18x18 video file would require four: one extra on the right and bottom to encode the extra pixels and one on the lower right to square out the video stream. These extra blocks and pixels are automatically cropped during display, so you never see them, but the pixels must be compressed nonetheless.

Obviously, this is a worst-case scenario, and there are two schools of thought on mod-16. One treats non-mod-16 streams like "ring around the collar," evidencing a total lack of sophistication on the part of the compressionist. However, there are some very relevant arguments against the importance of mod-16. First, not all mod-16 resolutions are a perfect 16:9 aspect ratio, forcing the compressionist to either crop pixels or adapt a non-16:9 aspect ratio, which distorts the video—however slightly. Second, the extra pixels are always at the edges, so the encoder can apply less data to these blocks without a noticeable loss in quality.

In addition, the importance of mod-16 resolutions decreases as the resolution increases because extra 16x16 blocks end up making up less of the total picture. For example, former Microsoft employee Alex Zambelli (now with Hulu), who helped configure the stream resolutions for

NBC's Olympics and Sunday Night Football streaming presentations, offered this observation. Using 320x176 (mod-16) versus 320x180 yields a 9 percent efficiency advantage. But 1920x1072 (mod-16) versus 1920x1080 yields only a 1.5 percent improvement. So as your streams get larger, mod-16 becomes less and less important.

Finally, 640x360 is the most widely used stream resolution in existence today, and it isn't mod-16. In fact, none of the resolutions below 768x432 in Table 2-1 are mod-16, which wouldn't be the case if the lack of mod-16 compliance significantly degraded quality. When theory clashes with reality, go with reality. Here's what Zambelli had to say regarding his Olympics and Sunday Night Football encodes:

> Most resolutions are mod-16, but in some cases, we had to settle for mod-8 or mod-4 to match a video resolution to a particular video player window size. For example, 720x404 was the Sunday Night Football player video window size, so we matched it with one of the encoded resolutions in order to ensure it played optimally without requiring any scaling.

In summary, when configuring your video, try using a mod-16 configuration. If mod-16 won't work, try mod-8, where both height and width are divisible by eight. Note that some encoding tools prohibit encoding with odd numbers of pixels, or at mod-2 configurations and below.

Frame Rate

Most video starts life at 29.97 or 24 frames per second (fps), or 25 fps in Europe. Usually, producers who shoot at 24 fps deliver at that rate, while some producers who shoot at 29.97 fps deliver at 15 fps or even 10 fps when distributing to devices with a very slow Internet connection. That's because dropping the frame rate by 50 or 66 percent reduces the number of pixels being encoded, just like dropping the resolution from 1280x720 to 640x360.

You can see in Table 2-1 that Apple recommends dropping the frame rate on the first and second files targeted towards cellular connections. Again, that's because losing a bit of playback smoothness is preferable to blockiness and other gross compression artifacts.

Bitrate (or Data Rate)

Bitrate (or data rate) is the amount of data per second in the encoded video file, usually expressed in kilobits per second (kbps) or megabits per second (Mbps). In Table 2-1, Apple recommends a video bitrate of 145 kbps for the lowest-quality file, increasing to 7800 kbps for the highest-quality file.

By now you're seeing a relationship between bitrate, resolution and, to a lesser degree, frame rate. At lower bitrates, which are necessary to deliver to devices with slower connection speeds,

Apple recommends lower resolutions and frame rates, which limits the number of pixels being encoded. This makes it easier for the encoder to produce a high-quality file without blockiness or other artifacts.

As an example, suppose you were producing a file using the parameters shown on the third line of the Apple table, 640x360 at 29.97 fps with a bitrate of 600 kbps for video. Now suppose instead of compressing the file to a resolution of 640x360, you decide to compress to 1280x720—a resolution with four times the number of pixels of the 640x360 file. To reach the 600 kbps bitrate, the encoder has to apply four times the compression, which very often noticeably degrades the image.

That's because, as discussed in Chapter 1, all streaming codecs use lossy compression, so the more you compress, the more quality you lose. For this reason, all other file characteristics (like resolution, frame rate or codec) being equal, the lower the bitrate, the lower the quality of the compressed file.

Bandwidth

One concept implicit to the Apple chart is that of bandwidth. Note that the streams on top, which are targeted towards cellular viewers (hence the "CELL" in the left column), have a lower total bitrate. This reflects the reality that most cellular connections are slower than Wi-Fi or direct Ethernet connections used by most desktop and notebook computers. Very appropriately, the table matches the total bitrate to the viewer's bandwidth, which is the viewer's connection speed to the Internet. (I have no idea what ATV means, though Wi-Fi I get.)

In the early days of streaming, producers encoded video to meet the bandwidth capabilities of their target viewers. That is, back when most viewers connected via modems, you had to produce postage-stamp-sized video compressed to somewhere south of 28.8 kbps or the viewers couldn't watch it. Today, with most non-mobile viewers connecting via broadband capable of 6 to 9 Mbps or higher, most producers encode their video to meet quality and cost concerns.

For example, if you scan the websites of television networks and/or large corporations, the typical videos average about 640x360 resolution and are produced at 800 to 1200 kbps, even though many viewers have the capacity to watch higher-bit-rate streams. That's because these producers have to pay for their bandwidth and have decided that 640x360 video at 800 to 1200 kbps provides a sufficiently high-quality experience to meet their viewers' needs. In short, back in the day, most producers encoded their files to meet the target bandwidth of their lowest-common-denominator viewer. Today, as bandwidth to the home has increased, choosing a bitrate is largely a cost/quality trade-off.

Of course, just when it was safe to go back in the water, mobile video delivery came to the fore—as did OTT devices connected to large-screen LCD displays. Now it's not enough to create one file that pleases those watching on middle-of-the-road 19-to-25-inch monitors. You have to go low to satisfy mobile viewers and go high to satisfy those watching in their living room. That's why the Apple table scales from a low of 145 kbps for mobile devices to 7800 kbps for a 1920x1080 movie quality stream.

Compression and Ben and Jerry's Ice Cream

Now that you know the basics, the easiest way to think about video compression is to compare it to a can of paint. Say you have a small can, like the size of a pint of Ben and Jerry's gourmet ice cream. If all you're painting is your front door, you're probably in good shape. On the other hand, if you're trying to paint the entire back wall of your house with that can, you're going to run into trouble. While you could spread the paint over the entire wall, the coverage would be sketchy, with lots of blotches of old paint showing through. To make it look really good, you simply need more paint.

So it is with video compression. The size of the paint can is the bitrate per second in the file. The size of the wall you have to paint are the pixels per second in the file. Anything that increases the number of pixels per second—whether it's a larger resolution or more frames per second—increases the size of the wall you have to paint. At some point, the can is simply too small, and your video will look ugly. The only solutions are to add more paint and encode at a higher bitrate, or to decrease the size of the wall by encoding at a lower resolution or frame rate.

The next concept, bits per pixel, essentially defines how much you're spreading the paint, and ties these concepts altogether into a neat little bow.

Bits Per Pixel

Bits per pixel is the amount of data applied to each pixel in the video file. You compute it by dividing the per-second video bitrate (e.g. 500 kbps) by the number of pixels per second (height x width x frame rate) in the video file. If you're not particularly mathematically inclined, you can use a tool called MediaInfo (shown in Figure 2-4) to do the calculation for you.

Why is bits per pixel such a valuable metric? Several reasons. Most importantly, it provides a single metric that represents how much data is allocated to each pixel in the file, which is the single most important determinator of file quality. If the bits-per-pixel value is too low, you don't have enough paint, and your file will look ugly. If it's too high, it will look great, but you're probably wasting bandwidth—you really didn't need that third and fourth coats for the wall to look good.

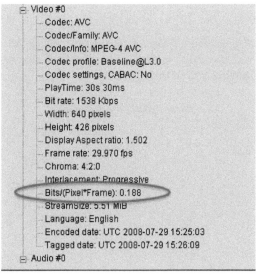

Figure 2-4. MediaInfo is the one tool on every computer in my office.

Note: *You'll learn more about MediaInfo in Chapter 3. It's an invaluable tool you can download for free at bit.ly/dl_mi.*

In addition, bits per pixel provides a single metric to compare different videos. For example, look at the two files compared in Table 2-2. These were two files produced by two accounting firms that I grabbed for comparison purposes. Which configuration looks right to you?

	Width	Height	Frame Rate	Data Rate (kbps)
Video 1	320	180	30	1,500
Video 2	720	392	29.97	1,072

Table 2-2. Two video files produced by two different accounting firms.

It's difficult to tell, right? If you have any experience with encoding at all, you're probably looking at Video 1 and musing, "320x240 resolution, pretty small; 1500 kbps, pretty high. Might be some inefficiency there, particularly compared to Video 2." But it's hard to put the comparison into precise words.

Now take a look at Table 2-3, which also shows the bits-per-pixel value of the two files. Now you're thinking, "Holy cow, Video 1 has close to seven times the bits-per-pixel value of Video 2! What were those idiots thinking?"

	Width	Height	Frame Rate	Data Rate (kbps)	Bits per Pixel
Video 1	320	180	30	1,500	0.868
Video 2	720	392	29.97	1,072	0.127

Table 2-3. The same two files with bits-per-pixel value in red.

What's the optimal bits-per-pixel value? Take a look at Figure 2-5, which shows the bits-per-pixel values (left axis) used by multiple sites, plotted against the resolution of the video files (bottom axis). You can take multiple lessons from this figure.

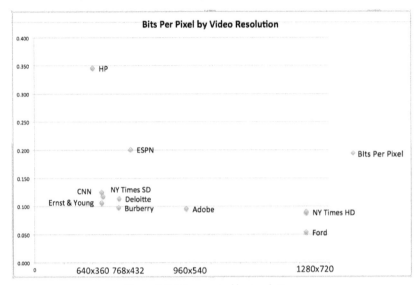

Figure 2-5. Bits per pixel by resolution.

First, the biggest clump of sites is clustered between about 0.1 and 0.13 for SD resolutions, and you can safely assume that these videos exhibited acceptable quality or better. From this, you can conclude that for these low-motion videos, 0.1 to 0.13 are pretty reasonable values. HP is a clear outlier at 0.350, which makes you wonder—again—what the person who encoded Video 1 in Table 2-3 was thinking.

Second, ESPN, the sports network, is at 0.2, which tells you that for higher-motion videos, you need a higher bits-per-pixel value. No surprise there. Finally, you can detect a slight decrease in bits-per-pixel value as video resolution increases. This is because codecs work more efficiently as video resolutions increase, so you can maintain quality at a progressively lower bits-per-pixel value. How much lower? Former Microsoft technology evangelist Ben Waggoner (now with Amazon) has quantified this as the Power of .75 rule, which he defined as follows:

> Using the "Power of .75" rule, content that looks good at 500 kbps at 640x360 would need (1280x720)/(640x360)^.75*500=1414 kbps at 1280x720 for roughly similar quality.

Essentially, as the resolution gets higher, a lower bits-per-pixel value will sustain the same quality level. On the off chance that you may not be up to speed on how to compute fractional exponents (I sure wasn't), I'll share tables that lay out this math after a short summary.

Applying Bits per Pixel

Taking all of this data into account, my rule of thumb is that a reasonable bits-per-pixel is around 0.1 for videos with low to average motion—your basic talking head or news video—ranging to 0.15 or higher for fast-moving videos. ESPN streams at around 0.178 to 0.2, which tells me that you might consider going a little higher for sports videos.

You should apply these values to video configured at 640x360 resolution (16:9) or 640x480 resolution (4:3). According to the Power of .75 rule, for lower-resolution videos, the bits-per-pixel value should increase with resolution. For higher-resolution videos, it should decrease. I used these concepts to create Table 2-4, which is computed for videos produced at 30 fps.

30 fps		Low Motion		High Motion	
Width	Height	Data Rate (kbps)	Bits per Pixel	Data Rate (kbps)	Bits per Pixel
16:9					
320	180	244,376	0.14	366,564	0.21
480	270	448,948	0.12	673,421	0.17
640	360	691,200	0.10	1,036,800	0.15
853	480	1,063,860	0.09	1,595,790	0.13
1280	720	1,955,009	0.07	2,932,513	0.11
1920	1080	3,591,581	0.06	5,387,371	0.09
4:3					
320	240	325,835	0.14	488,752	0.21
400	300	455,368	0.13	683,052	0.19
480	360	598,597	0.12	897,895	0.17
640	480	921,600	0.10	1,382,400	0.15

Table 2-4. Recommended data rates and bits-per-pixel values for video produced at 30 fps.

The top of the table deals with 16:9 videos, and normalizes the 0.1 low-motion and 0.15 high-motion rules at 640x360. I've applied the rule of .75 upward and downward to compute data rates and bits-per-pixel values at other resolutions. The bottom four lines are for 4:3 videos. At each resolution, I've suggested a data rate that would deliver the same quality as the data rate suggested for the 640x360/640x480 resolutions.

Obviously, the data rates and bits-per-pixel values are just suggestions. However, if you're producing at much higher than those values, your data rate may be excessive, unnecessarily increasing your bandwidth costs and making your videos harder to smoothly play for those on marginal connections. If you're producing at much lower and your video quality isn't up to par, perhaps you should re-evaluate. Here are tables for 24 fps and 25 fps.

24 fps		Low Motion		High Motion	
Width	**Height**	**Data Rate (kbps)**	**Bits per Pixel**	**Data Rate (kbps)**	**Bits per Pixel**
16:9					
320	180	195,501	0.14	293,251	0.21
480	270	359,158	0.12	538,737	0.17
640	360	552,960	0.10	829,440	0.15
853	480	851,088	0.09	1,276,632	0.13
1280	720	1,564,007	0.07	2,346,011	0.11
1920	1080	2,873,264	0.06	4,309,897	0.09
4:3					
320	240	260,668	0.14	391,002	0.21
400	300	364,294	0.13	546,442	0.19
480	360	478,877	0.12	718,316	0.17
640	480	737,280	0.10	1,105,920	0.15

Table 2-5. Recommended data rates and bits-per-pixel values for video produced at 24 fps.

25 fps		Low Motion		High Motion	
Width	**Height**	**Data Rate (kbps)**	**Bits per Pixel**	**Data Rate (kbps)**	**Bits per Pixel**
16:9					
320	180	203,647	0.14	305,470	0.21
480	270	374,123	0.12	561,184	0.17
640	360	576,000	0.10	864,000	0.15
853	480	886,550	0.09	1,329,825	0.13
1280	720	1,629,174	0.07	2,443,761	0.11
1920	1080	2,992,984	0.06	4,489,476	0.09
4:3					
320	240	271,529	0.14	407,294	0.21
400	300	379,473	0.13	569,210	0.19
480	360	498,831	0.12	748,246	0.17
640	480	768,000	0.10	1,152,000	0.15

Table 2-6. Recommended data rates and bits-per-pixel values for video produced at 25 fps.

Note that these tables apply only to high- and low-motion real-world videos. As you'll learn about in Chapter 7, the rules are much different for other types of videos—like animations, screencams, and other synthetic videos.

Tip: *For more on the importance of bits per pixel, check out my article "The Essential Key to Producing High Quality Streaming Video" at bit.ly/bits-per-pixel.*

Note: *When encoding for upload to YouTube or similar sites—or to an online video platform like Brightcove, Kaltura, or Ooyala—you should encode at full resolution and at a very high data rate. You can read more about this at bit.ly/encode_4_upload.*

Encoding in FFmpeg

Over the past few years, I've started working more and more with FFmpeg. It's an incredibly useful tool for scaling, file conversions, and encoding into the H.264, H.265, and VP9 formats. I cover some FFmpeg-related operations in Chapter 5 on the Moscow State University Video Quality Measurement tool. In each chapter where I discuss encoding into H.264 or H.265 formats, I'll show how to accomplish these in a GUI-based tool (Figure 2-1) as well as FFmpeg.

Let me start by saying that Frantisek Korbel's book *FFmpeg Basics*, which is available on Amazon, is a great general-purpose reference for FFmpeg operation. If you plan on using FFmpeg extensively, I recommend it wholeheartedly.

Note that Chapter 5 contains an extensive section on command line operation, and I recommend reading that before jumping into these operations.

> **Note:** *I'm not going to detail how to download and install FFmpeg, as there are many guides available for that. One I found useful is on wikiHow at bit.ly/install_ffmpeg. If you need more help, Google "How to install FFmpeg" and you'll find lots of answers.*

FFmpeg Basics

In this chapter, we covered bitrate, resolution, and frame rate, but you'll have to choose the video and audio codecs as well. Here's a sample FFmpeg script for doing all this.

```
ffmpeg.exe -i TOS_1080p.mp4 -vcodec libx264 -s 480x270 -r 15 -b:v 500k
-acodec aac -b:a 128k -ac 2 -ar 48000 TOS_270p.mp4
```

Here's an explanation for the commands used in this string.

`ffmpeg.exe` calls the program. If not located in the same folder, include folder information.

`-i TOS_1080p.mp4` names the input file. If not located in the same folder, include folder information.

`-vcodec libx264` chooses the video codec.

`-s 480x270` sets the resolution. If not included, FFmpeg will encode at the resolution of the source file.

`-r 15` sets the frame rate. If not included, FFmpeg will encode at the frame rate of the source file.

`-b:v 500k` sets the video bitrate.

`-acodec aac` chooses the audio codec. If you're producing an MP4 file, FFmpeg will convert to AAC even if you don't specify.

`-b:a 64k` sets the audio bitrate.

`-ac 2` sets the audio channels—choose 1 for monaural, 2 for stereo.

`-ar 48000` sets the audio sample rate.

`TOS_270p.mp4` sets the output file name.

Computing PSNR with FFmpeg

One of the video quality metrics that FFmpeg can provide is the Peak Signal-to-Noise Ratio (PSNR) you learned about in the Introduction. There are two elements to computing PSNR; first computing it, second recording it into a log file, because if you don't create the log file, the PSNR value doesn't get saved.

```
ffmpeg.exe -i TOS_1080p.mp4 -vcodec libx264 -s 480x270 -r 15 -b:v 500k
-acodec aac -b:a 128k -ac 2 -ar 48000 -psnr -report TOS_270p.mp4
```

Here's an explanation for the new commands used in this string.

`-psnr` - Tells FFmpeg to compute PSNR.

`-report` - Tells FFmpeg to store a log file, which it will name according to the date and time (`ffmpeg-20161207-143841.log`).

If you open the log file and scan to the bottom, you'll see PSNR values for Y, U and V (Figure 7). We'll exclusively use the Y value in this book, so that's the one you want.

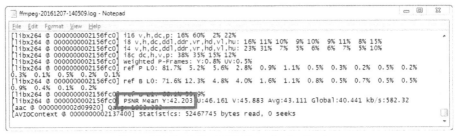

Figure 2-7. Here's the PSNR Mean for the Y value.

For those who care about such things, FFmpeg's numbers do not exactly match those reported by the Moscow State University VQMT Tool. In the nine cases that I checked, FFmpeg proved about 1.8% higher, averaging 38.6 compared to 37.9 for VQMT, which isn't significant. Scores were consistently higher, ranging from about 1.75% to 2.08%, rather than all over the map. If I didn't have VQMT to use, I would definitely fall back on FFmpeg.

OK, that's it for our basic file parameters. Now we have enough information to start talking about the tools you'll find essential for the procedures and workflows you'll learn in this book.

Chapter 3: Essential Tools

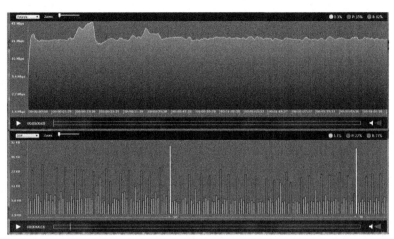

Figure 3-1. Two views from Telestream Switch: data rate view (top) and group of pictures (GOP) view.

In this book, I'll use multiple tools to glean information from compressed files. These are absolutely essential to the work that I do. In this chapter, I'll introduce you to these tools. Specifically, you will learn about:

- **MediaInfo.** A cross-platform tool for identifying encoded file details

- **Bitrate Viewer.** A free tool for viewing the data rate and group of pictures (GOP, explained in Chapter 9)

- **QuickTime Player.** Apple's player, which provides basic playback capabilities for MOV and MP4 files.

- **Telestream Switch.** A free tool for viewing data rate and I-frame, B-frame, and P-frame file data (bottom of Figure 3-1, which you'll also learn about in Chapter 9)

- **VLC Media Player.** As close to a universal player as exists on this planet

- **Beamr Video Comparison Tool (VCT).** A very useful tool for comparing the quality of two video files

- **HandBrake.** A free, cross-platform encoder for producing H.264 and H.265 files

- **FFmpeg.** A free, cross-platform command line tool for a number of tasks—including encoding, transcoding, and scaling

- **Charles Web Debugging Proxy.** A tool for constraining incoming bitrates and visualizing the segments downloaded during adaptive streaming.

- **Zond 265.** A tool that provides a visual in-depth analysis of HEVC/H.265 and AVC/H.264 video bitstreams.

Let's start with MediaInfo, a tool I have on every computer in my office.

MediaInfo

MediaInfo is a cross-platform tool that offers an extensive and often unique range of data, as well as the ability to export file-based information for printing or further analysis. It also supports pretty much every codec that I've ever tried to load—including Ogg Theora and WebM, plus the normal H.264, VP6, WMV, MOV, MPEG-1, and MPEG-2. And MediaInfo details the bits per pixel for the file, which is the single most important compression-related metric (see Bits Per Pixel in Chapter 2 for more information).

The Windows version is available in multiple languages—including simplified and traditional Chinese—can open multiple instances, and displays more data about the file than any other tool. You can download all versions at https://mediaarea.net/en/MediaInfo. The tool is free, although donations are gladly appreciated.

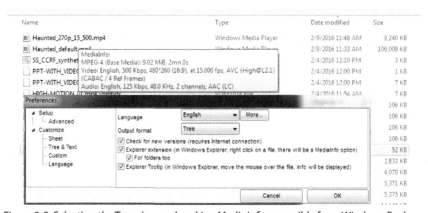

Figure 3-2. Selecting the Tree view and making MediaInfo accessible from Windows Explorer.

Both the Windows and Mac versions load files using drag-and-drop or via traditional menu or button controls. In the Windows version, you have six different views including text, HTML, and the Mac-style Tree view.

In Windows, you can set which view opens by default by clicking Options > Preferences (I like the Tree view). Here you can activate the Explorer Extension to make MediaInfo appear in the right-click menu for files in Windows Explorer. You can also activate Explorer Tooltip, which shows the file details you see below the Haunted_270p_15_500.mp4 file in Figure 3-2 when you hover your pointer over a file in Windows Explorer. Both options are very handy. Click Debug > Advanced Mode in the Windows version, and the program shows about three times the data, although most of the critical data is available in the Basic view.

The Mac version of MediaInfo can only export a simple text file, while the Windows version can output CSV, HMTL, text, and custom formats. The Windows version can also analyze multiple files simultaneously, either displaying all results in a single instance of the program or exporting a consolidated report.

For all files (Figure 3-3), both MediaInfo versions show the resolution, data rate and other basic stats relating to both the audio and video components—including whether they were encoded with constant- or variable-bit-rate encoding.

For H.264 files, you can see the profile used and whether the file was encoded with context-adaptive binary arithmetic coding (CABAC) or context-adaptive variable-length coding (CAVLC) entropy encoding. You can also see the number of reference frames and Bits/(Pixel*Frame), which I call bits per pixel.

Figure 3-3. Showing details of a file encoded in HEVC.

You get much of the same information about high-efficiency video coding (HEVC) files, as shown in Figure 3-3. In Advanced Mode in Windows, sometimes you can see B-frame interval (M=x, which means a B-frame interval of x-1) and I-frame interval (N=x), but this information is not always available. You have to purchase Telestream Switch to reliably extract this information.

Although the Mac version is less full-featured than the Windows version, it's the only option I found for analyzing a broad spectrum of files on the Mac, making it a natural for most producers. The tool also reveals enough unique file characteristics on Windows—like variable bitrate (VBR)/

constant bitrate (CBR) for Windows Media files, and profile and CABAC/CAVLC for H.264—to make it invaluable for most Windows producers.

> **Tip:** *You can see a video describing two of the tools, MediaInfo and Bitrate Viewer, at bit.ly/twovidanalysistools.*

Bitrate Viewer

Bitrate Viewer is a Windows-only tool available at bit.ly/BRV_download. The tool is free, although donations are gladly accepted (and justified). You can see the tool in all its glory in Figure 3-4.

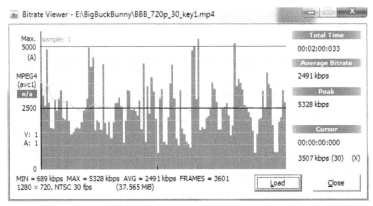

Figure 3-4. Bitrate Viewer shows you how the data rate varies over the duration of the file.

The individual spikes represent the size of a single group of pictures (GOP—see Chapter 9), while the wavy faint blue line hovering around the 2500 kbps line is the average data rate of the file. On the upper right, you can see the average bitrate, which is always handy, plus the peak bitrate in the file. On the lower left, you can see resolution and frame rate statistics.

I like Bitrate Viewer because it instantly identifies issues that may cause playback problems. For example, in the file shown in Figure 3-4, there are multiple GOPs that extend far above the 2500 kbps line, representing data spikes that could interrupt playback on a constrained connection like cellular. You'll learn how to avoid problems like this in Chapter 9.

QuickTime Player 7

QuickTime Player 7 can open multiple instances on Mac and Windows, which makes it a useful playback tool for many producers. QuickTime comes in two versions, Player and Pro ($29.99), with Pro offering more encoding and diagnostic features. On the Mac, there's also QuickTime X, which came with Snow Leopard and later operating systems, although it has much fewer diagnostic features than Version 7.

With the Player versions of QuickTime 7 (Windows and Mac) and both versions of QuickTime X, you can load a file, choose Window > Show Movie Inspector, and get the information shown in Figure 3-5. There is nowhere near as much data as MediaInfo, but sometimes it's helpful. If you upgrade to the Pro version of QuickTime 7 ($29.99), you can access unique data relating to hinted streaming files by choosing Window > Show Movie Properties, which also shows codec, frame rate, and data rate information. Typically, though, I just use MediaInfo for this data since it provides so much more.

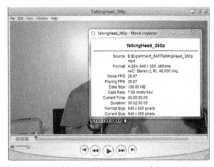

Figure 3-5. Information available in all versions of QuickTime, Mac and Windows.

Telestream Switch

Telestream Switch is file viewer and inspector that comes in three versions: Switch Player (free), Switch Plus ($49), and Switch Pro ($295). You can read about the various versions at telestream.net/switch. As you would expect, the most useful version is Pro, which is the version you'll need to view the file information shown in Figure 3-1. As far as I know, there is no competitive tool anywhere close to this price range that displays the GOP-based information. The Pro and Plus versions also come with the ability to perform some basic file edits, which is useful in a production environment, plus the ability to view closed captions in a number of formats.

From a diagnostic and playback perspective, Switch Player and Switch Plus are still finding their way. For example, information available for free in MediaInfo isn't available in Switch Player or Plus. VLC Media Player, discussed next, plays more file types and operates via drag and drop, while Switch only works via the traditional File > Open menu commands. This makes it tough to recommend downloading Switch Player, or paying for Switch Plus unless you need the edit/captioning features. If you've got the cash (or expense account) for Switch Pro, go for it— the GOP view is fabulous.

VLC Media Player

VLC Media Player is a cross-platform player available from VideoLAN (bit.ly/VLC_down) that plays pretty much any file you can throw at it, including files using the HEVC, VP9, Windows Media (WMV) and VP6 codecs—plus AVI and QuickTime files if the right codecs are loaded on the system. In addition, it's much less persnickety than QuickTime Player, so it often plays MOV or MP4 files that QuickTime refuses to load.

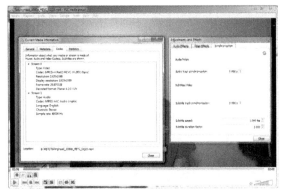

Figure 3-6. The popular VLC Media Player.

Interestingly, VideoLAN is a French company that doesn't believe in software-related patents and has steadfastly refused to pay royalties for H.264 or HEVC. For some reason, owners of these patent rights, like the MPEG LA patent group, haven't pursued VideoLAN for these royalties or to cease and desist. This makes VLC Media Player wonderfully convenient for video producers, and one of the few players that can play HEVC files.

Beamr Video Comparison Tool (VCT)

The Beamr Video Comparison Tool (VCT) is curious in that it's available as a free 90-day trial ([bit.ly/b_vct](bit.ly/b_vct)), but as far as I know, has never been offered for sale. The player, which is available for Windows only, can load up to two H.264 and/or H.265 files, with multiple views to facilitate comparing them.

For example, in the split-screen view shown in Figure 3-7, you can play both files, dragging the blue line in the middle one way or the other to see details in both files. Or, you can watch in overlay mode with one video atop the other, toggling between them via the Ctrl+Tab keystroke, which is a great way to see minor compression artifacts in a compressed file. Basically, if you want to compare two files during playback, it's the best tool available.

Figure 3-7. The Beamr Video Comparison Tool in split-screen mode.

HandBrake

HandBrake is a free cross-platform encoder available at handbrake.fr/downloads.php. Essentially, HandBrake puts a graphical user interface (GUI) over x264 and x265, providing a convenient mechanism for accessing features like constant rate factor (CRF) encoding, which we'll explore in Chapter 7.

Figure 3-8. Clearly, HandBrake doesn't take itself too seriously.

While HandBrake is great for experiments, it's cumbersome for production encoding, making the next tool a better choice for those performing frequent x264/x265/VP9 encodes.

> **Tip:** *You can watch my tutorial on HandBrake at youtu.be/rB7pgyn3tws.*

FFmpeg

FFmpeg is a tool that many developers use to create their own enterprise encoding tools; in fact, it powers the encoding farms used by YouTube, Netflix and many others. You can download the software and access multiple learning resources at ffmpeg.org.

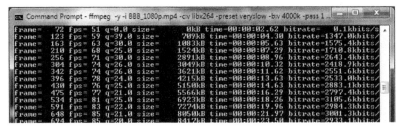

Figure 3-9. FFmpeg crunching through an x264 file.

Over the course of this book, we'll explore using FFmpeg to encode files with the x264, x265, and VP9 codecs; to convert files to YUV format to analyze in our objective metric tools; and to scale files to different resolutions. You were introduced to FFmpeg back in Chapter 2, and can learn about command line operation in Chapter 5.

Charles Web Debugging Proxy

According to the Charles Proxy website (charlesproxy.com), "Charles is an HTTP proxy/HTTP monitor/Reverse Proxy that enables a developer to view all of the HTTP and SSL/HTTPS traffic between their machine and the Internet. This includes requests, responses and the HTTP headers (which contain the cookies and caching information)." From my perspective, Charles is an affordable ($50) highly capable tool that I just started using for two specific features.

Figure 3-10. Setting a bandwidth limit (or throttle) in Charles Web Debugging Proxy.

First is the ability to set an artificial bandwidth throttle for testing. As an example, I've heard for years that VBR-encoded video delivers a lower quality of experience (QoE) than CBR under constrained playback conditions. However, my cable broadband connection delivers 85 Mbps download speed, so how exactly do I test under constrained playback conditions? Well, as you can see in Figure 3-10, Charles lets you set a bandwidth limit to simulate these constraints. Apply the limit and test with Speedtest.net, and you can verify the throttling.

The second feature is the data Charles displays in the session window, shown on the left in Figure 3-11. As you can see, I'm downloading data from three layers in the HTTP Live Streaming (HLS) adaptive group, which means at least two stream switches during the early seconds of file playback. This data helps me understand exactly what's happening during playback, so I can compare the quality of experience delivered by different encoding schemes.

Figure 3-11. Charles showing the fragments retrieved during HTTP Live Streaming (HLS) playback.

You can read all about these tests in my article on the Streaming Learning Center titled "Bitrate Control and QoE—CBR is Better" (bit.ly/VBR_CBR_QoE), which I also discuss in Chapter 8. In the meantime, if you're looking to debug your video playback experience, check out Charles. There's a free 30-day trial, and at $50 it's a steal. I know I'm just touching the surface of Charles' functionality, but these two features alone were well worth the purchase price.

> **Tip:** *You can see a video of Charles in action at youtu.be/vBJmDTMILlg.*

Zond 265

Zond 265 is a visual H.265/H.264 file analyzer from Solveig Multimedia (solveigmm.com). It costs $1,390, with a demo version available for tryout. The tool is targeted towards "developers of HEVC decoding/encoding/transcoding hardware and software" rather than encoding professionals, and will be overkill for most users. However, as of the time of this writing, it's the only tool I could find that lets you see the frames actually deployed in the bitstream—kind of like Switch does for H.264 files. As you can see in Figure 3-12, Zond also can show the PSNR and MS SSIM rating throughout the file, as well as an absolute ton of compression details, like the transform partitions shown in the figure.

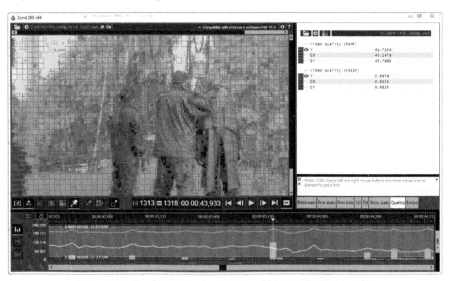

Figure 3-12. Zond 265 showing PSNR and SSIM in the TOS test file.

I learned of the tool as I was finishing this book, so did not use it while writing Chapter 11 on HEVC. I'll be using and writing about it in early 2017 as I compare HEVC codecs for a presentation at Streaming Forum 2017 in London. Again, if you're deep into HEVC codec development, or really into learning about how HEVC works, it's an essential tool. But much less so for the typical HEVC producer.

OK, that's it for essential tools. Now that you know what they are and what they all do, you're ready to tackle planning your testing, which you'll learn how to do in the next chapter.

Chapter 4: Testing Overview

00:01:03:05

Figure 4-1. A test clip taken from Sintel, an animated movie from the Blender Foundation. Note the timecode I've inserted.

This chapter presents an overview of the testing procedures used throughout the book. In this chapter you'll learn:

- how to create your test clips

- how and why to standardize your file naming conventions

- why it's critical to test file size and data rate after encoding

- tips on presenting your test data for maximum impact

- why it's essential to visually confirm your objective findings

- workstation requirement for crunching objective benchmarks.

Creating Your Test Clips

Once you've decided to start objective testing, your natural inclination is to jump right in and start to encode some clips. Unfortunately, unless you invest time thinking about the test clips you'll use, this ready-fire-aim approach often leads to suboptimal results and wasted time. So let's cover the high-level points of test clip selection and preparation.

Selecting Your Test Clips

When selecting your test clips, keep the following thoughts in mind.

- ***Your test clips should include all types of videos that you encode.*** At a high level, your test clips should represent the footage you encode in actual production. For this reason, you should have a clip or clips for all major types of videos that you encode. For a recent movie distributor client, that included animated movies and real-world movies. For a recent business client, that included screencams, mixed videos with PowerPoint, and talking head videos. If your typical videos include text or similar details, be sure to include these in the test videos. Artifacts on sharp detail are highly noticeable, so you may need to go for higher quality than ordinary video might dictate.

- ***Within these categories, the clips should include a reasonable mix of action and easy-to-encode segments.*** While it's important to test hard encoding cases, if these are infrequent in your day-to-day encoding, you don't want to unnecessarily prejudice your results by overemphasizing difficult-to-encode sequences.

- ***You can extract complete segments from longer clips, or create your own test clips from separate shorter components.*** I've used both approaches, but I've been gravitating more toward complete excerpts rather than synthetically created test clips from multiple sources.

- ***Be mindful of the frame rate of all of your test clips.*** Using clips with different frame rates complicates your testing and analysis because you must create unique presets for each frame rate. It's simpler if you can test at one frame rate. If you must test at several rates, like 23.976 and 29.97, be mindful of the fact that there's a difference between 29.997 and 30 fps (and 23.976 and 24), and that encoding at 29.97 to 30 fps can distort your results with some clips on some encoding tools. Maintain the precise frame rate of all test clips through the entire test cycle—from source to all test clips to all compressed clips.

- ***Your test clips should be relatively short.*** My test clips are typically two minutes long, but sometimes I use a five-minute segment as a torture test to finalize my results. Encoding and analysis can often take a long time, and using longer clips can limit the number of test cases you can produce.

- ***Be aware of copyrights.*** If you plan on publishing your results outside of your organization, mind the copyright issues. I've never had a problem when I've tested with copyrighted content, but I never post clips of copyrighted videos, and I restrict my use to occasional frames in a book or article.

Producing the Test Clips

After choosing the material, it's time to create your test clips.

- **Insert timecode into the clips.** Timecoding the test clips will simplify downstream debugging and technique comparisons, so you should absolutely add timecode to each test clip. Fortunately, most video editors include a timecode effect for this purpose. I used Premiere Pro's Timecode effect to insert the timecode into Sintel in Figure 4-1.

- **Create all iterations at once.** When using the Moscow State University Video Quality Measurement Tool (VQMT), you must compare the encoded file with a source file at the same resolution. Even if your source file is 1080p resolution, you may need test files in multiple resolutions like 720p, 540p, 480p, and 360p. When encoding for output at these resolutions, you'll use these files as the source, and it's easiest if you produce these files at the start. I have multiple output presets in Adobe Media Encoder, which simplifies the output process (see Figure 4-2). Note the separate presets for 23.976 and 29.97.

Test_640x360@23.976	H.264	640x360
Test_640x360@29.97	H.264	640x360
Test_720p@23.976	H.264	1280x720
Test_720p@29.97	H.264	1280x720
Test_854x480@23.976	H.264	854x480
Test_854x480@29.97	H.264	854x480
Test_1080p@23.976	H.264	1920x1080
Test_1080p@29.97	H.264	1920x1080

Figure 4-2. Multiple resolution files exported for a recent project.

- **Use the same mezzanine format you would normally use.** If you create your mezzanine files in H.264 format, as most producers do, use H.264 for your test files. You may want to use a higher bitrate than normal, like 50 Mbps for 1080p files, 30 Mbps for 720p files, and so on.

- **Keep names short and descriptive.** You probably will create multiple files from the test clips. When you're scanning files and results, shorter names are always easier to quickly grasp. When creating multiple file iterations, filenames should identify the file's unique characteristics. BBB_1080p.mp4 is preferable to Big_Buck_Bunny_1920x1080.mp4 because it provides the essential details in as few letters as possible.

- **Use uniform filenames.** If you are creating multiple test files, use identical nomenclature on all of them. This will simplify using the same batch files multiple times for different test files. If all of your 720p files are designated _720p (FileA_720p.mp4, FileB_720p.mp4, FileC_720p.mp4), it's easy to search and replace for just the filename in Notepad. On the other hand, if some of your 720p files are designated 1280x720, and others 720p, or just 720, reusing a batch file becomes vastly more complicated. A little bit of filename planning up front will simplify things down the road.

Encode Your Clips

Encoding parameters will change for each particular test, and I'll detail test procedures wherever they are relevant. Here are some key points to consider during this phase.

- **Test one encoding parameter at a time.** For example, if you're testing to identify the optimal key frame interval, don't adjust any settings other than the key frame. Run your tests, produce your results, and fine-tune parameters between tests. But don't address more than one parameter in each set of tests, or you'll produce inconclusive results.

- **Write down or otherwise record what you're testing.** It sounds pedantic, but it's very useful to write down or otherwise record the focus of each test (or round of tests), along with a brief statement of the overall configurations you'll use for each test. Since you'll likely be testing in between other activities over the course of multiple days (or weeks, or months), it's good to document exactly what you're testing and the parameters you're using, so you can hit the ground running each time you return to your testing.

- **Create presets or separate batch files for each test case.** With most encoding tools, you can apply a preset to a file, and then change the preset for testing purposes. For example, if testing for the optimal key frame interval, you could apply the same preset to the same file five times, and then change each preset to the various test cases. The alternative is to create a preset for each test case, which will simplify testing multiple source files and make it easier to verify your tests if you find an anomaly in your results. That's the approach I use and recommend.

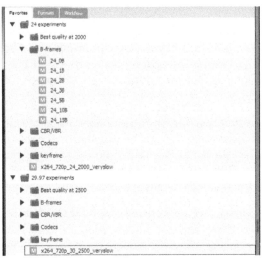

Figure 4-3. Sorenson Squeeze presets used for a round of testing at Streaming Media West 2015.

For example, when running a round of tests for a presentation at Streaming Media West in 2015, I started with a 720p preset that I had used for high-end encoder testing earlier that year. That was my baseline preset, which I duplicated for both 23.976 and 29.97.

Then I created different presets for the various tests that I performed. For example, in Figure 4-3, you see two sets of presets: one for 24 fps (24 experiments), the other for 29.97 fps (29.97 experiments). In the 24 fps preset, the open folder contains the presets applied to identify the optimal B-frame setting. When analyzing test results, if the 0 B-frame test file had a higher quality than the 15 B-frame file, which certainly would be anomalous, I could easily check to make sure the parameters applied to each file were correct. If you don't have these presets and do everything free form, you'll have to duplicate your tests to be sure, which wastes a lot of time.

- ***Pre-think all naming conventions.*** As with your test filenames, create short and descriptive names that quickly identify the file and parameters you're testing. A filename like BBB_720p_key1.mp4 conveys the critical information in as few letters as possible, and is much easier to visually parse than Big_Buck_Bunny_1280x720_keyframe1.mp4.

For programs that combine the source file and preset name to create the output filename (like Sorenson Squeeze), consider the optimal naming convention when naming the presets. In high-volume testing, overall operation is much simpler when you can simply use the output filename created by the program without any modification.

Verify Encodes

After encoding your clips, it's absolutely essential that you verify two aspects of the encoded clips: first the data rate, and second bitrate control. Both can dramatically impact your findings as described below.

Data Rate

Without question, the data rate of your clip is the most important determinant of file quality. It's important to recognize that not all encoding tools meet the target data rate set for each encode. For example, if a file is supposed to be 1 Mbps but the encoding tool produced the file at 2 Mbps, the fact that it has a great peak signal-to-noise ratio (PSNR) score is meaningless. For this reason, you absolutely have to check the file size of each encoded clip before performing any quality analysis.

Typically, I ensure that all encoded files are within 5 percent of the target. Figure 4-4 shows how I use Google Spreadsheets to help get that done.

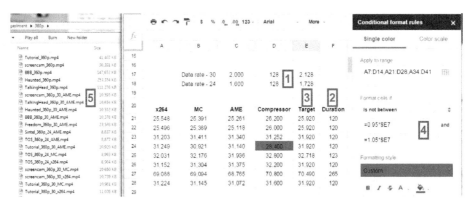

Figure 4-4. Making sure the file sizes are within 5 percent of the target.

Here are the relevant elements in Figure 4-4.

1. These fields contain the data rate of the test clips, including audio and video. There are two data rates, one for 30 fps and the other for 24 fps.

2. This field contains the duration of the test clip in seconds.

3. The target column shows the target file size of the encoded clip, calculated by multiplying the duration by the bitrate divided by 8 to convert bits to bytes (`duration x (seconds x bitrate/8)`).

4. Use the conditional format rules in Google Spreadsheets to create a red background for any field that isn't between 0.95 and 1.05 of the target. As you'll see, I use conditional formatting a lot to help identify errors and to highlight results in my tests.

5. Once the formulas and formatting is in place, start entering files sizes from File Manager. Re-encode any clip in red until it meets the target.

That ensures data rate compliance. Now let's look at bitrate control.

Bitrate Control

The file size of the clip tells you that you met the target bitrate, but you should also assess how the bitrate is allocated within the clip. That allocation can dramatically affect quality—particularly if one clip is encoded using constant bitrate encoding (CBR), while another is encoded with less constraint.

You see this in Figure 4-5, which is two file views in Bitrate Viewer (bit.ly/bitrateviewer), which you learned about in Chapter 3. The figure shows analysis of a clip encoded with Apple Compressor on top, and on the bottom a clip encoded with Sorenson Squeeze using the x264 codec. On the upper right of both screens you see the average bitrate. The Compressor clip is 582 kbps, while the Squeeze clip is 598 kbps. Although I encoded both clips using CBR, the peak bitrate for the Apple clip is almost twice as high as the Squeeze clip (1821 to 997 kbps).

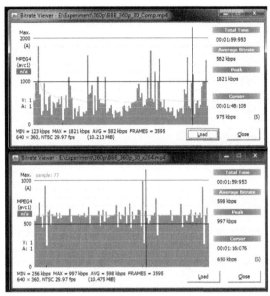

Figure 4-5. Checking the bitrate control of two encoded clips.

After seeing this, I would return to Compressor to make sure I encoded using CBR. If not, I would re-encode. If I did, even if the Compressor clip proved to be higher in quality than that of Squeeze, I would note that the Compressor clip exhibited less bitrate control, which could prove problematical when producing for adaptive bitrate streaming. Note that I'm not saying that Compressor can't produce accurate CBR clips; I'm saying it's something I need to go back and check before I compare the quality of the Compressor and Squeeze clips.

While I've used Bitrate Viewer to good effect for years, it does have issues loading some files and is a one-trick pony that provides only the information and functionality shown in Figure 4-5. Recently Telestream upgraded its Switch product (bit.ly/teleswitch) to include the two views shown in Figure 4-6, as well as file playback capabilities and some file information. But MediaInfo (bit.ly/mediainfo_dl) still provides much more data and is free.

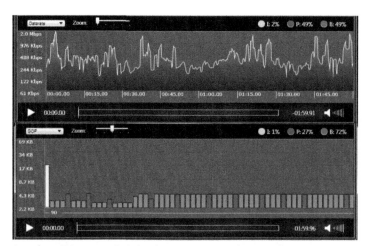

Figure 4-6. Two views from Telestream Switch—bitrate on top and group of pictures structure on the bottom.

Specifically, in the top view of Figure 4-6, you see a bitrate view very much like that shown in Figure 4-5—although with Switch you can move around and zoom in and out of the file view. On the bottom, you see the group of pictures (GOP) structure, with the yellow frame a key frame, the purple frames P-frames, and the blue frames B-frames (you'll learn about those in Chapter 9). Note the very useful B-frame percentage on the right in the bottom view. This is a view you can't get in Bitrate Viewer, or any other tool I'm aware of that costs under a few thousand dollars. To get this in Switch, however, you'll have to upgrade to the $300 version.

Choose Test Program and Algorithm

Once you have the encoded files verified, it's time to run your analysis. I detail how to perform these in the Moscow State University VQMT and SSIMWave's Video Quality-of-Experience Monitor (SQM) in the following two chapters. At a high level, the workflow is very similar in both tools. You can see an example from VQMT in Figure 4-7.

First you load the source file, then load the encoded file to compare to the source. With VQMT, you can load two encoded files, which is a great way to test and visualize the differences between two encoding options.

Next you choose a quality metric to apply. In the figure I'm using the VQMT test that I'll explain next chapter. Then you click Process to start the analysis.

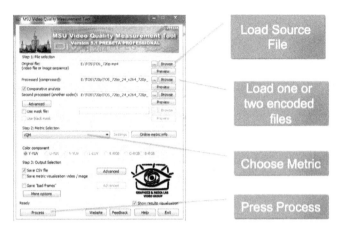

Figure 4-7. Typical test procedure for quality testing.

Collect and Present the Results

Both tests output a CSV file that contains the results. After creating a spreadsheet to analyze the results, I open each CSV file and copy and paste the results into the spreadsheet. You see this in Figure 4-8. By using keyboard shortcuts like Ctrl + C for copy and Ctrl + V for paste (or Command on the Mac), you can populate your spreadsheet in no time flat.

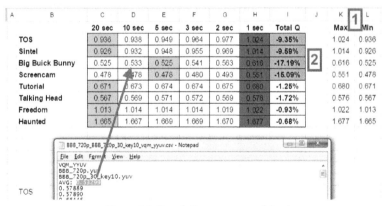

Figure 4-8. Populating your spreadsheet.

After inputting the results, use conditional formatting to identify the highest- and lowest-quality options in the results. For example, in Figure 4-8, I'm testing various key frame intervals. A brief glance at the table tells you that one second was the worst option in all test cases, while the best test cases were an interval of five seconds for Big Buck Bunny and Screencam, and 20 seconds for the other files.

Setting this up is very simple. At the extreme right in Figure 4-8 you see two columns for Max and Min. These use Google Sheets Max (`=MAX(C4:H4)`) and Min (`=MIN(C4:H4)`) functions to identify the highest and lowest numbers in the defined range. With the VQMT metric, lower scores are better. So in the results cells, I use conditional formatting to assign a green background to the value that matches the Min setting, and a red background to the value that matches the Max settings. This makes the data instantly scannable.

The Total Q column tracks the difference between the best and worst quality. Here I've used conditional formatting to present an orange background in all cases where the difference exceeds negative 5 percent. This allows me to quickly identify those files where the key frame interval makes a significant difference, and those files where it doesn't. There are many YouTube videos detailing how to use conditional formatting in Google Sheets and Excel, so you should have no trouble getting started.

I'm also a big fan of using charts to help draw conclusions from data, which is a topic we'll explore in detail in a later chapter. You can see this in Figure 4-9, which shows how the quality of three files vary at different data rates. Since I used the SQM metric, higher scores are better. The chart illustrates how increasing the data rate improves quality significantly at lower rates, but then hits diminishing returns.

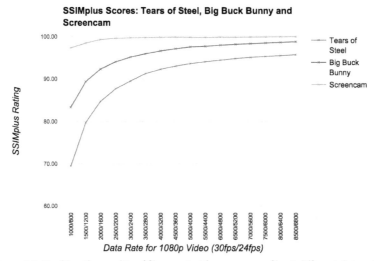

Figure 4-9. Tracking the quality of files created from a source file at different data rates.

I don't mean to divert into a separate discussion on data visualization, and certainly that's not an expertise that I claim. The point is that using simple tools available in the spreadsheets where you collect your data can really help you visualize and understand your results much more effectively than plain numbers. This can be important whether you're using the data yourself or presenting it to others.

Check the Actual Video Files

Overall numerical results are meaningless if they obscure a meaningful difference between some frames in comparative videos. For example, a comparison between variable bitrate (VBR) encoding and constant bitrate (CBR) encoding will show that VBR has only a slight advantage in either SQM or VQMT score. However, if you check the actual files, in many tests you will see that the CBR-encoded file suffers from several transient quality drops. These quality drops are shown in the VQMT Results visualization screen shown in Figure 4-10, represented by the red spikes in the graphs.

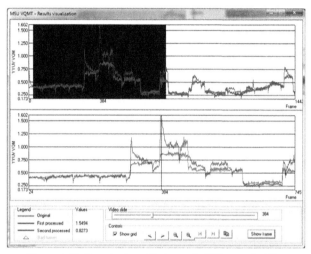

Figure 4-10. Transient quality issues in CBR encoded files.

In Chapter 5, you'll learn how to actually view the frames from the Results visualization screen. For now, understand that a close score between two files doesn't indicate a lack of transient differences that might dictate one encoding technique over another. The ability to easily identify this in the Results visualization screen is one of the reasons I use VQMT so frequently. In addition, you can use the Moscow State University tool to identify the lowest-quality frames in the encode, allowing you to quickly find those frames when using the command line version. You'll learn how to do this in Chapter 5 as well.

Whenever there is a significant difference between ratings, you should view the files and verify that the average user would actually notice the difference. For example, I've seen horrible PSNR scores resulting from a simple tonal change in the video that few viewers would notice without side-by-side comparisons. So you need to check the actual video files to verify the numbers. These standardized tests also don't pick up issues like loss of synchronization, and may not highlight motion-related artifacts like mosquitoes. For this reason, when drawing major conclusions from your tests, be sure to supplement the objective metrics with visual inspections both frame by frame and during full-speed playback.

Retest As Needed

In a perfect world, you would run the tests once, draw your conclusions, change your presets accordingly, and win massive plaudits from your bosses and viewing audiences. As you've no doubt already figured out, the world isn't a perfect place.

When performing this kind of objective testing, you have to filter results through your own logic and verify your tests when the results seem anomalous. For example, if one technique is dramatically worse than another, the file may have became corrupted during encoding or other processing. For example, sometimes Sorenson Squeeze inserts an extra frame at the start of an encoded clip, which drops the quality reported by virtually all objective metrics (and is why I always insert the timecode into my test files). Obviously you would have to correct this issue before drawing any conclusions about the technique or encoder.

The best advice I can offer is to follow your nose and go where the tests take you. Sometimes objective quality testing creates as many questions as it answers, and you may have to test and retest again to reach a valid conclusion.

This leads us to our final point: You'll need a hefty workstation for all this testing and retesting.

Get a Hefty Workstation

You probably already know that encoding video is one of the few tasks that really benefits from a powerful workstation. Interestingly, video quality measurement software, which performs extensive frame-by-frame comparisons, benefits even more from both faster central processing units (CPUs) and solid-state drives (SSDs).

During the summer of 2015, I compared the performance of an HP Z840 workstation with an older HP Z800 workstation. Both were dual-CPU computers with multiple cores, but the Z840 also benefited from HP's PCIe-based HP Z Turbo Drives (the Z Turbo Drive G2). You can see the decrease in encoding time in Table 4-1, and you can read this element of the three-part review at bit.ly/z840_encode. In four of five test cases, the decrease in encoding time exceeded 30 percent, triggering the green background shown in the third column.

Overall Performance			
Encoding	**Z840**	**Z800/ Z600**	**% Decrease**
Adobe Media Encoder	555	1,038	47%
Squeeze	331	528	37%
X265	166	375	56%
WebM	233	320	27%
Vantage	1,012	3,504	71%

Table 4-1. Decrease in encoding time between the Z840 and the Z800.

The benefits in processing VQMT ratings were even more striking, and are shown in Table 4-2. When converting MP4 files to YUV format, which may be necessary to run the command line version of VQMT, the Z840 outpaced the Z800 by 85 percent. In performing the VQMT analysis itself, the Z840 decreased processing time by 49 percent over the Z800.

Overall Performance			
Analysis	Z840	Z800	% Decrease
Convert to YUV	56	367	85%
MSU VQMT	860	1,701	49%

Table 4-2. Decrease in VQMT processing time between the Z840 and Z800.

If you've already got a pretty fast workstation, at the very least you should buy a large SSD to contain the files you will be analyzing. This will improve the performance significantly over traditional hard drives.

Now that you're familiar with the testing process, we can start really getting into it. Next chapter you'll learn how to get in-depth file analysis from VQMT.

Chapter 5: Working with MSU VQMT

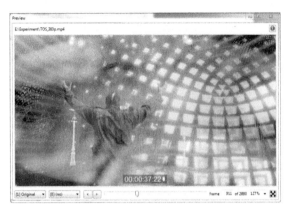

Figure 5-1. The frame visualization screen of the Moscow University Video Quality Measurement Tool.

The Moscow State University (MSU) Graphics and Media Lab has one of the most advanced compression-related curriculums in the world, as well as a very talented group of researchers and professors. The group has published multiple versions of an H.264 codec comparison that's the gold standard when it comes to picking a winner from the contenders. To facilitate these tests, MSU created the Video Quality Measurement Tool (VQMT), with help from Apple, Disney, and Cisco (among others). MSU offers a free version of the tool that can analyze files up to, but not including, 720p resolution—that's a great way to get familiar with the tool. For information on all versions, go to bit.ly/MSU_VQMT_DL.

Unlike SSIMWave and their Video Quality-of-Experience Monitor (SQM) tool, MSU created VQMT to be metric agnostic. In running its benchmark tests, the university relies heavily on peak signal-to-noise ratio (PSNR) and structural similarity (SSIM) testing. For reasons I'll explain in this chapter, I have gravitated towards the PSNR quality metric. The point is, to facilitate its own benchmark testing, MSU has created a very efficient tool for applying different metrics and easily visualizing the results. It has proven invaluable to me in multiple technology evaluations and consulting projects.

This chapter presents an overview of the tool and how it works in graphical user interface (GUI) and command-line modes. Specifically, you will learn:

- how to run VQMT from the GUI

- how to run VQMT from the command line

- how to perform the file conversions necessary for VQMT using the command line

- how to eliminate extra frames from the analysis in both GUI and command-line modes

- how to identify the lowest-quality frames in both GUI and command-line modes.

Note: *One of the most serious limitations of VQMT is that it can't analyze files with disparate resolutions. So if you encoded 1080p source into 360p output, you can't calculate the PSNR value of the 360p file directly in the GUI. Instead, you have to scale the 360p file to 1080p using FFmpeg, which you'll learn how to do in this chapter. If you do try to analyze files with resolutions different than the source, VQMT starts analyzing, then stops without displaying an error message. If this happens to you, 99 percent of the time, it's because of a resolution mismatch.*

Driving the GUI

Words and pictures are great for learning how to use a program, but some prefer screencam videos. If that describes you, go to bit.ly/VQMT_demo to watch a 7.5-minute demonstration of the program on YouTube. The experience is free, and no salesman will call.

As an overview, VQMT is a very flexible tool with lots of features and bells and whistles. I won't demonstrate every feature or mode of operation, but I will show you the basics necessary to analyze your files. Although I've been using the tool consistently for about 18 months now, I probably use only a very small portion of features and functionality in my practice.

Let's work through the individual steps of running the program from the user interface.

Loading Files

VQMT can process one or two files simultaneously, which is useful when comparing one technique, encoder, or codec with another. One significant advance in the last few releases has been the ability to analyze some files in their native format, like the MP4 files shown in Figure 5-2. The manual contains a complete list of video formats and codecs that the program supports, either natively or via AviSynth scripts. If you're working with a file that VQMT can't load directly, you'll have to convert the file to YUV, which I show you how to do in the "Converting with FFmpeg" section in this chapter. Once in YUV format, you can load the file directly into the VQMT interface.

Figure 5-2. Loading the original file and two processed files in VQMT.

Click Browse to load the files, which opens the Opening file dialog shown in Figure 5-3. If you click the Open with list box, you'll see a range of options for opening the file. With MP4 and YUV files, I've always been able to use the Auto option and simply browse to and select the file. If you need to load a file via any of the options in the Open with list box, check the user manual.

> **Note:** *You can drag and drop a file into the middle of the Opening file dialog and VQMT will try to figure out how to load it. When working with MP4 files, that's often the fastest way to load the files.*

Figure 5-3. Choosing the file and opening technique.

Click Next to open the next opening file dialog, shown in Figure 5-4, which I've expanded by clicking and dragging the bottom right edge down and to the right. In this dialog, if you click Offset, you'll be shown the controls on the bottom right of the figure that you can use to exclude frames from the analysis. You'll learn why this is important and how to do in a later section.

Figure 5-4. The second Opening file dialog.

If you input a YUV file, you'll have to manually type in the resolution of the file in the Opening file dialog (Figure 5-5). This is because the file header in YUV files doesn't contain this information. You'll also have to choose the pixel format using the Pixel format drop-down list just above the resolution fields. If you don't know the precise pixel format, experiment with the formats in the list box until the frame shown in the dialog looks normal. This is another case where expanding the dialog by dragging the bottom right edge down and to the right is very helpful.

Figure 5-5. Inserting the resolution and choosing the pixel format. Note that you can use the height and width in the file name to avoid having to do this (see the VQMT manual for details).

Choosing the Metric and Test Options

After selecting the test files, it's time to choose the metric another test options. You'll do this in the bottom of the VQMT interface as shown in Figure 5-6. Let's go through the various steps.

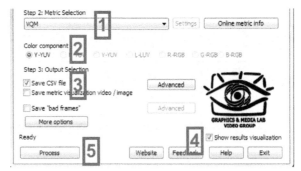

Figure 5-6. Choosing the metric and other options.

1. Choose the metric. As discussed previously, VQMT (currently in version 8) is metric agnostic, and supports many different objectives quality algorithms. The metrics I use the most are PSNR, MS SSIM, SSIM, and VQM.

2. Choose the Color component. Options here are only available if the selected metric supports components other than Y-YUV, which VQM doesn't.

3. Check Save CSV file. The Save CSV file box should be checked by default. If you uncheck it, you'll see the results visualization screen after VQMT finished processing, but the results won't be saved into the CSV file necessary to record the results. Starting in version 9 of VQMT, you'll be able to save CSV and JSON files after the analysis is complete.

4. Check Show results visualization. If the Show results visualization box is not checked, VQMT will save the CSV file, but won't show the Results visualization screen. This can be frustrating because you'll think the program is somehow broken when the results optimization screen doesn't appear after processing. So remember this checkbox if this happens. Starting in version 9, the Visualization window will always open.

5. Click Process. This is the magic Go button that starts the analysis process. Processing time will depend upon a number of factors including file resolution and duration, the selected metric, and the speed of your computer. VQMT shows a progress bar during processing to keep you apprised.

> **Tip:** *VQMT saves the CSV file in the same directory as the processed file (not the source). If there are two processed files in different directories, VQMT saves the CSV file in the directory of the second file.*

The Results Visualization Screen

After processing, VQMT shows the Results visualization screen shown in Figure 5-7. If this screen doesn't appear, it's almost certainly because you didn't check the box marked with "4" in Figure 5-6.

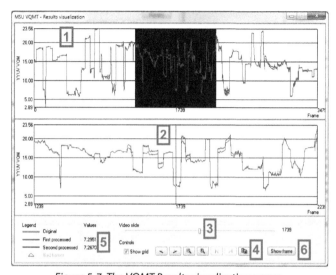

Figure 5-7. The VQMT Results visualization screen.

Let's review the information and controls shown in Figure 5-7.

1. Top graph. The top graph shows the scores for the file(s) tested for the entire duration of the file(s).

2. Bottom graph. The bottom graph shows a zoomed-in region of the top graph. That region is represented by the black box over the top graph.

3. Video slide. You can use the video slide to navigate through the analyzed video file(s). The slider starts halfway through the file. You can navigate through the files by dragging the slider with your cursor, or by using the arrow keys on your keyboard. As you move through the file, the number to the right of the video slide and on the bottom middle of the lower graph—1739 in the figure—updates to show the current frame number.

4. Controls. These controls perform multiple functions. The arrow keys move through the file, the Zoom in/Zoom out keys make the lower graph larger or smaller. The Copy command copies the lower graph into your clipboard to paste into an image editor or other program.

5. Values. These are metric values at the current frame location for the file(s) being analyzed. This is not an average score; it's the scores for that particular frame. To get the average score, you'll have to check the CSV file produced during the analysis.

6. Show frame. Click Show frame to view the current frame. For example, if I clicked Show frame while on the screen shown in Figure 5-7, frame 1739 would appear in the frame viewer shown in Figure 5-8.

Viewing the Frames

You view the frames in the Preview screen shown in Figure 5-8. Here are the relevant controls.

Figure 5-8. The VQMT Preview screen.

1. Toggling between the files. The most common activity performed in this dialog is comparing the original and compressed frames. You can load the frames from the respective files by clicking this drop-down list, or you can use the 1, 2, and 3 keys on your keyboard to toggle through the options. This is an amazingly effective way to view the actual quality deficits in the analyzed frames.

2. Switch into side-by-side mode. Use this drop-down list to enter side-by-side mode (see Figure 5-9).

3. File slider. Use this slider to move through the video file. Or you can use the arrow keys on your keyboard.

4. Frame number. This shows the frame currently showing. Note that you can enter any frame number into this field, and the program will show that frame.

5. Zoom level. Use this drop-down list to zoom into or out of the frame.

6. Full-screen toggle. Switch into full-screen mode. Controls will then appear on the top of the screen to zoom in and out, and exit full-screen mode.

7. Filename. The filename listed on the top left shows you which file the frames are from.

Figure 5-9. Side-by-side viewing mode in the Preview screen.

Viewing the Scores

As mentioned previously, VQMT outputs the test results to a CSV file saved to the location of the compressed file. When I'm compiling results, I typically open the CSV file in Notepad and copy and paste the average score into a Google Sheet. When analyzing a single file, the CSV file identifies the source and test files, as well as the average score.

When analyzing two files, the CSV file shows both scores as shown in Figure 5-10. The top two files are the same file, the source screencam file at 1080p resolution. The first test file was encoded using Adobe Media Encoder (File 1, with _AME in the filename), while the second was encoded with Apple compressor (File 2, with _Comp in the filename). VQMT presents the average scores in order, just as you would expect, with Score 1 for AME (0.05144), and Score 2 for Compressor (0.10148). Since lower scores are better in this test, AME produced a higher-quality file than did Compressor.

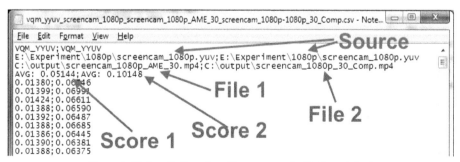

Figure 5-10. Results from two files compared with the original.

The data shown beneath the average scores are the frame-by-frame comparisons between the two tested files. If the test file had 3000 frames, you'd have 3000 lines of frame-by-frame results. The top line in the CSV file shows the test parameters (VQM) and color component (YYUV) for both tests.

Working the Command Line

I distinctly remember the first time I ever booted a computer, a circa 1983 Compaq "portable" that was the size of a sewing machine and weighed about 30 lb. You booted the computer by inserting a Microsoft boot disk into one of the two 5.25-inch floppy drives and pressing the on switch. Two to three minutes later, the A:\ prompt appeared, looking very much like what you see in Figure 5-11. This was literally the first time I ever touched a computer, and after all the ballyhoo about how great they were, I was pretty much underwhelmed. "What now?" I thought. I soon found out the answer to that question, and computers quickly became a fascination, then an avocation, and then an occupation.

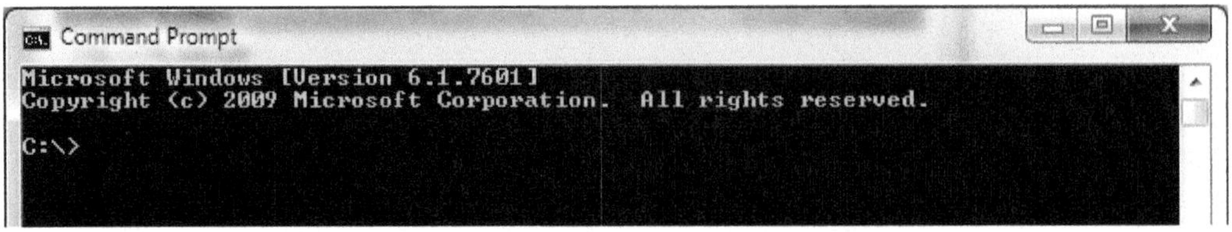

Figure 5-11. The MS-DOS C Prompt in the Command Prompt window. A bit vestigial, but still highly functional.

In the PC-compatible world, MS-DOS ruled until the launch of Windows 3.1 in 1993. Being computer literate in the pre-Windows days meant knowing your way around the command line. With the Windows graphical user interface, however, the command line became irrelevant for most users.

The primary exception relates to the ability to automate multiple operations via what's called a batch file. At a high level, batch file operation involves three components: the program you're running, the files you're processing, and the batch file itself. Take a look at Figure 5-12. The batch file is on the top line and it's named `VQMT.bat`. The program it's running is the command-line version of the VQMT tool.

The individual operations in the batch file are called arguments (also called switches or strings). The command line argument always starts with the program name (`msu_metric_64.exe`). As you can see in Figure 5-13, you refer back to the installed program on your C:\ drive by putting the reference in quotes, which lets Windows ignore the spaces between `Program` and `Files`, and `MSU` and `VQMT`. Without those quotes, Windows wouldn't know where to find the .exe file.

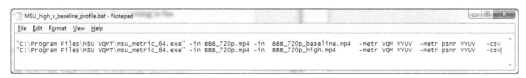

Figure 5-12. A simple batch file and the command line argument.

Then you identify the source file (`-in BBB_720p.mp4`) and compressed file
(`-in BBB_720p_baseline.mp4`). In Figure 5-13, you can see I'm running the test from the
same folder as both files so I don't have to identify the drive and folder (`C:\folder`). While
writing this book, I kept most source test files in the E:\experiment folder and produced
experimental files in a separate folder. I would run VQMT from this folder, and include the E:\
experiment address before the source file location in the VQMT (and FFmpeg) batch files.

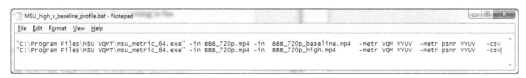

Figure 5-13. Here's the batch file itself.

Then you include the test or tests to run (`-metr VQM YYUV -metr psnr YUV`). If you're
comparing multiple metrics, as I did a lot while writing this book, the ability to run multiple
metrics simultaneously speeds up processing time and simplifies batch file creation.

The last command, `-csv`, ensures that you save a CSV file. I'll cover the arguments for VQMT in
more detail shortly, but this is sufficient to get us started.

Now if you just had one file to test, you could run it in the GUI. But if you have multiple files to
run, the command line is much simpler. Figure 5-13 shows the batch file I created to run two
tests comparing the quality of the H.264 Baseline and High profiles when encoding a 720p
version of the Big Buck Bunny test file. While writing this book, I used batch files with hundreds
of entries that took hours or even days to complete. Of course, since it was running in batch
mode, I was off doing other things (like sleeping). Once the processing was complete, I could
simply open the CSV files and copy the results into my spreadsheet.

Not all programs offer command-line operation, so you can't automate every Windows
program with batch files. VQMT obviously does, as does FFmpeg, which you'll use for a variety
of operations.

Introduction to Batch File Creation and Operation

Here's the basic setup and structure of running command line arguments. Note that I know just enough about batch files to automate the testing and analysis described in this and the following chapter. I'm certainly not a maven, and this section is designed to be an introduction to batch file operation for newbies, not an advanced course.

1. Plan the location of your files. As mentioned, I ran VQMT from its location on the C:\ drive, kept all source files in the same folder on my E:\ drive, and created a new folder for each experiment—into which I saved the test files. I created every VQMT batch in this test folder. For this reason, most VQMT batch files had the following components:

```
"C:\Program Files\MSU VQMT\msu_metric_64.exe"

-in E:\experiment\BBB_720p.mp4

-in BBB_720p_baseline.mp4
```

The first line ran VQMT on my C:\ drive; the second input the source file in the E:\experiment folder; the third input the encoded file which needed no address because it was in the same folder as the source file.

2. Create the batch file. I use Notepad to create batch files in Windows because it doesn't introduce any funky characters into the text like Microsoft Word can do. You need to know the specific arguments for each command line program, and I'll cover those for FFmpeg and VQMT shortly. Figure 5-13 shows a batch file in Notepad. Basically, you list the operations one by one and the program parses through the file and runs the requested analyses in sequence.

3. Save the batch file. Save the batch file with a .bat extension, which lets the operating system know that it's a batch file (`MSU_high_v_baseline_profile.bat`). Since I often have multiple batch files for different operations in the same folder, I try to name them accordingly. For example, I use the following conventions:

`MSU_` an MSU VQMT batch file.

`Encode_` an FFmpeg batch for encoding a file from source.

`Scaling_` an FFmpeg batch for scaling encoded output to YUV/Y4M for analysis.

This makes it much easier to find batch files for reuse. And trust me, you'll want to reuse as many batch files as you can.

4. Run the batch file. You can run the batch file by double-clicking it in Windows Explorer. The operating system will open the Command Prompt window, run the batch operations, and then close the window.

You can also run batch files directly from the command line in the Command Prompt window, which you will do occasionally to debug batch files with errors. If you're running a batch file from Windows Explorer, and the batch file has errors, you may see a quick flash of red, but the Command Prompt window will quickly close, so you don't have time to identify the problem. If you open the batch file directly in Command Prompt window, the error message will remain on screen, allowing you to debug the problem.

There are two ways to open the Command Prompt window, as shown in Figure 5-14. Working from the Windows Start menu, you can either choose the Command Prompt program if available in your start menu, or type "command" to search for the Command Prompt in the program search screen on the bottom of the figure. Then navigate to the folder containing the batch file, and type of the name of the batch file in the command line. To run the batch file shown in Figure 5-13, for example, you would type VQMT.bat at the prompt.

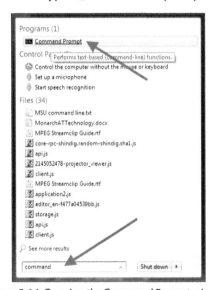

Figure 5-14. Opening the Command Prompt window.

Essential Command Line Commands

When you open the Command Prompt window, you typically will be in the C:\ drive and most of your batch files will likely be another drive or another folder. So job number one is navigating to the specific file location or location of the batch file. While there are myriad ways to do this, here are the simplest options.

- **Change drive.** Type the drive name and colon, but not a slash. For example, type e: to switch to the E:\ drive, and the prompt should change to read E:\. If you type in the slash, you'll get an error message.

- **Change folder in a drive.** Type `cd` (for change directory), then a space (press space bar), and then the name of the directory. For example, type `cd experiment` to move to the experiment folder on the current drive. If that was the E:\ drive, you would be in E:\ experiment.

- **Navigate closer to the root directory.** To navigate closer to the root—say from E:\experiment\Test to E:\experiment—type `cd..` (cd followed by two periods). Or, from any folder, type `cd\` to move to the root of that drive (E:\).

- **View all folders in a drive.** Once you get to a drive (or folder), you may need to see what folders are in the drive. To list all folders, type `dir *.` (dir followed by *.).

- **View all files and folders in a drive.** Once you get to a drive (or folder), you may need to see the files and folders there. To do so, type `dir` (dir).

- **View all files of a specific type in a drive or folder.** Once you navigate to a drive or folder, you may need to see which files are in that folder, particularly if you're trying to run a specific batch file. Type `dir *.bat` to locate all batch files in a folder. To list all files with a different extension (like MP4 files), simply substitute in that extension (`dir *.mp4`).

- **Paste a command line argument into the command prompt.** The simplest way to test a command line argument is to copy it into the Command Prompt. Note that Ctrl + V won't work; you have to right-click in the Command Prompt window and choose Paste.

Tip: *Both Macintosh and Linux computers support batch operation, but since the analysis tools covered here run primarily on Windows, I'm focusing on that platform. While batch file operation is very similar on Mac and Linux computers, the syntax for creating and running files, as well as navigating through directories, is different on those platforms. Once you know how to run batch files on one platform, it's pretty simple to learn operations on other platforms, but you'll need to find a detailed guide to explain the specific syntax and navigational commands.*

Running VQMT from the Command Line

VQMT command-line interface is a very rich environment with lots of options, including using scripts for programs like AviSynth to open and process files. It is very well explained in the product manual and you should consult that for reference. In particular, the new manual has several batch file examples that should simplify creating your own batch files. I recommend that you check the manual if you decide to go beyond the example provided here.

Note that the command line options have changed from version 4 to version 5. While command line strings from version 4 will continue to run under version 5, the new syntax is simpler and you should consider migrating your batch files to the new version as soon as possible.

Here I'm showing the simplest possible command string for comparing a compressed MP4 file with the source, running the VQM metric, and saving off the CSV file. Although this is simple, it's all you need. Note that I've excluded path information to save space; you'll need to add your specific file address for each file as well as the VQMT .exe file.

```
msu_metric_64.exe -in BBB_720p.mp4 -in BBB_720p_main.mp4 -metr VQM
YYUV -csv
```

Here's an explanation of the various components.

`msu_metric_64.exe` the program name. If the program isn't located in the same folder as the batch file, you must list the path to the program file as well.

`-in BBB_720p.mp4` the name of the source file. Include path information if the source file isn't located in the same folder as the batch file.

`-in BBB_720p_main.mp4` the name of the file to compare to the original. You can input multiple files here, though I've always performed the analysis one file at a time for simplicity. Again, insert `-in` to identify each file.

`-metr VQM YYUV` the metric or metrics, and color component, which varies by VQMT test. Depending upon the test, you can run it in different color components—like the Y, U, or V components of the YUV color space, or R, G, or B components of the RGB color space. YYUV is the only option for the VQM test.

> **Note.** *You can run multiple tests simultaneously, but you need to add* `-metr` *before each test, and identify both the test and color space for each test. See Figure 5-13 for this syntax.*

`-csv` saves the CSV file. By default, the command line version saves the CSV file in the same folder as the batch file, but you can insert a path for the CSV file in the command line argument if desired. See the VQMT manual for details.

Working with YUV and Y4M Files

The developers at MSU have done a great job incorporating new formats into the tool, so you can test MP4 files, HEVC files (in MP4 containers), and VP9 files (in WebM format) without conversion. If you're working with other formats, you may have to use FFmpeg to convert to YUV/Y4M format to test these with either the VQMT GUI or command line.

What's the difference between YUV and Y4M? YUV is a dumb file with sequential raw frames and a YUV extension. As you saw in Figure 5-5, if you input a YUV file into the VQMT GUI, you'll have to input the resolution and choose the input format manually. As you'll see below, you'll have to do the same when analyzing a YUV file using the VQMT command line.

In contrast, when you create a Y4M file in FFmpeg, the program stores the resolution information and format metadata in the header. When you see Y4M, think metadata. As a result of this metadata, you can use a Y4M file as easily as an MP4 file; you don't have to specify resolution or format in either the GUI or command line.

This makes Y4M the easier format to use. As you'll see, creating a Y4M file is just a matter of specifying that file extension in the FFmpeg script. Why are we talking about YUV at all? Because some older versions of VQMT don't properly display the frames in the Results visualization screen when using Y4M as compared to YUV. The calculations are all fine, but if you click Show frame in the Results visualization screen, the Y4M file will be stuck on the first frame. I know VQMT exhibits this behavior in version 5.2, but that Y4M files work fine in version 7. Can't tell you about version 6.

So, if you're working with an older version of VQMT, you may want to use YUV files so you can visualize the results. With newer versions, Y4Ms are the way to go.

Working with YUV Files

When working with my YUV files, the VQMT command string changes because the file header does not include information about the color space of the file, or the resolution. To run these files, you'll have to specify both format and resolution in the command string as shown here:

```
msu_metric_64.exe -in BBB_360p.yuv IYUV -in BBB_360p_bl.yuv
-metr psnr YYUV -sc 1 640x360
```

To specify the file format, you insert it after the first YUV file, like the bolded **IYUV** after BBB_360p.yuv. You don't need to specify the format after all the files, just the first. You specify the resolution at the end of the string (like the bolded **640x360**).

Again, with Y4M files, you don't have to specify either—just use them like MP4 files.

> **Tip.** *The most common mistake I make in multiple-resolution YUV testing with VQMT is forgetting to change the resolution in the command line argument when I change from one resolution to another. To minimize the risk of this, I include the resolution of the test in the batch file name, like BBB_MSU_360p.bat. That way, when I copy the batch file to reuse it, I have a reminder to change the resolution if and when necessary.*

Converting with FFmpeg

FFmpeg is a Swiss Army knife-type tool with exceptional functionality. It's simple enough that most video professionals can easily pick it up, and powerful enough to run encoding operations at sites like YouTube. FFmpeg is an open-source tool that you can download at ffmpeg.org/download.html.

There are many websites that explain FFmpeg functions, as well as detail the various switches and arguments. The most comprehensive source that I've seen is Frantisek Korbel's book *FFmpeg Basics: Multimedia handling with a fast audio and video encoder*, which is available on Amazon. You shouldn't need the book for converting files to YUV format, though.

You'll learn about FFmpeg throughout the book. Here we'll focus on conversion and scaling functions, starting with simple conversion from one format to another. You'll need to do this to analyze a file that VQMT doesn't input natively. For example, when I first started working with VQMT, it didn't input VP9 or HEVC files natively, so I had to use FFmpeg to convert them to YUV.

This is command string that I use. Since FFmpeg uses the native frame rate and resolution of the file unless told to do otherwise, you don't have to specify either of these to make the conversion.

```
ffmpeg -i BBB_720p.MP4 -pix_fmt yuv420p -vsync 0 BBB_360p.y4m
```

`ffmpeg` calls the program. If the program isn't located in the same folder as the batch file, you must list the path to the program file as well.

`-i BBB_720p.MP4` identifies the input file. Include the path if the source file isn't located in the same folder as the batch file.

`-pix_fmt yuv420p` identifies the file formats. The argument `-pix_fmt` tells FFmpeg to change the file format, while the `yuv420p` identifies the target format. If you use `yuv420p`, it matches up with the `IYUV` specified in the VQMT command line shown previously.

`-vsync 0` tells FFmpeg to preserve the same video sync in the output file as in the input file. I'm not 100 percent sure that the `vsync` command is necessary—I inserted it in an attempt to eliminate some sync issues with a particular encoder, which it did, and it's never caused a problem with other encoders.

`BBB_360p.y4m` the name of the target output file. If you insert a specific path, FFmpeg will save the file in the designated location. I'm specifying Y4M for reasons discussed earlier. If you need a YUV file, just use that extension.

I've used variations of this command line argument roughly a gazillion times. If you're converting files to process with the command-line version of VQMT, give it a shot and see if it works for you.

Scaling in FFmpeg

Since VQMT is compatible with most formats I use these days, I convert files to Y4M format mostly to scale them to the original resolution of the input file. You'll learn about scaling in Chapter 7. The short story is that when you produce 360p output for streaming, you often encode from a 1080p source file. As mentioned earlier, you can't compare the 360p-encoded file to the 1080p source file directly in VQMT; you have to scale the encoded file to 1080p and compare them. Here's the command line for doing that, with the new arguments in bold.

```
ffmpeg -i  BBB_360p.MP4 -pix_fmt yuv420p -vsync 0 -s 1920x1080
-sws_flags lanczos BBB_1080p.y4m
```

Here's an explanation of the new switches in the command line argument.

`-s 1920x1080` changes the resolution to 1080p.

`-sws_flags lanczos` tells FFmpeg to use the Lanczos filter to perform the scaling.

I used the Lanczos scaling method after finding a white paper from graphics card vendor NVIDIA that stated this was a primary method used on the company's graphics cards. Since I was trying to simulate the quality perceived when a graphics card scaled video, this seemed appropriate. Lanczos is not the default method for FFmpeg, although the documents don't appear to specify what the default method is (see bit.ly/ff_scale). I compared the quality of a file produced with Lanczos against one produced without specifying a method (which obviously used the default method), and the default method rated higher. So, when scaling to simulate a graphics card, use Lanczos; when trying for top quality, don't specify and use the default (although you can Google and find plenty of tests that disagree with my results).

> **Tip.** *If you know how to create a script in AviSynth, you don't have to pre-convert your files to YUV. Check the VQMT manual for more details. I'm not an AviSynth user, so I've always pre-converted with FFmpeg.*

> **Tip.** *If you are applying similar tests to multiple source files, you may be able to reuse these batch files by copying and pasting them to the new folder, and using Notepad's search and replace function to swap out the source file name. If you minded the recommendations in Chapter 1 and standardized file names and nomenclature, this should be a fairly simple operation.*

> **Tip.** *SSIMWave Video Quality-of-Experience Monitor (SQM), which you learn how to use in the next chapter, can analyze files with disparate resolutions, so you don't need to pre-convert any files to YUV.*

Eliminating Excess Frames

As mentioned earlier, one of the most significant issues that arise when using VQMT is when the encoder inserts extra frames at the start of the encoded clip. Obviously, this prevents VQMT from comparing the proper frames in the input and compressed files, and produces an erroneous score. With version 4 of VQMT, you had to trim the frame from the compressed or YUV file, which was time consuming, and involved an extra processing step that you always worried somehow affected the score.

Interestingly, when I reviewed SQM, I noted that it had a very simple adjustment tool that avoided this problem, and pointed this out to the MSU programming team. Two beta versions later, the fix in the GUI and command that I describe below appeared. Coincidence? I think not. Actually, MSU acknowledged that I was the instigator of the change, of which I'm both proud and relieved, because it's a problem I frequently face.

You'll know you have a problem when VQMT reports an outrageously high score, like 5.223452. You'll scan the file, and in most cases, it will look fine, and you'll wonder what happened. This is why I put timecode in all my test files. Without it—particularly if you're fading in from black—it's almost impossible to tell when the extra frame is inserted. With timecode inserted, you can preview the file in the main VQMT interface, and if you see two different frames with the same timecode, you know you have a problem.

Figure 5-15. Removing an extra frame from the encoded file.

In the GUI, follow the instructions shown from Figures 5-2 to 5-5. Then, as shown in Figure 5-15.

1. Click Offset. This reveals the controls shown in the figure.

2. Click over to the first frame you want included in the file. In virtually all instances where I've experienced the problem, the encoder added a single frame to the start of the clip. To eliminate this, go to frame 1 as shown in the figure.

3. Click A to eliminate the selected frame from the start of the clip.

Then click Finish as normal, to return to the main VQMT interface. If you preview that file, you should see that VQMT has excluded the extra frame.

If you click the offset type drop-down box, you'll see three options: seek, skip, and auto, which is the default. I asked my contact at MSU to explain the differences, and this is what he sent.

- *Seek.* Seeking to selected frame. Seeking can be unsafe, produce unstable picture for some codecs.

- *Skip.* All frames before start frame will be decoded. For big offset, this can be slow.

- *Auto.* Select automatically. Seek will be used if seeking is safe for this file or offset is quite big.

I use auto and leave it at that.

To eliminate the extra frame in the command-line interface, just add `-range 1-` to the end of the string. For example, to eliminate a single extra frame inserted into the encoded file, add the `-range 1-` as shown here:

```
msu_metric_64.exe -in BBB_720p.mp4 -in BBB_720p_main.mp4 -metr VQM
YYUV -csv -range 1-
```

I've experienced the extra-frame problem working with different desktop encoders, including Sorenson Squeeze and HandBrake. I've also experienced it with files created using command-line strings, including VP9 and HEVC. In all cases, the encoder inserted only a single frame at the start of the clip. In the tests are performed recently, both the GUI and the command-line fix described above eliminated the issue. Kudos to the MSU team.

Low Frame Quality

In Chapter 8 we start exploring the concept of low frame quality. The theory is that you need the configuration that delivers not only the best overall quality, but also avoids transient quality issues. So there we start tracking the lowest-quality frame, a value that you can acquire in either the command line or GUI. Let's start with the command line. To identify the lowest-quality frame, add the bolded switches to the command line we've been working with.

```
msu_metric_64.exe -in BBB_720p.mp4 -in BBB_720p_main.mp4 -metr VQM
YYUV -csv -sbf -bfnum 0 -bft origproc
```

Here's what the new switches mean.

-sbf turns on save bad frames.

-bfnum 0 the number of bad frames saved, with 0 equaling one bad frame saved (go figure).

-bft origproc identifies the bad frame type, which can be origproc, procproc, firstbetter, or secondbetter (check the manual for definitions). Use origproc when comparing a single file to the original, and VQMT identifies the frames with the maximum difference between the original and first processed file (orig:proc). Since the first processed file is always perfect, this identifies the lowest-quality frame(s) in the video.

When you're analyzing two files, you have to use one of the final three options, which identifies the frames with the largest quality differences between the two compressed files. Often these are not the absolute lowest-quality frames, making this analysis useless if you're seeking the lowest-quality frames. Figure 5-16 shows what the frame looks like after it's saved. You can see the name of the video, the file it was compared to, the metric value, and the frame number. z

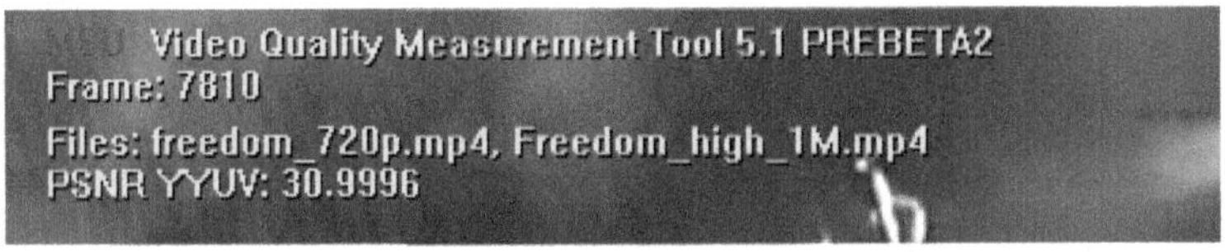

Figure 5-16. The lowest-quality frame in this encode was frame 7810.

You can run the same analysis in the GUI by clicking the Save bad frames checkbox in the GUI front panel, and clicking the Advanced button to see the settings shown on the right in Figure 5-17. If you have two files loaded, as I do in Figure 5-17, you have to choose one of the final three options. Remember to set the output folder before processing.

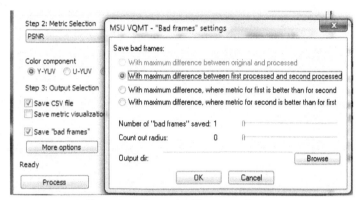

Figure 5-17. Saving bad frames in the GUI.

Figure 5-18 shows how VQMT annotates the saved frames from both test files. With PSNR values of 48.3601 and 50.063, the two frames tagged show where the disparity between the Baseline and High profiles is the greatest, but not the absolute lowest-quality frames. I really don't care that there's a big difference at those PSNR levels because no viewer would notice it. I wanted to find the lowest-quality frames in the file, and analyzing two compressed files in the GUI doesn't get you there.

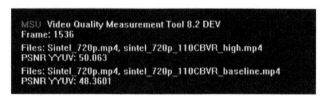

Figure 5-18. Frame output when comparing two encoded files.

Now you know how to compute a variety of objective metrics via the VQMT command line and GUI. In the next chapter, you'll learn how to use another tool, the SSIMWave Video Quality-of-Experience Monitor (SQM).

Author's note: *I wish to thank Moscow State University's Dr. Dmitriy Kulikov and Georgiy Osipov for their tech read of this chapter, and many helpful suggestions.*

Chapter 6: Working with SQM

Figure 6-1. The new visualization screens for the SSIMWave SQM.

The SSIMWave Video Quality-of-Experience Monitor (SQM) tool offers a different value proposition from that of Moscow State University's format-agnostic Video Quality Measurement Tool (VQMT). Specifically, the tool is built around the company's SSIMplus algorithm, which was co-invented by Dr. Zhou Wang, the company's co-founder, and co-inventor of the SSIM algorithm, which recently won an Engineering Emmy from the Television Academy (bit.ly/ssimplusemmy).

According to tests performed by company researchers available at bit.ly/SSIMPlus_VQM (see Figure 2 of the Introduction), the newer SSIMplus algorithm provides the most accurate matching between SSIMplus scoring and actual subjective ratings of all tested algorithms, which included SSIM and VQMT. Today, the SQM tool is the only way to access the SSIMplus algorithm.

In this chapter, you will learn:

- the unique features of the SQM tool

- the feature sets of the three operating modes: graphical user interface (GUI) mode, batch mode, and command line interface (CLI) mode

- how to operate SQM in all three modes

- how to visualize the results in QoE Visualizer.

SQM's Unique Features

Unlike most metrics produced by VQMT, SQM's ratings correlate with expected subjective evaluations, so a score of 80 to 100 predicts that live viewers will find the video excellent in quality, 60 to 80 predicts that viewers will rate the video good in quality, and so on down to zero. In contrast, while metrics like VQMT can tell you which video has higher quality than another, it doesn't correlate to any level of viewer perception.

Beyond this, SQM offers multiple additional features not available in VQMT. First, you can select device-specific profiles like smartphones, tablets, computer monitors, and smart TVs, and SQM will render a score that predicts how viewers watching video on those devices will rate the video. This is important, because what looks good on a smartphone doesn't necessarily look good on a 65-inch 4K TV. There's even an expert mode to predict quality when the viewer is exceptionally close to the screen. SQM can also predict scores at resolutions different than the source resolution, which simplifies operation dramatically—no conversions to Y4M required.

Beyond cross resolution, SQM can perform cross-frame-rate testing (120 fps, 60 fps, 30 fps, 24 fps); cross-bit-depth testing (8-bit, 10-bit for SDR); cross-pixel format testing (YUV420, 422, 444, 411 etc); and cross-scan type (interlaced, progressive) testing. The cross-bit-depth measurement for HDR video quality of experience (QoE) is in the product roadmap. Note that many of these features are available only in the command line version, as specified shortly.

Driving the GUI

As with VQMT, SQM is a flexible tool with lots of features. I won't demonstrate every feature or mode of operation, but I will show you the basics necessary to analyze your files using multiple device profiles.

Let's work through the individual steps of running the program from the user interface.

Loading Files

SQM compares a single encoded file to the source (called the reference). Load the files by clicking the folder icon on the bottom left of the interface (Figure 6-2).

Figure 6-2. Click the Folder icon to open the file selection screen shown in Figure 6-3.

Figure 6-3 shows the file selection screen. You know the drill for most of these actions, but let's dig in.

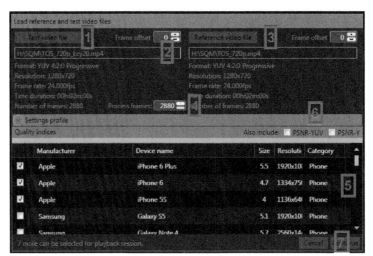

Figure 6-3. Choosing test parameters.

1. Load the Test video file. The test file is the encoded file you'll compare to the source.

2. Exclude any extra frames. If the encoder inserted duplicate frames at the start of the clip, exclude them using the Frame offset control. As an example, click 1 if the encoder inserted a single extra frame at the start of the clip.

3. Load the Reference video file. This is the source video file. Again, use the Frame offset control to exclude any extra frames.

4. If desired, limit the application of the test. If you only want to test the first 100 frames, insert this into the Process frames control. Note that by using the Frame offset and Process frames control, you can isolate any discrete section in the file. For example, if you use Frame offset at 100 for both files, and limit Process frames to 200, you'll analyze the second 200 frames in the file.

5. Choose settings. This is where you choose the device settings for measuring quality. The test will always deliver a composite SSIMplus Core score. If you're encoding for mobile delivery, check several smartphones and tablets, using the scroll bar on the right to view all available devices. When targeting computer playback, check several computer monitors of various sizes. If the video is for TV playback, there are multiple devices for that. Any device with (Expert) in the title means the viewer will watch from very close to the screen. Otherwise, the test assumes normal viewing distances.

6. Choose additional tests. SQM can calculate peak signal-to-noise ratio (PSNR) using in the YUV or Y color spaces.

7. Click Continue to close the dialog and run the test. Otherwise choose Cancel to choose two new files.

You now should see the interface as shown in Figure 6-4. Here are the components in the interface and how to run the test from here.

Figure 6-4. Running a test in SQM.

1. Press Play to start the test. The Play button toggles to the Pause button, which you click to pause playback. Note that SSIMWave may add full playback controls to future versions of the tool, but they were not available in the version that I tested. This means that there will be no way to scroll back and forth in a file until those controls appear.

2. Test video. This displays the test/encoded video.

3. The quality map. According to SSIMWave, the quality map "predicts the quality at every pixel in every frame in the test video."

4. Quality map/source file toggle. This control toggles the right display window between the quality map and the source file. Note it is not available when encoded video and source video have different resolutions.

5. Device scores for that frame. These bars show the SQM scores for the displayed frame for the selected devices in real time as the tool processes the videos.

6. Score graph over time. These graphs track the scores for the devices over time.

7. Quality threshold. SQM lets you set a quality threshold below which any frames are reported. The default quality threshold is set at 70, which is shown in the display graph area. This makes it easy to identify when any frames in the video fall below the minimum quality standards.

When you finish or stop the test, the tool shows the spreadsheet icon in the bottom left as shown in Figure 6-5. Click this to view and save the scores in a CSV file.

Figure 6-5. Click the spreadsheet icon to save a CSV file.

Viewing the Results

In both GUI and batch mode, SQM exports a CSV file with the results. If viewed in a spreadsheet, the results look like those shown Figure 6-6.

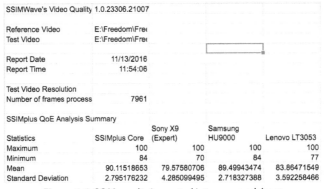

SSIMWave's Video Quality	1.0.23306.21007			
Reference Video	E:\Freedom\Free			
Test Video	E:\Freedom\Free			
Report Date	11/13/2016			
Report Time	11:54:06			
Test Video Resolution				
Number of frames process	7961			
SSIMplus QoE Analysis Summary				
		Sony X9	Samsung	
Statistics	SSIMplus Core	(Expert)	HU9000	Lenovo LT3053
Maximum	100	100	100	100
Minimum	84	70	84	77
Mean	90.11518653	79.57580706	89.49943474	83.86471549
Standard Deviation	2.795176232	4.285099495	2.718327388	3.592258466

Figure 6-6. SQM results imported into a spreadsheet.

As mentioned, the SSIMplus Core score is always shown, along with scores for the selected devices. The score that matters is the mean score. Interestingly, note how much lower the Sony X9 (Expert) score is then either of the other two devices or the core score. That's because expert mode assumes the viewer is watching from very close to the screen, where he or she could easily spot artifacts in the video.

Figure 6-7 shows what the CSV file looks like when opened up in Notepad. As you can see, with multiple devices selected, it's tougher to discern which metric relates to each device, which makes recording the results more prone to errors. Once you go beyond three or four devices, it's best to import the CSV file into a spreadsheet and grab your results from there.

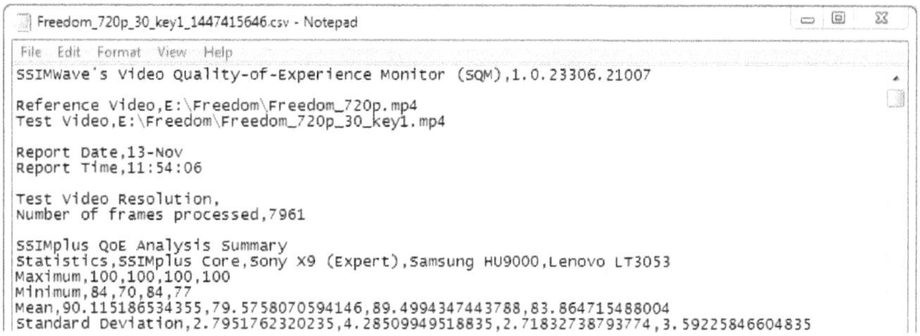

Figure 6-7. The same results shown in Notepad, which can get confusing.

Running SQM in Batch Mode

When you run SQM in batch mode, you create a batch file, load that into the program, and run it from there. I find this approach easier than true command-line operation because the program checks the batch file when you enter it into the program, so you can detect any errors before you get started. On the other hand, as you'll see, pure command line offers a lot more types of tests than either of the GUI modes.

Creating the Batch File

Figure 6-8 shows the structure of the batch file. The top line shows an actual batch entry, under which I've pasted a snippet from the manual that defines the entries. As shown in the figure, you'll list the test video first, including the full address information, and then the source video, again with complete file address. The next entry lets you specify the frame offset for the ***test*** video, which you'll use if the encoder inserts an extra frame at the start of the video. The next entry specifies the offset for the ***reference*** video, and the total number of frames to be tested. The last entry sets the quality threshold.

The middle line of the figure is there to illustrate which entry is which, and won't appear in your actual Notepad file.

> **Note:** *Use the vertical character to separate entries in batch mode. This is located above the Enter key on a Windows keyboard with the Shift key pressed.*

If you're not adjusting any of the offsets, or setting a quality level, none of these entries are necessary. The command string shown on the bottom of the figure shows the typical command line I run, which just includes the test file followed by the source file, with no other modifiers.

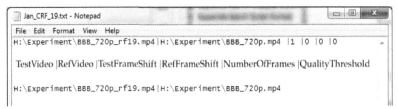

Figure 6-8. The command string structure for SQM in batch mode.

Tip: *Files loaded into the SQM batch interface are not technically batch files since they don't run a program in the Command window. I always save the files as a text file with a .txt extension, but SQM will load files with a .bat extension as well. Whatever extension you use, you should create the files in Notepad rather than Word, to avoid any extraneous characters that could corrupt the batch file.*

Loading Batch File

Here's how you load the batch file into SQM and run the batch.

1. Convert SQM to Batch Mode. On the bottom left of the SQM interface, click the Switch to batch mode icon (Figure 6-9).

Figure 6-9. Converting SQM to batch mode.

2. Load the batch file. On the upper left of the batch mode interface, click Open batch file list. Locate and select the batch file as normal.

Figure 6-10. Loading the batch file.

If there is an error in the batch file, SQM displays a purple message adjacent to the open batch file list (Figure 6-11). Typically, the problem relates to the file name or location.

Figure 6-11. Ruh roh, problem with the batch file.

Fix the problem and reload the file. If all the name, location, and syntax information is correct, you'll be rewarded with a green filename next to the Open batch file list command. This tells you that the batch file is correct and SQM is ready to run.

Figure 6-12. Green means that the batch file is correct and SQM is ready to go.

3. Choose the device profiles. In the SQM interface, choose the desired device profiles (Figure 6-13, 1).

Figure 6-13. Finalizing the SQM batch settings.

4. Choose other metrics to run. If desired, click the PSNR-YUV and/or PSNR-Y checkboxes to calculate these metrics (Figure 6-13, 2).

5. Start running the batch. After finalizing all settings, click the Fast Forward button in the bottom middle of the SQM interface to start running the batch (Figure 6-13, 3).

Run time will depend upon the length and configuration of the files, as well as the speed of your computer and hard drives. The batch will continue until the end; I've run batches that have taken days to complete.

> **Tip:** *SQM is very particular about the batch files it will successfully load. As an example, if you have any extraneous words or even spaces in the file, SQM may display the error message shown in Figure 6-11. When creating batch files for SQM, I'm very careful not to leave any extra spaces in any lines, or any descriptive text at all.*

> **Tip:** *Note that SQM does not use significant CPU resources when performing its analysis. However, you can load multiple instances of the tool simply by clicking the program icon again and again. Split the files you have to test into multiple batch files and you can significantly reduce test time.*

Running SQM in Command Line Interface Mode

Command Line Interface (CLI) mode is available in a separate download that you can install anywhere in your file structure (the Windows GUI version installs itself normally in the Program Files folder on your C:\ drive). Like the GUI version, the CLI version is locked to a dongle that you obtain when you purchase the software.

The CLI version can perform all operations that the GUI and batch mode can perform, plus the others listed below. It can also automatically align frames, eliminating problems caused by encoders inserting extra frames into the encoded filed. Here's a complete list of operations available in CLI that aren't available in the GUI.

> *1. Cross-frame rate comparisons.* Compare videos with different frame rates.
>
> *2. Expert mode.* Enables all supported devices.
>
> *3. Spatial region-of-interest (ROI) selection*. Prioritize regions within the frames.
>
> *4. Multiple speed options*. Reduce processing time with minor compromise on QoE prediction accuracy.
>
> *5. Customized measurement period in seconds.*
>
> *6. Mean Square Error calculation*.
>
> *7. Support for program/transport streams.* Video program ID (PID) support for multiple program transport streams.
>
> *8. Linux OS support.*
>
> *9. Source and overall video QoE measurement.* The CLI version can test the quality of the source video, and factor that into the QoE of the compressed video.

Overall, a lot of great functionality that will be useful to advanced users.

Creating Batch Files

The command line version comes with a readme file that documents operation. The basic structure is this:

```
SQM.exe -r referenceVideo -d testVideo -dev ssimpluscore
[optional values]
```

Here's a simple command line that I used for testing.

```
SQM.exe -r TOS_1080p.mp4 -d TOS_180p.mp4 -dev
ssimpluscore:iphone6plus -rf report.csv
```

Unless `SQM.exe` is located in the same folder as the batch file, you'll need to add the path to the exe file at the start of the command line. Note the colon (`:`) after `ssimpluscore:` where you can insert devices, each separated by an additional colon. The readme file contains a handy list of those devices. Finally, the `-rf report.csv` produces the CSV file with the test results you'll likely need.

As mentioned previously, I like using batch mode because the program checks the batch before it starts running, eliminating most errors. However, the CLI version performs more functions, and is easier for programmers to automate, making it a very valuable addition to the GUI version.

> **Tip:** *Chapter 5 has a useful introduction to command line and batch file operation. If you're unfamiliar with how batch files work, you might want to start there.*

Visualizing Your Results

In early 2016, SSIMWave released the SSIMWave QoE Visualizer for the SQM. As an overview, you run the tool within a browser, dragging .csv files into the interface to load the data from the files, and switching into play mode to play the files as you would in the SQM interface.

You open the Visualizer from the QoE-Visualizer folder in your Windows installation folder;

```
C:\Program Files (x86)\SSIMWave\SSIMWave Video QoE Monitor\
QoE-Visualizer
```

The utility is labeled `visualizer.html` in that folder, and works best if you open it with the Google Chrome browser. If Chrome is your default browser, just click `visualizer.html` and Chrome should load the Visualizer.

Opening Visualizer and Loading Files

After opening the Visualizer, you drag CSV files produced by SQM into the designated region in the tool. Don't move your test files after running the SQM tests, because if you change the file location in the CSV files, you won't be able to play the files within the Visualizer.

Figure 6-14. Dragging .csv files into the visualization tool.

The visualization tool will take a few moments to crunch the data, and then will present the results shown in Figure 6-15, which is essentially a multiple-file view of the data shown in the main tool. Note that you can delete any of the test files input into the program by clicking the trash icon beneath the filename on the upper left. You can also load additional files into the tool by dragging them into the file bar.

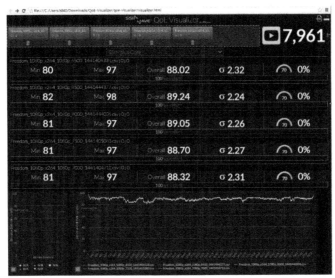

Figure 6-15. The QoE Visualizer tool showing the collective file results.

On the upper right of the visualization tool interface, there are three controls for printing the results (Figure 6-16, 1), saving a collective .csv file with the results from all the files (Figure 6-16, 2), or switching into video playback mode (Figure 6-16, 3).

Figure 6-16. The upper right of the QoE Visualizer tool.

Playing the Files

Figure 6-17 shows the file playback interface. Select the file to play by clicking it in the file bar on the upper left. The selected file appears in blue (Figure 6-17, 1).

You can play the file by clicking the spacebar, or click any spot in the quality graph to move to that location. A small black dot will appear where you clicked in the file (Figure 6-17, 2). If you analyzed for multiple devices, you can choose the results to display in the graph window by clicking the drop-down list directly above the video playback window (Figure 6-17, 3).

Figure 6-17. The file playback interface.

During playback, you can drag the thin vertical line shown above the video to view the source and encoded files. On the bottom left of the graph, you can view export options for data shown in the graph (and not the video frames), which include downloading a PDF file and multiple image formats of the quality graph (Figure 6-18).

Figure 6-18. Export options for the quality graph.

Tip: *In the beta version documented above, there are no playback controls. You use the spacebar to stop and start playback, and can click in the frame graph to move the play head to any location in the file.*

That's SQM. This ends the preliminaries. Now that you know the basics and how to use the tools, it's time to jump in and start applying them to our compression-related decisions.

Author's note: *I wish to thank SSIMWave's Dr. Kai Zeng for his tech read of this chapter, and many helpful suggestions.*

Chapter 7: Choosing Data Rate

Figure 7-1. Encoding at constant quality in HandBrake.

Now you know basic file parameters and about objective testing; it's time to put it to use. Of all the encoding decisions that you make, the data rate decision is the most important. We'll spend much of the rest of the book fine-tuning various encoding decisions, but get this one wrong and you can irreparably compromise quality. This is one decision that you have to get right.

We touched on data rate (also known as bitrate) back in Chapter 2, where you also learned about bits per pixel. Now, using the information that you learned in the interim chapters, we're going to take that understanding to a whole new level.

Specifically, in this chapter, you will learn:

- that all files encode differently, and that a technique called constant rate factor (CRF) encoding can identify the data rate necessary to maintain consistent quality across all of your files

- that while increasing the data rate of your files almost always improves quality, you typically reach a point of diminishing returns beyond which increasing the data rate delivers minimal value

- that a reasonable goal for file encoding is to find the lowest data rate that eliminates noticeable artifacts.

Note that this chapter addresses single file encodes only, although we will revisit much of this analysis in the chapter on adaptive streaming. I'm also assuming that you're using a single encoding ladder for all videos, or for all videos within a specific type of videos. If you're interested in per-title encoding, check out Chapter 16.

Finding the Appropriate Data Rate

I wish I could tell you that finding the appropriate data rate for any particular resolution file is a simple matter. Unfortunately, in my experience, it's not. On the plus side, for most organizations, it's a decision that you make once every two or three years and then use for the next 24 to 36 months. So spending time to make the right decision up front is worthwhile.

There are many idiosyncratic factors involved in identifying the optimal data rate, not the least of which is the inherent difference in content between most video files.

You can approach the data rate decision in multiple ways. As you will learn shortly, Netflix has created a brute force analysis for computing the appropriate data rate for each file it distributes. Very effective, but not that efficient. Unless you have access to a room full of math PhDs, it's probably beyond your capabilities.

The second approach is to hunt around and find the data rate used by other reputable sources, and simply use those data rates. There's validity here, and we'll check the data rates used by Hollywood at various points in this chapter. But unless your video content is exactly the same as the files encoded by those other sources, this information could have limited value.

Still another approach involves encoding files to multiple data rates and attempting to identify the lowest rate that meets your subjective quality requirements. This analysis is essential, and we'll discuss this shortly as well.

From my perspective, however, the simplest and most straightforward starting point is to encode your files using CRF encoding and gauge the result. So let's start there, taking a brief roundabout to discuss what Netflix announced in December 2015.

Netflix Per-title Encode Optimization

On December 14 2015, Netflix released a seminal blog post titled "Per-Title Encode Optimization" (bit.ly/NF_pertitle). In the post, Netflix announced that it was customizing the encoding for each title in its library—and, equally importantly, why.

Netflix explained the why by sharing the results of an experiment during which the team encoded 100 titles at 1080p resolution using constant quantization parameter (QP) rate control at multiple QP values with the x264. At a high level, QP encoding seeks to deliver a certain quality level, and it varies the data rate to achieve this. Netflix encoded each file using four different QP levels, which produced four files with varying data rates. The team then measured the peak signal-to-noise ratio (PSNR) for each clip at each level, and plotted the bitrate/PSNR points in the graph shown in Figure 7-2.

Looking at the two files at the bottom of the graph, the lavender and aqua lines, you see that even though the QP encoding resulted in files with very high data rates of 20 Mbps and beyond, the PSNR level, which was around 38 dB for both files, was comparatively low. This indicates that these files are challenging to encode.

At the other end of the spectrum, the light blue line pointing nearly vertical at the top of the graph topped out at over 48 dB at less than 2 Mbps, despite using the same QP value as the two encodes at the bottom. That's dramatically higher quality at less than 10 percent of the data rate, indicating that that the top light blue line represents an easy-to-encode file.

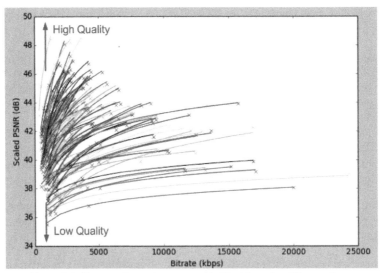

Figure 7-2. How quality varies among Netflix titles using QP encoding.

From these results, Netflix concluded:

> Given this diversity, a one-size-fits-all scheme obviously cannot provide the best video quality for a given title and member's allowable bandwidth. It can also waste storage and transmission bits because, in some cases, the allocated bitrate goes beyond what is necessary to achieve a perceptible improvement in video quality.

Netflix then goes on to describe how it creates that custom encoding ladder, which I discuss in Chapter 16. Again, while Netflix's technique is beyond most casual readers, you can achieve a reasonable facsimile thereof using the workflow we're about to discuss.

Before we move on to how you'll accomplish this, I wanted to use some Netflix comments in the blog post to tie PSNR scores to subjective ratings, which Netflix is obviously qualified to do. Specifically, for that hard-to-compress file at the bottom of the graph, a PSNR level of 38 dB is "acceptable." At other points in the discussion, Netflix says that scores under 35 dB will often show encoding artifacts, while scores above 45 dB produce no perceptible quality improvements. In other words, pay attention to files with scores of 35 dB and below. Also, encoding files to a data rate of 45 dB and beyond is likely a waste of bandwidth.

Constant Rate Factor (CRF) Encoding

Interestingly, a few days before the Netflix announcement, I had turned in an article to Streaming Media titled "How to Use Objective Quality Measurement Tools" (bit.ly/ABR_via_obj).

After briefly describing objective quality metrics, the first section described how to use CRF encoding to assess the complexity of your clips, essentially, a preview of this chapter.

It turns out that I wasn't the first to come up with this idea. In the days following the Netflix post, I found another blog post (bit.ly/crf_4abr), which predated my article submission, but recommended the same procedure I'm about to describe. So let's jump in.

About CRF Encoding

Where constant QP encoding uses a fixed quality parameter, CRF encoding adjusts the QP value over different scenes within a video to improve quality. How does CRF encoding work? Here's a brief description from Werner Robitza's "CRF Guide" (slhck.info/articles/crf).

> When you use a constant rate factor, it varies the QP slightly. When a scene has a lot of action and motion, it will raise the QP (compressing more). This is because your eye will be distracted by everything going on, and won't have the image on screen for enough time to see the heavier compression. When a frame doesn't have a lot of motion, it will lower the QP, compressing it less. This is because your eye will have more time to look at the image, so you want it to be as much like the source as possible.

In other words, constant QP encoding applies a fixed quality parameter to the entire file, while CRF encoding varies the parameter to adjust to changing content within the file. Both adjust the data rate to achieve a fixed quality level. This is very different from techniques that vary quality to achieve a fixed data rate like constant bitrate encoding (CBR) and variable bitrate encoding (VBR), which you'll learn about in Chapter 8.

Although Netflix used QP in its analysis, I asked the team about CRF for an article that I wrote for Streaming Media about the Netflix technique (bit.ly/SM_NF). David Ronca, Director of Encoding Technologies at Netflix, clarified that, "We started with QP and recently migrated to CRF. The results are about the same." I prefer CRF to QP because it adapts to changing content within the file, so that's where I started.

Here's the critical point. There are some instances, primarily with synthetic clips, where you might use CRF encoding for final distribution. For most real-world video clips, however, you'll need to control the data rate, so you'll use a traditional encoding mechanism like CBR or VBR. For these clips, you'll use CRF to assess the data rate necessary to produce that file at an acceptable quality level. In essence, the analysis and workflow goes like this:

- Use CRF to identify the encoding complexity of the file, and the data rate necessary to achieve a certain quality level.

- Change your existing CBR/VBR-based presets to these targets, and encode as normal for distribution.

Using CRF

Briefly, when you encode with CRF encoding, you choose a CRF value, not a target data rate. You can see this back in Figure 7-1, where I chose a CRF factor of 23. Figure 7-3 shows how CRF values affect quality; specifically, the lower the value, the higher the quality. It's counterintuitive, but that's how it works.

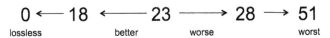

Figure 7-3. How CRF values affect video quality. From "CRF Guide."

How does CRF help us gauge encoding complexity? The crux is this. You encode disparate clips like those shown in Table 7-1 at the same CRF value to produce similar output quality. Then measure the data rate of the clips to see what data rate is necessary to produce that quality level when encoding with CBR or VBR. If the data rates vary significantly, you know that you should customize your encoding parameters for each major type. If not, your one-size-fits-all solution is working just fine.

With this as background, let's take a quick look at the best clips I used in this analysis, and how I produced the CRF encodes.

My Test Clips

As you will see throughout this book, different types of videos respond to various compression options much differently. For this reason, if you're working with different types of videos, like animation and real-world videos, or screencams and talking heads, you should create short test files and test all types of files. Here are the files that I tested in this and future chapters.

- **Tears of Steel.** A Blender Foundation movie—mostly real-world video with some animation

- **Sintel.** Another Blender Foundation movie—all animation, but very lifelike rather than cartoonish

- **Big Buck Bunny.** Yet another Blender Foundation movie—all animation, but more cartoonish than Sintel

- **Screencam.** A section of a VQMT demo video you can watch at bit.ly/vqmt_demo

- **Tutorial.** A PowerPoint presentation with talking head video grabbed from a Udemy course called "Encoding for Multiple Screen Delivery" (bit.ly/tut_vid)

- **Talking Head.** A simple talking-head video of yours truly in my office

- **Freedom.** Multicam concert footage (HDV/AVCHD) of the fabulous Josiah Weaver at the

Greensboro Coliseum (vimeo.com/6044024)

- **Haunted.** Footage from a trailer I shot with a DSL for the Haunted Graham Mansion (bit.ly/haunted_graham)

These clips are very diverse, from screencam to very high-motion concert footage with a couple of distinct animation types in between. Now let's see how I encoded them.

Encoding with CRF

I produced my CRF encodes in an encoder named HandBrake, which is free, so you can duplicate my tests with your own files (handbrake.fr/downloads.php). If you're unfamiliar with the program, you can find a useful tutorial at bit.ly/Ozer_HB. For these tests, the only settings I adjusted were to choose Constant Quality at a rate factor (RF) value of 23 (Figure 7-4, 1), the veryslow preset (2), and the high profile (3).

Figure 7-4. Up close and personal in HandBrake.

Note: *I demonstrate how to create CRF encodes with FFmpeg at the end of the chapter.*

I used RF 23 because it's generally the default for most programs that offer this feature. As you'll see, the results also dovetail nicely with Hollywood's perception of acceptable quality. I duplicated this for all eight test files at 1080p resolution, measured the PSNR and SSIMWave Video Quality-of-Experience Monitor (SQM) scores, and show the results in Table 7-1. I also identified the score for the lowest-quality frames to make sure that the CRF encode didn't produce ugly frames that would force you to reduce the CRF value to avoid.

Note: *When producing your CRF encodes, you should otherwise use parameters identical to your production encodes. For example, for Table 7-1, I encoded using the very slow x.264 preset, a keyframe interval of 3 seconds (with no keyframes inserted at scene changes), and 3 B-frames strictly enforced. You'll learn what all this means in later chapters. If you'll be performing this analysis for real, you should read ahead and get comfortable with these concepts because they will affect your results.*

1080p Results

Table 7-1 is noteworthy in several regards. First, the SQM values are all 91 and higher, indicating that all videos should have excellent quality as perceived by real viewers. All overall PSNR values are over 40, indicating that artifacts shouldn't be an issue with any encoded files. Several files exceed 45, indicating that you could likely cut the data rate without anyone noticing.

Looking at the low PSNR scores, the rule of thumb is that any scores below 35 could indicate visible issues, so the 32.62 recorded by Big Buck Bunny is a concern. A quick visual look at the frame indicates that few viewers would notice any extra degradation. So the quality is good overall, and doesn't produce any transient quality issues at the low end.

CRF23	Frame Rate	Description	Data Rate	SQM	Overall PSNR	Low PSNR
Tears of Steel	24	Movie	4,485	94.28	41.71	36.96
Sintel	24	Complex animation	5,002	94.45	41.53	34.36
Big Buck Bunny	30	Simpler animation	3,375	95.91	43.64	32.62
Screencam	30	Camtasia	1,200	98.83	46.85	36.06
Tutorial	30	PowerPoint and talking head	690	97.93	47.28	41.49
Talking Head	30	Simple talking head	2,638	93.24	44.09	40.58
Freedom	30	Concert	5,467	91.56	41.87	38.63
Haunted	30	DSLR movie-like production	6,064	92.05	42.23	36.74

Table 7-1. Data rates at CRF 23 encodes for 1080p video.

The most significant finding is the disparity in data rates that delivered a relatively consistent quality level, which varied from 690 kbps to 6064 kbps, a difference of over 800 percent. Clearly, synthetic videos like screencam-captured video and PowerPoint-based content warrant special treatment, because you can achieve excellent quality at a fraction of the data rates of real-world video files. With most encoders, once you choose a target data rate for these types of files, the encoder will deliver that rate even though it could deliver the same quality at much lower data rates. So you have to use a different preset or presets to achieve these file savings.

Note that Tears of Steel and Sintel were both produced and encoded at 24 fps. To compare their data rates to the other 30 fps files in the test, you'd have to add 20 percent to their data rates, which boosts their comparable data rates to around 5800 kbps. This compares to 3,375 for Big Buck Bunny, which was produced at 30fps, or the same quality at approximately 58 percent the data rate. If you're encoding simpler animations, you should encode them differently from real-world videos, or even complex animations like Sintel, which encode more like real-world videos.

Similarly, the talking-head video offered higher quality than the 30 fps concert and movie-like footage at less than half the data rate, which may warrant a separate encoding category for many simple talking-head enterprise videos.

If the videos listed in Table 7-1 represented a meaningful cross-section of the videos I produced regularly, I would argue for separate presets, or groups of presets, as follows:

- real-world videos and simulated real world animations (TOS, Sintel, Freedom, Haunted)

- cartoonish animations (Big Buck Bunny)

- talking-head videos (Talking Head)

- screencam/PowerPoint tutorial (Screencam/Tutorial).

I would use the data rates produced by the CRF encoding as a starting point. For most real-world videos, I would switch to either CBR or VBR for the final encode.

So, if CRF showed 4400 kbps to be an appropriate target for movie videos, I would change my existing preset to target that data rate. Then I would encode and measure quality again to ensure that the quality level produced by my production encoding technique (CBR or VBR) was similar to the quality level produced by the CRF encoding. In particular, I would make sure to repeat the lowest-quality frame measure because CBR in particular can produce some serious ugly frames in your videos. I would repeat the lowest-quality frame measure for most encoding decisions, including buffer size, B-frame interval, and reference frame setting. You'll see that I do this in the chapters ahead.

As an example, referring to Table 7-1 above, using CRF encoding, Tears of Steel produced a file at 4,485 kbps, with an SQM rating of 94.28, and a PSNR value of 41.71. Using 2-pass VBR, and encoding to a target of 4,400 kbps, FFmpeg produced an SQM rating of 94.03 and a PSNR of 41.53, and the lowest frame quality was 38.56. The numbers are not identical, but close enough to confirm that CRF encoding was an accurate predictor for actual production encodes.

For perspective, Table 7-1 tells us that real-world 24fps footage should look excellent (according to SQM) at between 4,485 kbps (Tears of Steel) and 5,002 kbps (Sintel). Let's seek some external validation of that assumption.

Hollywood Confirmation

What does Hollywood say? To find out, I downloaded multiple 1080p files from iTunes and measured their data rate, presenting the results in Table 7-2. As you can see, there's a great deal of uniformity here—most likely because these studios use only a few encoding houses to produce these files.

Program	Owner	Width	Height	Frame Rate	Target Video DR	Bits Per Pixel
Angie Tribeca	Tuner	1916	1076	23.976	5,060	0.102
Better Call Saul	Sony	1916	1076	23.976	5,169	0.105
Blackish	ABC/Disney	1920	1080	23.976	4,953	0.1
Brooklyn 999	Universal	1920	1080	23.976	5,094	0.102
Family Guy	FoxTV	1920	1080	23.976	5,173	0.104
Fresh of the Boat	20th Century	1920	1080	23.976	4,946	0.099
Full Frontal	TBS	1920	1080	23.976	5,238	0.105
I am Cait	E!	1440	1080	23.976	5,261	0.141
Sherlock	BBC	1920	1080	25	5,062	0.098
The Affair	Showtime	1912	1080	23.976	4,959	0.1
Last Man on Earth	20th Century	1920	1080	23.976	5,117	0.103
Transformers	Hasbro	1920	1080	23.976	5,128	0.103
Average					5,097	0.105

Table 7-2. Average data rate for downloadable 1080p files on iTunes.

The general consensus appears to be that 5,097 kbps at 1080p produces sufficient quality for iTunes viewers. To this, you can add the two rates Netflix used for 1080p video before it implemented per-title encoding, which were 4,300 and 5,800 kbps (which average out to 5050 kbps, bit.ly/SM_NF).

Now Hollywood producers use the best gear, and great lighting, and compression-friendly techniques like limiting the depth of field of many shots. They also use top encoding firms to produce their videos. So overall, you would expect their file efficiency to be outstanding. Still, if you're producing 1080p video and your data rates significantly exceed 5097 kbps, you may be able to lower your output data rate without dramatically impacting quality.

How low should you go? Well, that's always the hard part, and we'll get there next. Before moving on, though, let's reflect on what we learned about CRF.

First, it does a great job distinguishing the encoding complexity of our files. Second, the 5097 kbps average data rate shown in Table 7-2 for iTunes encodes is pretty close to the 5002 kbps produced with a CRF value of 23 for Sintel as shown in Table 7-1. Increasing quality to a CRF rating of 22 boosted Sintel's data rate to 5703 kbps, which is clearly too high. For Tears of Steel, however, a CRF rating of 22 increased the data rate to about 5.2 Mbps, which is really close to the Hollywood average. So, at least at 1080p resolution, you can argue that a CRF value of between 22 and 23 comes close to delivering what Hollywood perceives as acceptable quality video.

What to do with this information? Well, try encoding your videos at a CRF value of 22. If the data rate is acceptable to you, you could be done; you can tell your boss or client that the quality approximates the quality of Hollywood productions distributed via iTunes.

Certainly using this technique with easier-to-encode videos like simple animations and screencams, you should end up with a very compact file. Try encoding to this data rate using your normal encoding technique, like two-pass VBR, and you should produce a distributable file that's likely much lower than you ever would have anticipated. Again, though, be sure to check the lowest-quality frames.

What if you need to produce acceptable quality at the lowest possible data rate? That's what we cover in the next section.

> **Note:** *Why do I share iTunes stats with you as opposed to videos from other sources? Two reasons. First, the data is accessible—just download the files and measure the data rate and other parameters. At this point, most channels that stream their video use digital rights management techniques to prevent downloading the files. Second, since this is premium content sold on iTunes, you can argue that if you match the quality, your quality is certainly "good enough."*

How Low Should You Go?

Figure 7-5 shows the impact of data rate on the SQM quality of the three clips; Tears of Steel in blue, Big Buck Bunny in red, and Screencam in yellow. Two data rates are shown on the lower axis, both with the same bits per pixel value. The first is 30 fps, for Big Buck Bunny and Screencam, and the second 24 fps for Tears of Steel. These clips were all encoded using 2-pass VBR encoding with a maximum data rate of 150 percent of the target—all of which will be perfectly clear to you once you read Chapter 8. The key point is I didn't use CRF encoding for the test clips shown in the table, so the results are different, though very similar.

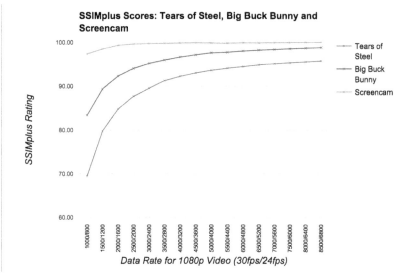

Figure 7-5. Different clips benefit differently from higher data rates.

Screencam, which is a synthetic clip, hits close to 100 at 1500 kbps. This tells you that data rates in excess of that are a waste, so you should distribute at somewhere between the 600 kbps shown for CRF and perhaps 1000 kbps.

Big Buck Bunny crosses over 95 at about 3000 kbps, making additional data rates a waste beyond that figure. However, Tears of Steel, the most complex video analyzed, didn't cross the 95 threshold until hitting 6000, about 1 Mbps higher than Hollywood distributes iTunes movies of the same configuration. More than the other two clips, Tears of Steel continued to improve at higher and higher data rates, though the improvements become increasingly marginal.

When attempting to find the lowest possible data rate, objective quality metrics become less helpful, and you'll need to examine the videos subjectively. In this regard, each file has two relevant data rates, as shown in Figure 7-6. The first eliminates most noticeable artifacts, like blockiness or distortion, and this represents the absolute minimum for most producers.

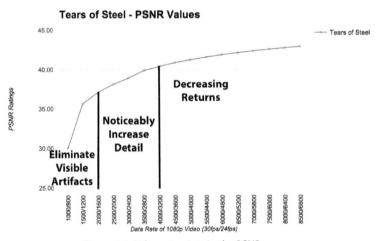

Figure 7-6. Relevant points in the PSNR curve.

Once artifacts are gone, there's a range where the detail noticeably increases with each data rate increment. You can see this in the curve of the PSNR value in Figure 7-6. From 1600 to 3200 kbps, PSNR improves 3.3 dB; from 3200 to 4800 kbps the benefit drops to 1.44 dB. Generically, Hollywood has drawn the line at about 5100 kbps—although obviously this should vary for each video file. If you're encoding for archival purposes, or for collector's editions that will be pored over frame by frame, you may want to go to 6800 kbps, or even far beyond. The point is that it's an unfortunately soft number.

Finding the Number

Whenever I subjectively evaluate the video quality, I refer to the categories shown in Table 7-3, which categorizes video artifacts into two classes: those seen by average viewers and those only seen by expert viewers. When choosing the minimum data rate for videos, I make sure that none of the artifacts in the average column are present. When choosing the maximum data rate, I make sure that all artifacts noticed by expert viewers are gone.

Artifact	Average	Expert
Blockiness	X	X
Choppiness	X	X
Loss of Text Detail	X	X
Loss of Object/Facial Detail	X	X
Jaggies	X	X
Bleeding	X	X
Background Distortion	X	X
Mosquitoes		X
Ringing		X
Pulsing		X
Banding		X

Table 7-3. Video artifacts seen by average and expert viewers.

I created this table for a consulting project back in 2014, after researching articles defining the most common video artifacts, and differentiating those most apparent to average and expert viewers. Most relevant was and article titled "Video Quality Impairments 101 for MSO's" by Daniel Howard, then of VQLink (bit.ly/vid_art2). In the article, Howard differentiates between artifacts seen by average and expert viewers. A rough taxonomy would be:

- **Average viewers.** Blockiness (obvious blocks in the video), choppiness (dropped frames).

- **Expert viewers.** Blockiness, choppiness, blurriness, mosquito noise (motion around the edges of moving objects), ringing (rings around moving objects), pulsing (a noticeable shift on key frames, which he calls background breathing) and interlacing artifacts that are not relevant here.

Another article, "Can Small Be Beautiful? Assessing Image Resolution Requirements for Mobile TV" (multiple authors, bit.ly/vid_art3), discusses that average viewers complain most about the loss of detail in text—probably because it's the most obvious. Loss of object and facial detail are also common complaints. Another article, "Compression artifacts in modern video coding and state-of-the-art means of compensation" by Andreas Underweger (bit.ly/vid_art1), added the familiar staircase, or jaggies artifact.

Other common compression artifacts include:

- **Bleeding.** Highly saturated colors bleed from the source object to the background—although in my experience, these artifacts are distracting and apparent to most viewers.

- **Banding.** Colors form visible bands in the video, usually in smooth regions.

- **Background distortion.** Either moving or still image distortion obvious in smooth backgrounds.

I distribute these into their respective columns in Table 7-3, which I refer back to whenever I'm trying to gauge the subjective quality of encoded videos. Whenever you perform a similar analysis, keep these rules in mind:

- **Watch at native resolution or full screen.** Many artifacts are visible within a video when zoomed to 200 percent or higher. However, most viewers watch at either the native resolution or full screen. Remember, you're not looking for any artifacts; you're looking for artifacts that the average viewer would notice during normal watching. A great tool for this is the Beamr Video Comparison Tool shown in Figure 7-7, and discussed back in Chapter 3.

- **Watch at full frame rate.** Unless your typical viewer will watch at slower speeds, or frame by frame, you should watch at full frame rate during this analysis.

- **Confirm artifacts aren't in the source file.** Whenever you identify an artifact in the video, check the source video to make sure it wasn't present in that file.

Figure 7-7. The Beamr Video Comparison Tools is great for comparing videos at native or full-screen playback.

For perspective, remember that occasional artifacts are generally acceptable to viewers. We see them on video delivered to our living room via cable, satellite, and OTT—as well as on web videos from credible sites like ESPN and CNN. However, consistently poor quality has a host of negative results, primarily that your video may fail at its essential purpose, whether that was to train, educate, or produce a sale.

With this structure in place, let's take a look at 720p results.

720p Results

The results from the 720p analysis are more complicated, as you can see in Table 7-4. In essence, there are two sets of results:

- **Files encoded from the 1080p source and compared to the 1080p source.** To accomplish this, you input the 1080p source into the encoder, and output the 720p file, a common workflow. When applying the objective test, you scale the 720p output to 1080p and compare it to the original 1080p source.

- **Files encoded from 720p source and compared to the 720p source.** To accomplish this, you create a 720p mezzanine (mezz) file from the 1080p source. You then input the 720p mezz file into the encoder to produce the 720p output, which you compare to the 720p mezz file to produce your objective results.

Not surprisingly, the files produced and analyzed in the first case fare the worst. That's because there are scaling artifacts in the encoded video, plus a loss of detail as compared to the 1080p source, plus any compression artifacts. In particular, the synthetic video files with lots of sharp lines, like Screencam and Tutorial, showed the lowest scores.

If you check back to Table 7-1, you'll see that the results are significantly lower than those achieved by 1080p output encoded at CRF 23. This reflects the reality that 720p video can never reach the theoretical quality of the 1080p source because some detail is simply gone, and scaling from 1080p to 720p often leaves subtle artifacts reflected in the lower scores. Would a viewer notice the difference? Probably not as much as the scores might indicate, which is why I created the second set of files.

Again, to create the second set of files, I scaled down the 1080p source to 720p in Adobe Premiere Pro, and output high data rate MP4 files as 720p source files for these encodes. Then I encoded the second set of 720p files using CRF 23. As you can see, the data rates vary a bit from the files in the first group created directly from the 1080p source, but not significantly. However, the second set of scores are much higher—particularly for the synthetic clips.

CRF23	Frame Rate	From 1080p Source				From 720p Source			
		Data Rate	SQM	Overall PSNR	Low PSNR	Data Rate	SQM	Overall PSNR	Low PSNR
Tears of Steel	24	2,255	82.44	38.70	32.88	2,318	90.45	40.79	31.46
Sintel	24	2,336	81.60	36.69	30.19	2,433	89.97	40.59	31.46
Big Buck Bunny	30	1,837	83.42	38.63	29.06	1,873	92.43	42.57	31.34
Screencam	30	666	87.56	25.89	23.39	682	97.45	46.61	31.46
Tutorial	30	414	85.34	32.68	31.38	433	95.45	46.20	43.57
Talking Head	30	920	81.68	41.49	31.46	957	89.72	43.73	39.95
Freedom	30	2,439	79.60	38.90	31.46	2,498	87.05	41.26	37.84
Haunted	30	2,194	80.93	39.82	31.46	2,183	88.08	42.12	36.64

Table 7-4. Two sets of results from 720p files.

Why are these scores better? Because I compared the encoded 720p file directly to the source 720p file, rather than scaling it up to 1080p and comparing it to the 1080p source file. In this comparison, the scaling artifacts and loss of detail incident to scaling from 1080p to 720p are present in both the source and the encoded files. In the first analysis, 720p compared with 1080p, scores are reduced by the inherent loss of detail and scaling artifacts, plus any compression loss. The second analysis, 720p to 720p, only measures the compression loss. Which set of scores is "correct"? Interesting question.

Certainly if you're encoding 720p source videos, the results from 720p source are more relevant. Even if you're not, however, I wanted to present both sets of scores to reassure you that 720p videos encoded using CRF 23 aren't as bad as the 1080p source scores might indicate.

Just to confuse matters even further, the viewing resolution also plays a role here. For example, suppose you watched a 1080p video and a 720p video on a device with a maximum screen resolution of 720, or in a 720p browser window. During playback, the 1080p video would be scaled down to 720p, injecting the same loss of detail and scaling artifacts that drove the score of the 720p file down in the first set of tests. Here, the quality perceived by the viewer would be very similar even though the PSNR scores might be very different.

On the other hand, suppose you scaled the two videos to full screen on a 4K monitor, or even a large screen 1080p monitor. Here, the loss of detail in the 720p file should be much more obvious. As surprising as it sounds, however, for most clips, this loss of detail is only obvious when you have a 1080p file to compare the 720p file to. Otherwise, it's very hard for viewers to, in effect, see what isn't there. For the record, all tests are at full-resolution display unless otherwise noted.

Which technique should you use while testing? It's a complicated question, and to be honest, one I'm coming to grips with while writing this book. Certainly there are some absolutes, like:

- When attempting to find the optimal data rate for a particular resolution, as we are here, encode from 720p source and compare to 720p source. The objective scores will more accurately reflect the reality of how the files will be perceived.

- When attempting to find the best resolution for encoding at a certain data rate (as we will in Chapter 15), encode from 1080p source and compare to 1080p source—particularly if you anticipate that the files will be viewed at full screen.

As I write this, though, I can hear math PhDs from around the world screaming at me to trust the math, and always use the first method (at least when full-screen viewing is anticipated). Overall, when your tests all involve files encoded at a single resolution, I would encode and compare at that resolution. If comparing files produced at different resolutions, particularly for full-screen display, you have to encode and compare at full resolution.

To address the lowest PSNR scores briefly, I checked the lowest-quality frames in both columns, and found none that looked noticeably impaired.

How Does Hollywood Encode 720p Files?

OK, we've run our CRF 23 tests; let's see what outside sources tell us about the appropriate data rate. Unfortunately, since Hollywood no longer distributes shows at 720p, there are few Hollywood-based examples, and I present the current shows I could find in Table 7-5, along with some historical data from articles that I've written or research performed along the way.

Program	Owner	Width	Height	Frame Rate	Target Video DR	Bits Per Pixel
David Spade - Standup	Comedy Central	1280	720	29.97	3,237	0.117
Geekbeat	Revision 3	1280	720	29.97	1,936	0.070
Joel Osteen	Joel Osteen	1280	720	29.97	2,000	0.072
Fighter and the Kid	Fox Sports	1280	720	29.97	2,500	0.091
ESPN - 2011	ESPN	1280	720	29.97	2,500	0.091
NBA League Pass (2012)	Turner	1280	720	29.97	3,500	0.127
iTunes 2013	Various	1280	720	23.976	4,097	0.185
					2,824	0.088

Table 7-5. Average data rate for downloadable 720p files on iTunes.

As you can see, the data rate for current shows ranges from 1936 to 3237 kbps, and average just above 2400. Back in 2011, ESPN encoded its 720p videos to 2500 (bit.ly/ESPN_vidspecs), while a year later, Turner encoded its live videos to 3500 (bit.ly/Turner_NBA). Back in 2013, when Hollywood was still releasing 720p files on iTunes, the average data rate was 4097. However, the peak 720p rate used by Netflix until its recent switch to per-title optimization was 3000 kbps, with a separate file available at 2350—the last of which comes close to CRF23 output values for Sintel and Tears of Steel. From where I sit, if your 720p data rate exceeds 3500 kbps or so, you probably have some fat to cut. This is certainly verified by the graph shown in Figure 7-8.

How low can you go? As we saw with 1080p clips, the answer varies by the clip type. Use the same analysis described earlier to find the lowest data rate for your clips and your application.

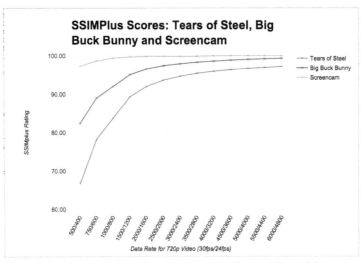

Figure 7-8. Different clip types benefit more or less from additional data rates.

Now let's take a quick look at 640x360 (360p) clips.

360p Results

While 360p files don't offer the same opportunity for bandwidth savings as 1080p or 720p files, it's probably the most widely supported output resolution, and it's certainly one that you want to get right. So let's spend a few minutes identifying and discussing the now familiar data points.

Table 7-6 shows the result from encoding files to 360p using a CRF value of 23, again using two procedures. The first encodes the 1080p source file to 360p, and then compares the encoded file to the 1080p source (after scaling as described above). I produced the second file from previously scaled 360p source, and compared the 360p-encoded files to that 360p source.

| CRF23 | Frame Rate | From 1080p Source | | | | From 360p Source | | | |
		Data Rate	SQM	Overall PSNR	Low PSNR	Data Rate	SQM	Overall PSNR	Low PSNR
Tears of Steel	24	809	29.90	34.04	30.51	901	83.85	38.47	34.10
Sintel	24	751	29.70	35.59	30.93	812	83.51	38.94	32.09
Big Buck Bunny	30	661	30.23	35.59	28.06	683	87.23	40.72	29.83
Screencam	30	207	31.73	31.27	29.41	213	95.37	45.55	35.66
Tutorial	30	169	31.00	29.44	28.16	178	92.53	45.03	42.45
Talking Head	30	252	29.92	37.79	33.95	292	85.22	43.20	36.14
Freedom	30	828	33.99	34.57	27.03	893	79.37	39.09	35.33
Haunted	30	577	29.75	36.00	24.23	597	83.77	40.76	36.31

Table 7-6. Two sets of results from 360p files.

The first set of results are understandingly dismal, since tremendous detail is lost when scaling 1080p source down to 360p. While I don't dispute the math behind the results, I do dispute the SQM ratings. Even at full screen, most of the real-world files look fine. After all, we watch 640x360 video all day long from sites like CNN and ESPN, even at full screen, and very few people complain. In my opinion, the second set of results is more reflective of the actual degradation from compression artifacts, and certainly how the video would be perceived if viewed in a 640x360 window, rather than full screen.

Again, while there are some low PSNR scores that might indicate a problem, a quick glance over the frames saved by the Moscow State University Video Quality Measurement Tool revealed no problems that would be noticeable to most viewers.

Program	Owner	Width	Height	Frame Rate	Target Video DR	Bits Per Pixel
Angie Tribeca	Turner	640	478	23.976	1,497	0.204
Better Call Saul	Sony	640	478	23.976	1,545	0.211
Blackish	ABC/Disney	640	480	23.976	1,571	0.213
Brooklyn 999	Universal	640	480	23.976	1,471	0.200
Fresh of the Boat	20th Century	640	480	23.976	1,564	0.212
Full Frontal	TBS	640	480	23.976	1,542	0.209
I am Cait	E!	640	480	23.976	1,579	0.214
Sherlock	BBC	640	480	25	1,495	0.195
The Affair	Showtime	638	480	23.976	1,465	0.200
Last Man on Earth	20th Century	640	480	23.976	1,492	0.203
Transformers	Hasbro	640	480	23.976	1,563	0.212
We Bare Bears	Hasbro	640	480	23.976	1,563	0.212
iTunes Average					**1,529**	
Netflix	Netflix	640	480	23.976	1,050	0.143
ESPN - 2011	ESPN	640	360	29.97	1,400	0.203
NBA League Pass (2012)	Turner	640	360	29.97	1,200	0.174

Table 7-7. Data rates used for 640x480 and 640x360 videos.

What do Hollywood and other sources say? I present several sets of results in Table 7-7, most of which are the encoded parameters from 640x480 files downloaded from iTunes, which average 1529 kbps. Note, however that the higher vertical resolution of a 640x480 file means that it has 33 percent more pixels than a 640x360 file. To reach the equivalent data rate, you would need to multiply 1529 by 75 percent (360/480), for a score of 1147, which is reasonably close to Netflix's pre-per-title optimization standard of 1050 kbps. Back in 2011, ESPN distributed 640x360 videos at 1400 kbps. Turner distributed NBA video at a maximum of 1200 kbps, while also distributing a 640x360@600 kbps stream.

Figure 7-9 shows how the velocity of quality improvement slows substantially for the Screencam video after 400 kbps, and at about 1 Mbps for Big Buck Bunny and Tears of Steel. Before automatically assuming that Hollywood is correct and boosting your data rates to their levels, perform a similar analysis and see how much of a quality improvement the extra data rate actually delivers.

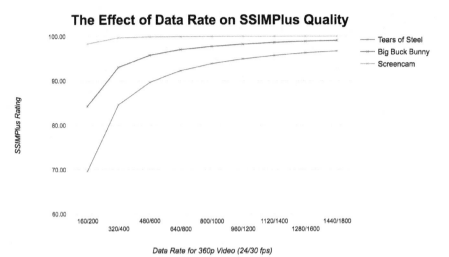

The Effect of Data Rate on SSIMPlus Quality

— Tears of Steel
— Big Buck Bunny
— Screencam

SSIMPlus Rating

Data Rate for 360p Video (24/30 fps)

Figure 7-9. The impact of data rate on SSIMplus quality at 360p.

Note that I ran some ad hoc tests with the 360p version of Tears of Steel, and found that a CRF setting of 21 delivered a data rate of 1171 kbps, while boosting the PSNR value from 38.47 to 39.75, and the SQM score from 83.85 to 86.62. If you were trying to ascertain the Hollywood equivalent for your 640x360 clips, I would use a CRF value of 21, not 23.

CRF Encoding in FFmpeg

Encoding with CRF in FFmpeg is simple. Just insert the -crf control in the command string, followed by a space and then the value, from 0 to 51.

```
ffmpeg -i TOS_1080p.mp4 -c:v libx264 -crf 23 -g 48 -keyint_min 48
-sc_threshold 0 -bf 3 -b_strategy 2 -refs 5 TOS_1080p_CRF23.mp4
```

As mentioned earlier, you should encode with CRF using the other parameters you'll use with your file, like keyframe parameters (-g 48 -keyint_min 48 -sc_threshold 0), B frame parameters (-bf 3 -b_strategy 2), and reference frame parameters (-refs 5). The only CRF specific parameter in the argument is the bolded **-crf** 23, where you can substitute any value from 0 to 51 for 23. Lower values will deliver higher quality, and 0 is a close to lossless encode (Figure 7-3). Remember, most programs use a value of about 23 as the default, although that may be a bit too rich for many applications.

> **Note:** *Don't confuse CRF encoding with capped CRF encoding, which is a form of production-level encoding discussed in Chapter 16.*

Applying These Findings

In the next few chapters, you'll see the results of various tests that identify the optimal encoding configurations for the eight video files identified above. Obviously, it only makes sense to perform these tests at the data rate most applicable to each file; for your information, these are the data rates used going forward for the various files and testing resolutions.

	Chapter 7		
	1080p	720p	360p
Tears of Steel	5000	2000	900
Sintel	5000	2000	900
Freedom	6000	2500	900
Haunted	6000	2500	900
Big Buck Bunny	3000	1500	600
Talking Head	3000	1500	600
Screencam	1000	600	200
Tutorial	1000	600	200

Table 7-8. Data rates for future testing.

Note: *After attempting to improve the low frame quality with bitrate control techniques (Chapter 8) and frame adjustments (Chapter 9), I punted and ended up increasing the data rates for the Screencam and Tutorial files to 1600, 1000, and 400 kbps. If you're going to model your own computations after mine, use the ones from Chapter 9.*

As you'll read about in Chapter 16, YouTube performs per-title encoding on each video after assessing its encoding complexity via a neural network. Just as a reality check, I uploaded all the source files to YouTube, downloaded the encoded files, and checked their data rates. You can see the results in Table 7-9.

	1080p	720p	360p
Tears of Steel	3873	2547	578
Sintel	3883	2674	544
Freedom	4115	2646	573
Haunted	4125	2134	420
Big Buck Bunny	3049	2111	448
Talking Head	2475	1091	305
Screencam	1354	1004	172
Tutorial	1185	1010	179

Table 7-9. YouTube equivalents.

While the numbers are different, the pattern is very similar. How does YouTube quality compare? Hehe. Nice question, that. Unfortunately, I couldn't measure the comparability quality because the YouTube files had a slightly different frame cadence than the ones that we produced. That's likely because YouTube converts their files twice: once to a mezzanine format to iron out any compatibility issues caused by the diverse range of files uploaded to the service, and the second into final output. A frame or two added here or there isn't something any viewer would notice, but throws any objective benchmarks completely out of whack.

My data rates are a bit higher at 1080p, but that's because we were conforming with Hollywood data rates, not YouTube's. If you're targeting Hollywood quality, go with my numbers. If you're a UGC shop, use YouTube's as a starting point. But I'd measure quality, particularly at the 360p stream level, before deploying them. The main point is that if you're encoding all files using the same encoding ladder, you need to be thinking about some kind of per-title approach, either via the techniques discussed in this chapter, or in Chapter 16.

Two Other Applications

There are two other applications where objective quality metrics really helped isolate the appropriate data rate. One relates to mezzanine clips uploaded to an encoding service, the other to the optimal data rate used for live streaming.

Uploading Mezzanine Clips

Most producers edit in a program like Adobe Premiere Pro, and then output a mezzanine file to input to their encoder. One consulting client asked what data rate they should use for their 1080p, 24 fps clips. I produced the files at 10 Mbps increments from 10 to 50 Mbps, and measured using the Video Quality Metric (VQM). Lower scores are better, but in these tests, all four clips were almost total flat lines, with an average difference of less than .5 percent. Based upon this data, the client continued uploading at 10Mbps.

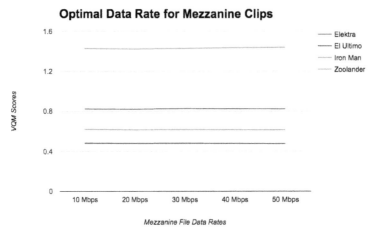

Figure 7-10. Impact of data rate on mezzanine file quality.

Optimal Data Rate for Live Events

A common workflow for live events is to output a single stream from the event, and transcode to multiple adaptive bitrate layers in the cloud. Since outbound bandwidth is costly, the big question is what data rate is appropriate. I addressed this in an article titled "Choosing the Optimal Data Rate for Live Streaming" (bit.ly/opt_livedr). The live output that I tested at various data rates was a 720p stream at 30fps, which I transcoded to 720p and 360p versions.

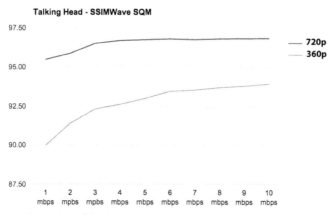

Figure 7-11. How the quality of the live source impacts the quality of the transcoded versions.

Figure 7-11 shows one of the primary results, using the SQM metric. As you can see, the 720p clip comes close to peaking at 3 Mbps, while the 360p clip improves from 92.5 to about 93.75 when the outbound data rate increased from 3 to 10 Mbps. Since any score in the 90s indicates that the subjective viewer would rate the clip as excellent, you could argue that a stream of 1 Mbps is sufficient.

A higher data rate is always better when it comes to streaming video. When transcoding, in particular, it may not make as much difference as you think.

Summary and Conclusion

Lots of material covered in this chapter, so I wanted to include a quick summary and conclusion. Here are the main things you learned in this chapter.

- ***Different types of videos encode differently.*** If you're encoding multiple types of videos, a one-size-fits-all solution will waste bandwidth on some clips and produce substandard quality on others.

- ***CRF encoding is a useful tool for identifying these disparities.*** CRF encoding can identify which clips are simple or hard to encode, and suggest the appropriate data rate for production bitrate-based encoding.

- ***Switch to bitrate-based encoding for actual production.*** CRF encoding can produce data rate spikes that inhibit smooth delivery. For this reason, you should use a bitrate-based encoding technique—either constant bitrate (CBR) or variable bitrate (VBR)—for your actual production encodes.

Chapter 8: Bitrate Control

Figure 8-1. Sometimes CBR-encoded video exhibits transient quality glitches like this one in the movie Zoolander.

Whenever you encode a file, you have to choose the bitrate control technique, or how the video data rate is allocated within the file. For most producers, this means a choice between constant bitrate (CBR) and variable bitrate (VBR) encoding. While these choices have been available since the dawn of H.264 (and MPEG-2 and before it, for that matter) there still is no consensus as to which is best to use.

In general, the CBR-versus-VBR decision involves a debate between quality and deliverability. It's generally accepted that VBR produces better quality than CBR, although it probably doesn't make as big a difference as you might think. Despite the quality advantage, many producers use CBR over concerns that variances in the VBR bitrate will make their files harder to deliver—particularly over constrained bitrate connections like 3G and 4G. As you'll learn later in this chapter, these concerns are appropriate. Otherwise, in this chapter, you will learn:

- how VBR and CBR work

- differences in both overall and low frame quality

- how both techniques vary from a delivery perspective

- what the Video Buffering Verifier (VBV) is and how it affects bitrate control and quality

- best practices for encoding with CBR and VBR

- how to encode CBR and VBR files in FFmpeg.

Note: *Capped constant rate factor (CRF) encoding could be considered a bitrate control technique, but it's sufficiently different from the VBR-versus-CBR decision that it's covered separately in Chapter 16.*

Techniques Defined

Most encoding tools provide the bitrate control options shown in Figure 8-2, CBR or VBR. With CBR selected, only the Target Bitrate selector shows; with VBR, both the Target and Maximum Bitrate configurations appear. Note that one-pass VBR is seldom used, so I won't address it in this chapter beyond a short mention below.

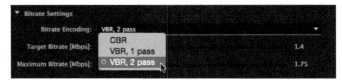

Figure 8-2. What will it be today, CBR or VBR?

Let's use the file shown in Figure 8-3 to illustrate the difference between CBR and VBR. As you can see, the file has fives scenes, as follows:

- **Low motion.** Talking head

- **Moderate motion.** Woman cooking pita bread on an outdoor oven

- **Low motion.** An integrated-circuit chip-cutting machine in operation

- **Moderate motion.** A musician playing the violin

- **High motion.** Walking through a narrow street holding camcorder to chest while panning from side to side.

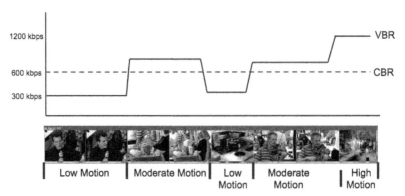

Figure 8-3. CBR applies the same data rate to the entire file, while VBR varies the data rate to match scene complexity.

With CBR, the dotted red line, the bitrate is constant throughout, a flat line at 600 kbps. In contrast, VBR varies the bitrate according to the complexity of the video file—lower in the easy-to-compress talking-head sequence, and higher in the high-motion sequence towards the end.

One question I always ask in my seminars is, "Which file is bigger, CBR or VBR?" Most students tend to guess VBR because of the variance in bitrate, but the answer is they should be the same, or very close. You'll see proof of that over the next two screenshots.

CBR Defined

Figure 8-4 shows a Bitrate Viewer data rate graph of the file shown in Figure 8-3 encoded using CBR. You can see the low-motion sequence at the start, moderate-motion next, and so on. (I inserted thumbnails from the video into the image as a reminder; they are not shown in the actual program.)

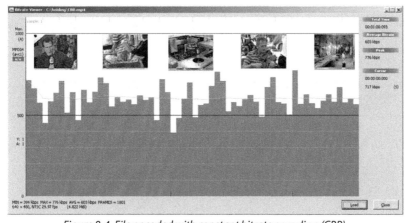

Figure 8-4. File encoded with constant bitrate encoding (CBR).

In the figure, the spikes represent the data rate for each group of pictures (GOP, which you'll learn about in Chapter 9) in the video, while the faint wavy line hovering over the black 500 kbps line represents the average data rate. While there are individual spikes in the graph, the average is pretty consistent. I encoded the file to a target data rate of 600 kbps. On the upper right, you can see that the average data rate was 603 kbps, while the peak data rate was 776 kbps. This level of variation is typical, and varies from encoder to encoder, though no encoder produces a perfect flat line when outputting x264 into an MP4 container, which we're doing here.

Note that CBR can be one-pass or two-pass, which is usually designated in the selection control when both options are available. When neither one-pass nor two-pass is designated, as in Figure 8-2, the encoder is using one-pass CBR, which means that the file is encoded in a single pass.

In contrast, most VBR is two-pass: one to scan the file and gauge the complexity of the scenes, the second to actually encode the file. In Figure 8-2, you see both one-pass and two-pass VBR options. One-pass makes no sense because the encoder can't effectively vary the data rate without knowing what's ahead. For this reason, one-pass VBR is almost never used for streaming, although it may be useful when encoding for archiving where quality is more important than meeting a target bitrate.

VBR and Constrained VBR

Figure 8-5 shows the same file encoded using VBR. Unfortunately, the scale is different for the two images, primarily because there were data rate spikes in the VBR file that extended beyond 1 Mbps. But if you ignore this and concentrate on the per-second spikes and faint average data rate line, you can see that both are low for the talking head portion of the file, then boost significantly for the moderate-motion sequence of a Druze woman tossing a pita.

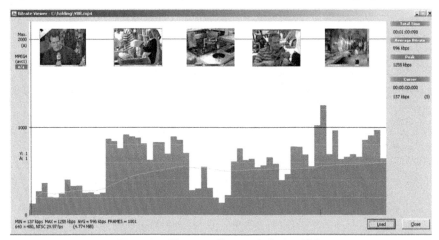

Figure 8-5. The same file encoded using VBR.

Then, the per-second and average data rate settles down for the section showing the integrated-circuit cutting machine, then increase for the violinist, and peak for the high-motion section at the end. In short, the per-second data rate and average data rate follow the underlying motion in the video file.

Again, I encoded this file to a target of 600 kbps. On the upper right of Figure 8-5, you see that the average bitrate was 596 kbps. It's not exactly the 603 kbps averaged with the CBR encode, but close enough to make the point that the average data rate should be very close irrespective of the technique used. However, the peak bitrate was 1255 kbps, compared with 776 kbps for CBR—quantifying, in part, the much greater stream variability shown in the VBR file.

Most VBR encoding is actually constrained VBR, where you set both the target data rate and the maximum data rate as shown in Figure 8-2, where the target is 1.4 Mbps, and the maximum

1.75 Mbps. This tells the encoder to produce an average bitrate of 1.4 Mbps, but never to exceed 1.75 Mbps. As discussed earlier, this typically involves two passes: one to scan the file and gauge scene complexity, the next to actually encode. Whenever you encode for streaming delivery, you should use constrained VBR, and we'll spend more time on this below.

Note that I encoded the file shown in Figure 8-5 using what's called 200 percent constrained VBR, telling the encoder to average 600 kbps with a maximum rate of twice that target, or 1200 kbps. Again, the encoder wasn't perfectly on target, delivering a peak bitrate of 1255, but it's close. Typically, the maximum constraint used in practice is 200 percent.

Another commonly used constraint is 110 percent. Here, the maximum is set to 110 percent of the target, or 660 kbps in our example. Also common is 150 percent constrained VBR, where the maximum is set to 150 percent of the target, or 900 kbps in our example.

CBR Versus VBR Quality

There are two aspects to comparing the quality of CBR- and VBR-encoded files: quality of the entire file and transient quality issues. In short, VBR delivers slightly better quality over the life of the file, but in most files the difference is modest. However, as you'll see, CBR-encoded files can exhibit short but dramatic quality issues like that shown back in Figure 8-1. Avoiding these types of issues is why most producers use some form of VBR over CBR.

Overall Results

Table 8-1 shows the results when comparing one-pass and two-pass CBR against 110 percent, 150 percent, and 200 percent constrained VBR, using PSNR as the gauge, so higher scores are better. Data rates vary from clip to clip, and were those calculated in Chapter 7. For example, I produced the Tutorial and Screencam clips at 1000 kbps, and the Tears of Steel and Sintel clips at 5000 kbps. The highest peak signal-to-noise ratio (PSNR) value for all clips wavered between 40 and 46.81 dB—a pretty tight range. To complete the picture, I encoded Freedom and Haunted at 6000 kbps, and Big Buck Bunny and Talking Head at 3000 kbps.

For each video, green shading means the highest-quality score of the five, while red means the lowest. The column on the extreme right, Total Quality Delta, shows the total difference between the highest and lowest scores. The Delta from 110 percent to 200 percent shows the difference between these techniques. The row 1080p Average shows the average values for this table, as well as the overall winner and loser. The 720p Average line shows averages from a similar comparison performed at 720p (with the 720p results not shown separately).

As you would expect, 200 percent constrained VBR is the overall winner at both resolutions. No surprise here—this technique gives the encoder the most wiggle room to adjust data rate to match scene complexity. Note, however, that the overall delta is only 2.46 percent at 1080p, much less if you remove the synthetic Screencam (7.8 percent) and Tutorial (4.49 percent) files from the equation. At 720p the average is a bit higher, with synthetic clips Screencam (8.55 percent) and Tutorial (4.66 percent) well above the overall average.

PSNR	200% VBR	150% VBR	110% VBR	CBR 2-Pass	CBR 1-Pass	Total Quality Delta	Delta - 110% to 200%
Tears of Steel	41.97	41.89	41.60	41.40	41.41	1.36%	0.88%
Sintel	41.34	41.13	40.67	40.56	40.17	2.83%	1.64%
Big Buck Bunny	41.73	40.98	40.00	39.70	40.07	4.88%	4.14%
Talking Head	44.23	44.22	44.17	44.12	44.15	0.25%	0.14%
Freedom	42.06	42.02	41.84	41.83	41.65	0.98%	0.53%
Haunted	42.07	42.07	42.01	41.90	42.06	0.40%	0.15%
Tutorial	46.81	46.56	45.27	45.08	44.71	4.49%	3.29%
Screencam	39.71	38.31	36.89	36.96	40.01	7.80%	7.11%
1080p Average	42.49	42.15	41.56	41.44	41.78	2.46%	2.20%
720p Average	41.35	41.18	40.82	40.77	40.76	1.71%	1.28%

Table 8-1. As you would expect, 200 percent constrained VBR is the absolute winner.

Intuitively, you would expect to see the most difference between 200 percent constrained VBR and CBR in clips varied content. That's because when the encoding complexity is consistent through the clip, there are no hard-to-encode or easy-to-encode sequences—they are all the same. This explains why there is such little quality variation in the very low-motion talking head sequence (0.25 percent differential).

However, it doesn't explain the relatively small differences in the Freedom concert video (0.98 percent), and the movie-like Haunted video (0.40 percent), which contain both high- and low-motion scenes. If you compare the CBR and 200 percent constrained VBR files in Bitrate Viewer (which I didn't show here), there is significantly more variation in data rate in the Haunted video. Sometimes you just have to test to measure the difference; you can't assume it will or will not be there.

Figure 8-6 shows the Table 8-1 results graphically. As you can see, for many files, the bitrate control technique makes little difference. For the synthetic Screencam and Tutorial files, the bitrate control technique makes a very significant difference. A bit less so for the two animated files, Sintel and Big Buck Bunny.

Whenever you test a small number of files, you risk producing results that are idiosyncratic to those files. However, these numbers at least suggest that if you're producing screencams, tutorials, and animations, you should check carefully to make sure that the selected bitrate control technique optimizes quality. This message comes through even stronger after looking at the lowest-quality frame analysis.

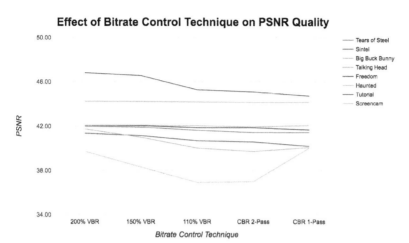

Figure 8-6. The effect of bitrate control technique on PSNR quality.

Lowest -quality Frame Analysis

What about the lowest-quality frame analysis? You can see this in Table 8-2. To provide perspective (as mentioned previously), Netflix has commented that PSNR scores below 35 dB can look degraded to viewers, though you really never know until you actually examine the frame. Certainly the quality degradation in the lowest-quality frame in the Big Buck Bunny clip is noticeable, as is the lowest-quality frame in the Screencam, Tutorial, and Freedom clips. But the lowest-quality Sintel frame isn't that noticeable, even at 26.94 dB, and the lowest-quality frame in the rest of the clips are pretty much in the safe zone.

Low PSNR	200% VBR	150% VBR	110% VBR	CBR 2-Pass	CBR 1-Pass	Total Quality Delta	Delta - 110% to 200%
Tears of Steel	37.07	36.37	34.91	34.67	34.99	6.47%	5.81%
Sintel	31.24	29.06	30.30	29.73	26.94	13.75%	3.01%
Big Buck Bunny	24.85	23.60	23.12	22.82	23.19	8.15%	6.95%
Talking Head	40.25	40.16	39.62	39.60	39.65	1.60%	1.55%
Freedom	36.62	36.41	35.81	35.62	30.93	15.55%	2.21%
Haunted	35.99	36.31	35.87	35.90	35.99	1.21%	0.33%
Tutorial	42.68	41.35	33.10	36.48	27.60	35.33%	22.45%
Screencam	27.39	23.86	23.02	23.93	23.82	15.94%	15.94%
1080p Average	34.51	33.39	31.97	32.34	30.39	11.94%	7.36%
720p Average	34.09	33.59	32.57	32.34	31.88	6.46%	4.44%

Table 8-2. Lowest-quality frames by bitrate control technique.

Why are almost all the lowest-quality frames in the CBR clips? Basically, CBR encodes are much more constrained than VBR, and can force the encoder to produce very small frames to meet the target bitrate. These small frames can cause transient quality problems.

To visualize this in situ, check out Figure 8-7, which compares the one-pass CBR Screencam file (in red) to the 200 percent constrained VBR Screencam file (in blue). As you can see, the PSNR values for both files vary consistently throughout both graphs.

If you were able to scan through the actual frames, you would notice two things. First, where the red line dips, the quality deficits in the one-pass CBR file are very noticeable. However, when the blue lines head south, the low scores in the 200 percent constrained VBR file appear minor. If you played the two files side by side, or even sequentially, most viewers would prefer the 200 percent constrained VBR file, even though the overall scores of the file are very close.

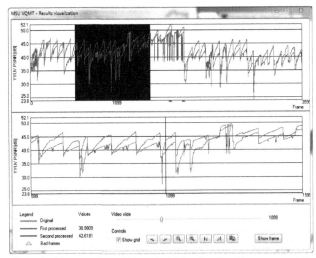

Figure 8-7. Screencam file in the Moscow State University Video Quality Measurement Tool Results Visualization screen showing PSNR scores. Red is one-pass CBR, blue is 200 percent constrained VBR.

The second thing to notice in Figure 8-7 is that some regions, the one-pass CBR file quality drops to very low levels, like the red line dipping well below the 30 PSNR line in the middle of the bottom graph. This is a transient quality drop that I mentioned above, and is shown in Figure 8-8. Even though the issue rarely persists beyond one to four frames, it's very noticeable nonetheless.

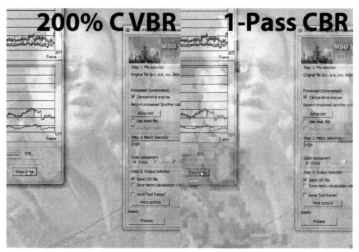

Figure 8-8. CBR files suffer transient quality drops like this one.

Switching from one-pass to two-pass CBR didn't eliminate these issues in the Screencam file, but tended to minimize them in others. To be fair, with the Screencam file these issues were also present in the 110 percent and 150 percent constrained VBR files, as shown in Figure 8-8, although it finally cleared up at 200 percent constrained VBR. Remember that Screencam files are unique in both the level of sharp detail contained in the file and the data rate applied, which was 1000 kbps for 1080p video in these tests.

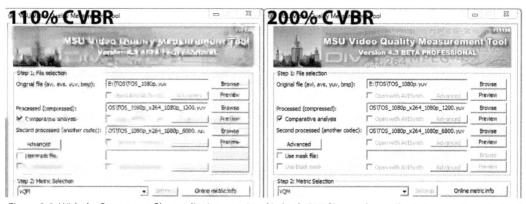

Figure 8-9. With the Screencam file, quality issues existed in both CBR files, and even the 110 percent constrained VBR, although the 200 percent constrained VBR looked perfect.

The aggressive data rate challenges the encoder to deliver very good quality with a very low bits-per-pixel value. On the other hand, it creates an opportunity, since at 1000 kbps, even the variability in the 200 percent constrained VBR should be fairly easy to deliver over most connections.

Of course, if you encoded the Screencam clips at 5000 kbps, both CBR versions would likely look just fine. If your priority is to minimize data rate variability, as opposed to the overall data rate, you should be able to encode Screencam clips at a higher data rate and encode with one-pass CBR without any transient quality issues.

200 Percent Constrained VBR to the Rescue?

OK, CBR encoding can lead to transient quality issues—you get it. Let's take a macro view and see where changing the bitrate control technique can eliminate, or at least minimize, the problems. You can get a glimpse of the answer in Figure 8-10.

As you can see, the lowest-quality frames in the Screencam and Big Buck Bunny files improve slightly at 200 percent constrained VBR, but it's not a night-and-day difference. With 200 percent constrained VBR, most of the visible problems disappear, but the lowest-quality frame levels are still low. This is a case where you might want to consider raising the overall data rate of the file to eliminate ugly frames, even if overall quality is acceptable.

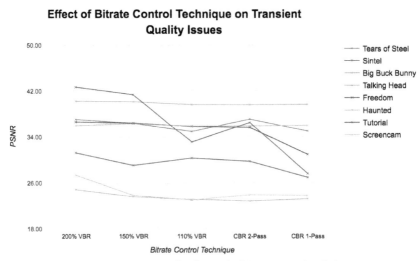

Figure 8-10. Lowest-quality frames by bitrate control technique.

The Freedom video, a music video that contains the highest motion of all the test clips, saw very significant quality degradation with one-pass CBR. Even though the total PSNR score only varied by about 1 percent, the lowest-quality frame dropped in quality by 15.55 percent, and the lowest-quality frame produced via one-pass CBR contained blocks that viewers would definitely notice.

Again, the results of the Tutorial video, if confirmed through testing of additional files, might dictate using 200 percent constrained VBR for all of these file types. Certainly given the low bitrate of these files (1000 kbps for 1080p), encoding at 200 percent constrained VBR shouldn't present a significant delivery risk.

> **Note:** *I know this is sounding a bit jumbled at the moment, but I summarize my recommendations at the end of the chapter with Table 8-6. The bottom line is that for most videos, you should use 110 percent constrained VBR to avoid the transient quality issues associated with CBR, and the deliverability issues associated with 200 percent constrained VBR.*

Other Factors in Bitrate Control Selection

In "Technical Note TN2224" (bit.ly/appletn2224), Apple details how to encode when deploying HTTP Live Streaming (HLS), the mandated technique for distributing to iOS devices, which we'll explore in detail in Chapters 13 to 15. One of the dictates is "Bit Rate Variability — Should not exceed 10% of target bitrate." Essentially, this means to use CBR or 110 percent constrained VBR.

In a later document titled "HLS Authoring Specification for Apple Devices" (bit.ly/A_Devices), Apple refined the specification, stating that "For VOD content the peak bit rate SHOULD be no more than 200% of the average bit rate." So this means no more than 200 percent constrained VBR. Though this document was originally targeted solely for Apple TV devices, in August 2016, Apple expanded its role (and title) to all Apple devices.

Before this change, there was an interesting mix about how actual producers responded to Apple's dictates. In March 2016, I ran a survey on the Streaming Learning Center to understand the bitrate control techniques used by most producers. Unfortunately, the survey generated only 16 responses, though 10 indicated that they were producing more than 100 files a week. Admittedly, the number of respondents is too small to be statistically significant, but 16 responses are better data than solely my opinion, so I'll share the results here.

Figure 8-11 shows the techniques used by the respondents, with the total percentage exceeding 100 percent because the survey permitted multiple responses. The survey had options for both VBR and constrained VBR, and I'm guessing that all respondents who selected VBR really meant constrained VBR. If you combine these two responses, total VBR users equal those using CBR. The bottom line is that many producers use both techniques, depending upon the target.

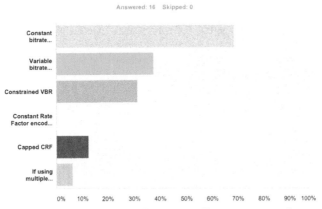

Which bitrate control technique do you use for your files? (Check all that apply).

Answered: 16   Skipped: 0

Figure 8-11. Bitrate control techniques used by survey respondents.

Another question asked those using VBR the level of constraint. As you can see in Figure 8-12, 110 percent was the most popular configuration—probably to meet the now obsoleted Apple dictate in TN2224. The next most popular constraint was 150 percent of the target, followed by 125 percent and 200 percent. No respondents exceeded 200 percent constrained VBR.

If you're using Constrained VBR, what maximum bitrate constraint are you using?

Answered: 7   Skipped: 9

Figure 8-12. Constraint level used by survey respondents

Figure 8-13 shows some of the more interesting results of the survey. That is, of those producing HLS files, the majority of producers ignore Apple's recommendation entirely. Interestingly, of the 10 respondents who were producing more than 100 files a week, five followed Apple's recommendation religiously and five ignored it completely.

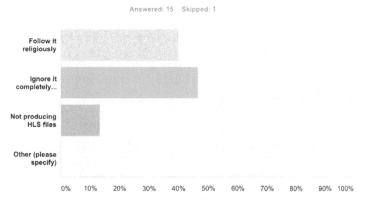

If you're producing HLS files, do you follow Apple's recommendation that bitrate variability should not exceed 10% of the target bitrate?

Answered: 15   Skipped: 1

Figure 8-13. Adherence to Apple's "Technical Note TN2224."

When I posted the results of the survey to the Streaming Learning Center website, we received some interesting comments. One came from Sylvian Corvaisier, who runs a company called iReplay.fr, which offers a service that creates Apple TV channels for its customers. Corvaisier commented:

> We are one of the providers which have been applying the 110% constrained VBR for HLS streams for more than 2 years. The point is not to be strictly in line with Apple recommendations for app submission ... but to get best quality possible (especially on linear streams) and to get the heuristics used to switch from one stream still to work as expected.

In other words, it's not just about quality and deliverability, it's about getting the player to switch streams when it's supposed and not to switch when it's not supposed to. Another comment came from Sandy MacInnis, a highly respected compressionist from Broadcom. He stated:

> Using VBR with a peak rate that is much greater than the average is of course attractive in terms of picture quality, but it's a problem when the network throughput is constrained to significantly less than that peak, such as the nominal rate plus 10%. In many cases there is a weak link in the network, such as throughput of a crowded Wi-Fi hotspot, or a weak Wi-Fi link with low throughput, so a peak rate beyond 110% may be an issue.

Here, MacInnis is taking a realistic look at the Internet and playing the deliverability card, saying that 110 percent is probably deliverable, while 200 percent constrained VBR may not be.

VBR and CBR Deliverability

Soon after performing that survey, I discovered a tool called Charles Web Debugging Proxy, which allowed me to do two things to isolate the impact on bitrate control over file deliverability. First, it enabled me to constrain the data rate of the incoming bandwidth on a computer to any arbitrary level. So if I wanted to test performance at an incoming bandwidth of 3200 kbps, I could. Figure 3-10, back in Chapter 3, shows how this works.

The second feature is the ability to identify which fragments the player is downloading for playback. You can see this back in Figure 3-11, but I'll duplicate here as well as Figure 8-14. You see the segments on the left of the figure.

Figure 8-14. Charles showing the fragments retrieved during HLS playback.

With Charles in hand, I decided to create the ultimate VBR-versus-CBR quality-of-experience test. To do so, I created an eight-minute test file that alternated 30 seconds of talking head with 30 seconds of ballet. Then I encoded the file using CBR, 200 percent constrained VBR and 110 percent constrained VBR, using the layers shown in the encoding ladder in Figure 8-15. Then I uploaded all the streams to a website, and created separate web pages for each.

Video Streams			
Codec	Width	Height	Bitrate (kbps)
H.264	1920	1080	4500 (VBR)
H.264	1280	720	3100 (VBR)
H.264	1280	720	2100 (VBR)
H.264	960	540	1500 (VBR)
H.264	640	360	1000 (VBR)
H.264	480	268	550 (VBR)
H.264	320	180	260 (VBR)

Figure 8-15. The VBR encoding ladder used for these tests.

To measure quality of experience (QoE), I restricted the bandwidth of the playback station to 3200 kbps and 4500 kbps, played each file, and then tracked the bitrate of the segments retrieved by the player in each test. I tested using JW Player to play the HLS files, and the native HLS player in the Mac version of Safari. You can see the results for JW Player for bandwidth constrained at 3200 kbps in Table 8-3.

Layer	Bitrate	VBR - JWPlayer			CBR - JWPlayer		
		Segs	Percent	Bandwidth	Segs	Percent	Bandwidth
0	4500		0%	0		0%	0
1	3100	8	20%	24,800	2	6%	6,200
2	2100	7	18%	14,700	32	94%	67,200
3	1500	3	8%	4,500		0%	0
4	1000	22	55%	22,000		0%	0
5	550		0%	0		0%	0
6	260		0%	0		0%	0
Total		40	100%	66,000	34	100%	73,400

Table 8-3. Quality-of-experience results for 200 percent constrained VBR and CBR.

The table shows that the CBR version delivered the smoothest experience, with 94 percent of the segments retrieved and played at 2100 kbps. In this mode, the player downloaded only 34 segments for a total of 73.4 MB of data. In contrast, during VBR playback, the viewer spent the most time at 1 Mbps, and 40 segments downloaded. Examining the actual segment order indicated that there were as many as five stream switches in the VBR file, compared with three in the CBR.

So not only did VBR deliver lower-quality fragments, it cycled the viewer through more stream changes, including multiple trips into very low-quality segments that the viewer would be sure to notice. Sure, VBR downloaded less data, 66 MB compared with 73.4, but the QoE was noticeably worse.

You can read about all the other experiments in the original article on my website at bit.ly/cbr_qoe, and watch two YouTube videos that shows some of these experiments. You'll note that I tested with 110 percent constrained VBR, which downloaded seven packets from the 1500 kbps file, but none from the 1000 kbps file. The bottom line was that the QoE of the CBR file was still better, but 110 percent constrained VBR delivered much better QoE than 200 percent constrained VBR.

Balancing Quality and Deliverability

So where does that leave us? As I mentioned at the beginning of this chapter, this is a balance between quality and deliverability. From a quality perspective, with real world clips, including animations, transient quality issues are hard to predict. The *Zoolander* sequence is very fertile ground, because it contains multiple camera flashes that produce very significant changes from frame to frame, leaving little wiggle room for a CBR encode. Still, I've seen very noticeable transient quality issues in a simple camera switch on an otherwise very low-motion clip. Regarding transient quality issues in real-world clips, it's best to hope for the best, but expect the worst.

I didn't use the *Zoolander* clip for most tests because I like to limit the usage of copyright clips. In all real-world clips that I tested for the book, two-pass CBR avoided the transient issues, which is the strongest argument for using two-pass CBR over one-pass CBR. If your goal is the least stream variability with the best chance for avoiding transient quality problems, two-pass CBR is the way to go. On the other hand, 110 percent constrained VBR also avoids the transient quality issues, should be equally easy to deliver, and produces slightly better overall quality than two-pass CBR.

If you're looking for overall top quality, however, 200 percent constrained VBR is a better option. From a deliverability perspective, with a top data rate of 6000 kbps for the Haunted and Freedom clips, the 12,000 kbps peak is a bit scary particularly for mobile networks. On the other hand, if you're encoding clips for delivery over a robust network, deliverability isn't really a factor and you should go with the highest quality option.

With Screencam, only 200 percent constrained VBR avoided all transient quality-related issues, which should be a viable option given the low data rate of the clip. In the Tutorial clip, which is mixed PowerPoint and a small talking head video, one-pass CBR did produce some noticeable quality issues, which two-pass CBR (and all constrained VBR clips) avoided. Given the overall low data rate on these clips (1000 kbps), and the higher quality produced by 200 percent constrained VBR, I would use 200 percent constrained VBR if at all possible. That said, I'm only testing one screencam or tutorial clip each. If you're distributing lots of either type of clip, you should run your own comparisons and make your conclusions based upon that data.

With these decisions made, let's transition to how to produce top-quality CBR and VBR encoded files. I'll preface this section with the comment that all encoding interfaces are different and offer different controls. Some encoders, like Sorenson Squeeze, offer multiple H.264 codecs, and vary the interface to present options relevant to that codec. So unless you're using the exact same version of the product detailed in the screenshots, you'll be working with a different interface. If you've read the foregoing, no worries—you've got this. If not, skim through and you should be able to figure things out.

Producing CBR

When producing files with CBR encoding, options will vary depending upon whether you're streaming live or creating on-demand files. If you're creating on-demand files, some encoders let you choose between one-pass and two-pass encoding, as shown in Figure 8-16, which is a screen from Sorenson Squeeze Desktop 10. When two-pass is available, select it, and then insert the target data rate, which is shown as 576 kbps in the figure.

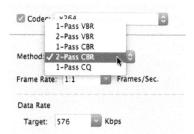

Figure 8-16. Choosing between one-pass and two-pass CBR in Sorenson Squeeze Desktop 10.

When two-pass isn't available, as we saw in Figure 8-11, the encoder almost invariably uses one-pass. This cuts the encoding time by 50 percent or so, but can create the transient quality issues discussed earlier. If this is the case, you're probably better off using 110 percent constrained VBR rather than one-pass encoding.

A note on CQ encoding: As used in Squeeze, CQ is another name for CRF encoding, which we discussed in Chapter 7. CRF encoding is valuable primarily for file benchmarking and archiving. Capped CRF, a technique that encodes via CRF with a maximum bitrate, is more valuable for distribution. We cover capped CRF in Chapter 16.

Producing VBR

Most programs have one of two different interfaces for VBR encoding. The most traditional is that shown in Figure 8-17, again from Sorenson Squeeze. You choose 2-Pass VBR, then set the target, then set the constraint, which in Squeeze can either be a bitrate or percentage.

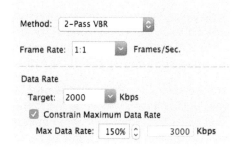

Figure 8-17. VBR encoding in Sorenson Squeeze.

The other technique is shown in Figure 8-18, from Telestream Episode Pro 7. Here you set the Average Bit Rate, which is the target, and the VBV Max Bit Rate, which is the maximum. But there's also the VBV Size setting, which throws another wrinkle into the mix, and leads us into the last substantive topic of the chapter.

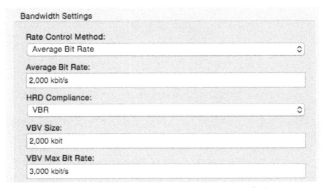

Figure 8-18. VBR encoding in Telestream Episode Pro 7.

Note: *Some encoding tools offer one-pass, two-pass, and multi-pass encoding. I've tested the quality of multi-pass encoding in the past, and found that it delivered very little extra quality, if any, and extended encoding time significantly. Don't dismiss it out of hand, but don't automatically use it, either. By now you should know how to run your own tests and draw your own conclusions about whether the extra encoding time is worth it.*

Working with VBV

VBV stands for Video Buffering Verifier, and it refers to how much video data is stored (or cached) in the player. Here's a description of the VBV schema from Tom Vaughan, Vice President and General Manager, Video at MulticoreWare, which developed the highly regarded x265 HEVC codec.

> We would suggest that you describe how VBV works using the "leaky bucket" model. The vbv-bufsize is the size of the bucket. The vbv-maxrate is the maximum rate that the bucket (decoder buffer) can be filled (the maximum transmission rate). The water in the bucket is made up of a series of encoded video frames, but the size of each frame can vary widely.

> The bucket is emptied at a steady frame rate by the decoder. As the encoder encodes frames, it models this leaky bucket to verify whether the frames it is encoding could be decoded by a decoder that has the specified VBV parameters. If a sequence of frames is too large, the bucket may run dry, and the next frame to be decoded may not be available in the bucket when it is time to decode it. Both VBV parameters are important, as the bucket only runs dry when the combination of the bucket size and fill rate are too small for the frames the encoder wants to encode.

In simpler terms provided by Amnon Cohen-Tidhar, System Architecture Team Leader at Amimon, "Video scenes are not monotonous, so for uniform quality some parts requires more bits than other. Under constant bitrate (CBR) the bitrate remains constant throughout the clip. VBV settings tells the encoder how much it allows to deviate from the CBR to move bits from 'boring' parts to 'action' parts."

The bottom line is that the VBV schema is designed to optimize quality without overrunning or exhausting the player buffer. In the olden days of hardware decode in DVDs and video CDs, the VBV buffer size was specified in the on-board chipsets, and you had to carefully encode the stream so that the buffer wouldn't overrun or underrun. Today, when most players are either in software, or in vastly more capable hardware, the controls shown in Figure 8-16 are used more to control the bitrate and quality of the video than to ensure player compatibility.

Telestream (or really, any encoder that uses the x264 codec, which is a lot of them) doesn't expect you to know the VBV buffer size of the device you're encoding for. Rather, it expects you to use these configuration options to control the bitrate—more specifically, the variability of the bitrate. So let's focus on how that works, then the impact of those settings, and then we'll look at the compatibility side.

Bitrate Control with the VBV Settings

Controlling the bitrate with VBV settings is simple. Set the Average Bit Rate at the target, and the VBV Max Bit Rate at the maximum bitrate. For CBR, use the same value for Average Bit Rate and VBV Max Bit Rate as shown on the left in Figure 8-19. For constrained VBR, set the VBV Max Bit Rate to the maximum desired bitrate as shown in the middle and example on the right in Figure 8-19.

Figure 8-19. Bitrate control via Average Bit Rate and VBV Max Bit Rate.

As you'll see at the end of this chapter, this is precisely how you control the bitrate when encoding with FFmpeg via a command line. It's also how you control many of the apps and cloud platforms that implement x264.

VBV, Quality, and Stream Variability

How does the VBV Size setting affect the stream? If you ponder the leaky bucket construct for a moment, you probably would conclude that smaller buffers should reduce quality, because the encoder has less wiggle room to adjust the data rate upwards or downwards to match scene complexity. On the other hand, a smaller buffer should produce a stream with less variability precisely for the same reason. Conversely, you would expect a file with a large buffer to enjoy higher quality, but also more stream variability. Let's test these assumptions.

To create the results shown in Table 8-4, I encoded the *Zoolander* clip to 1080p at 4 Mbps using one-pass CBR encoding with the buffer settings shown on the left. I checked the peak bitrate of each file in Bitrate Viewer (see Figure 8-5), and used this value to compute the maximum data rate variance. I computed PSNR and low PSNR with MSU VQMT.

Zoolander - 1080p 4 Mbps	Data Rate	Peak Rate	Data Rate Variance	Overall PSNR	Quality Delta	Low PSNR	Quality Delta
Half Second Buffer (2MB)	4,112	4,859	18.17%	36.441		26.11	
One Second Buffer (4 MB)	4,164	5,004	20.17%	36.673	0.64%	27.69	6.05%
Two Second Buffer (8 MB)	4,159	5,220	25.51%	36.886	0.58%	29.03	4.85%
Three Second Buffer (12 MB)	4,208	5,561	32.15%	37.014	0.35%	30.49	5.03%
Four Second Buffer (16 MB)	4,196	5,935	41.44%	37.056	0.11%	31.93	4.74%
Total Variance					1.68%		20.67%

Table 8-4. The impact of buffer size on data rate variance and video quality.

As you can see, the file encoded with a four-second buffer had the highest variance and the highest quality, which are shown in chart form in the next two figures. As you can see in Figure 8-20, increasing buffer size has a significant impact on data rate variance. Basically, if you're encoding in CBR mode and truly want a CBR stream, you should limit the buffer to one second, perhaps even half a second.

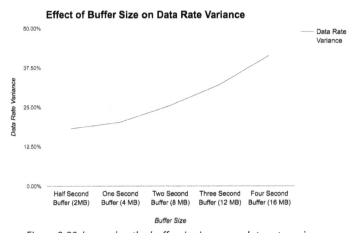

Figure 8-20. Increasing the buffer size increases data rate variance.

As shown in Figure 8-21, encoding with a larger buffer size increases overall quality slightly, but improves low frame quality much more significantly. As shown in Table 8-4, while overall quality only increased by 1.68 percent when boosting the buffer size from half a second to four seconds, low frame quality improved by 20.67 percent.

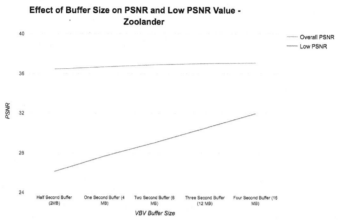

Figure 8-21. Increasing the buffer size increases overall quality slightly, but low frame quality significantly.

How representative are these numbers? In addition to the one-pass CBR, I encoded the *Zoolander* clip to the same parameters using two-pass CBR, and the Tears of Steel clip to the same parameters using both one and two-pass CBR. The aggregate overall quality improved by 1.25 percent (compared with 1.68 percent for the *Zoolander* clip in one-pass CBR mode), while the aggregate low-quality differential for the four test cases was 9.11 percent, compared with 20.67 percent. So you probably won't see this boost in low frame quality on all test cases.

Note that increasing the buffer size has a similar impact on stream variability when encoding with constrained VBR. For example, I encoded the 1080p version of Tears of Steel to 2 Mbps using 150 percent constrained VBR with a VBV buffer of one and two seconds. With a one-second buffer, the maximum data rate variance from the overall target was 50.1 percent, which is what you would expect with 150 percent constrained VBR. With a buffer of two seconds, the variance was 82 percent—almost 60 percent higher. So whether you're encoding with CBR or constrained VBR, you should expect buffer values in excess of one second to affect stream variability.

What's the takeaway? If you're encoding with CBR, and truly want a CBR stream, you have to keep the buffer small. If you do, be sure to check low frame PSNR quality to make sure that your selected data rate does not produce transient ugly frames. If you're producing with constrained VBR, a smaller buffer size will also deliver a stream closer to your target parameters.

> **Tip:** *When you encode with a small buffer size, particularly when using one-pass CBR encoding, there's a very significant chance that the encoder will undershoot the target. As an example, to produce the 4 Mbps Zoolander file with a buffer size of half a second (2MB), I had to target average and max rates of 5 Mbps. So be sure to check file size when encoding with low VBV buffer sizes to make sure the encoder is on target.*

Maximum Buffer in Practice

What maximum buffer values are used in practice? Table 8-5 details values found in files produced for streaming and podcasts. For streaming, I grabbed videos from the sites listed, while downloading the podcasts from iTunes. To learn the target, max data rate, and max buffer settings, I inspected the files in MediaInfo (Chapter 3). Sometimes, the command line information is saved in the Encoding Settings box shown in Figure 8-22. This doesn't always happen, but when it does, you've got the precise recipe used to encode the file.

Streaming	Bitrate	Max Rate	Buffer	Buffer Seconds
NYTimes	1500	1800	1500	1
BusinessInsider	2200	2200	4400	2
Bleacher Report	600	600	1200	2
CNET	400	800	800	2
MSN	2166	2166	10830	5
Mashable	1500	1500	3000	2
Vimeo (4K)	16500	24200	66000	4
Metacafe	1000	1000	2000	2
Average				2.5
Podcasts				
Apple: Achieving Wellness	5000	25000	31250	6.25
Fox: Bill O'Reilly	1000	1000	500	0.5
Chasing Conan	CRF	4950	13500	2.73
This Week in Tech	500	1500	6000	12
Average				5.4

Table 8-5. Buffer durations of video files from varying sites.

As you can see, most streaming files use a one- or two-second buffer, most likely to limit stream variability for the files delivered over the Internet. The numbers are much higher for the few podcasts that provided the information—although Apple, which obviously knows iTunes and its devices, used a buffer duration of over six seconds. Obviously, deliverability isn't a factor for downloaded podcasts, and the longer buffer times should increase the quality to some degree.

```
Encoding settings        cabac=1 / ref=3 / deblock=1:0:0 / analyse=0x3:0x113 / me=hex / subme=7 / psy=1 /
                         psy_rd=1.00:0.00 / mixed_ref=1 / me_range=16 / chroma_me=1 / trellis=1 / 8x8dct=1 /
                         cqm=0 / deadzone=21,11 / fast_pskip=1 / chroma_qp_offset=-2 / threads=12 /
                         lookahead_threads=2 / sliced_threads=0 / nr=0 / decimate=1 / interlaced=0 /
                         bluray_compat=0 / constrained_intra=0 / bframes=3 / b_pyramid=2 / b_adapt=1 / b_bias=0 /
                         direct=1 / weightb=1 / open_gop=0 / weightp=2 / keyint=250 / keyint_min=25 / scenecut=40 /
                         intra_refresh=0 / rc_lookahead=40 / rc=abr / mbtree=1 / bitrate=5000 / ratetol=1.0 /
                         qcomp=0.60 / qpmin=0 / qpmax=69 / qpstep=4 / vbv_maxrate=25000 / vbv_bufsize=31250 /
                         nal_hrd=none / filler=0 / ip_ratio=1.40 / aq=1:1.00
```

Figure 8-22. This data isn't included in every encoded file, but it's incredibly useful when it is.

Note that the Bill O'Reilly video is 640x360 and encoded in the Baseline profile, which means it plays on very old devices, going back to the iPhone 4 and iPod touch 4. If you were encoding podcasts for these devices, I would follow Fox's lead on a fairly small buffer size. On the other hand, the This Week in Tech video is encoded at 864x480 resolution using the Main profile, which excludes the aforementioned older devices, and uses a 12-second buffer. The Apple video is 1080p, and uses the High profile, so it's targeted towards the newer class of iOS devices, and uses a 6.25-second buffer.

I don't know the VBV-related specs for all iOS devices. It's a bit off topic for this book, so I'm not going to explore further. The most conservative approach is to copy the parameters shown in the table, and customize the buffer size for the lowest-common-denominator playback device.

For streaming, the size of your VBV buffer should be dictated by your concerns over stream variability. If you want your streams to meet your CBR or even constrained VBR targets, use a buffer size of one second. If you don't care about variability, a larger buffer will improve quality, especially for your lower-quality frames.

> **Note:** *I posted this section of this chapter to my website for comments, which was useful, and you can see the comments at bit.ly/vbv_explained. Most I've already incorporated into the chapter. Since I'm not covering live streaming in this book, I'll mention Alex Zambelli's comment: "Larger VBV sizes increase end-to-end latency in live streaming workflows. Every second added to VBV duration adds 2 seconds (1 encode + 1 decode) to end-to-end latency."*

Applying These Findings

How to synthesize this data? You see the summary in Table 8-6. Going forward, regarding bitrate control and the video buffer verifier, I'm lumping Sintel in with the other real-world videos and using 110 percent constrained VBR with a one-second video buffer verifier as the best blend of quality and deliverability.

	Chapter 7			Chapter 8		
	1080p	720p	360p	Target	Max	VBV
Tears of Steel	5000	2000	900	100%	110%	1 sec
Sintel	5000	2000	900	100%	110%	1 sec
Freedom	6000	2500	900	100%	110%	1 sec
Haunted	6000	2500	900	100%	110%	1 sec
Big Buck Bunny	3000	1500	600	100%	200%	1 sec
Talking Head	3000	1500	600	100%	110%	1 sec
Screencam	1000	600	200	100%	200%	2 sec
Tutorial	1000	600	200	100%	200%	1 sec

Table 8-6. Applying the data from this chapter.

With simple animations like Big Buck Bunny, my primary concern is avoiding transient quality issues. So, I'll use 200 percent constrained VBR with a one-second buffer to limit stream variability. I'll encode these files at a generally lower data rate than most real-world videos, so hopefully the stream variability issues won't cause to many delivery issues.

Finally, I'll produce screencams and tutorial files at a very low data rate, so again my concern is providing the codec with sufficient flexibility to avoid transient quality problems. I'll encode both using 200 percent constrained VBR, but use a two-second buffer for the Screencam file, which appears to need more help than the Tutorial file.

Bitrate Control and Buffer Size in FFmpeg

Choosing the bitrate control technique and buffer size in FFmpeg is simple. I'll use the test video file discussed around Figure 8-4 to demonstrate your alternatives. This file was eight minutes long, and alternates 30 seconds of talking head video with 30 seconds of high-motion ballet. You learned the `-b:v` code for bitrate control back in Chapter 2. To encode this test file using single pass bitrate control, you would use:

```
ffmpeg -y -i Test_1080p.MOV -c:v libx264 -b:v 5000k Test_DR_5M.mp4
```

This produces a file that looks like Figure 8-23, where the data rate would vary according to content. The overall data rate of 5062 is pretty accurate, but you'd be concerned that data rate spikes in the file could hinder deliverability. The answer? Two-pass encoding.

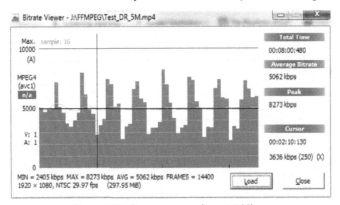

Figure 8-23. One-pass encoding at 5 Mbps.

How do you control data rate with two-pass encoding? Using the same two controls discussed above, maximum bitrate and VBV buffer size. That is, you use:

`-b:v 5000k` as the target, as before.

`-maxrate 5000k` to set the maximum bitrate. So 5000k would be CBR, 5500k would be 110 percent constrained VBR, and 10000k would be 200 percent constrained VBR.

`-bufsize 5000k` to set the size of the VBV. For this real-world video distributing via streaming, I'd use a VBV size equivalent to the data rate of one second of video (5000k).

Two-Pass Encoding in FFmpeg

Here's how two-pass encoding works for CBR encoding.

```
ffmpeg -y -i  test_1080p.MOV -c:v libx264  -b:v 5000k -pass 1  -f mp4
NUL && \

ffmpeg -i  test_1080p.MOV -c:v libx264  -b:v 5000k -maxrate 5000k
-bufsize 5000k -pass 2  test_1080p_CBR.mp4
```

Here is a description of the new controls added to the command line.

Line 1. During this pass, FFmpeg scans the file and records a log file documenting the complexity of the file.

`-y` overwrites existing log file. If you encode multiple files using FFmpeg, this tells the program to overwrite the existing log file. Without `-y`, FFmpeg will stop the batch to ask if you want to overwrite the log file each encode. Or you can name the log file for each encode with the `-passlogfile` switch.

`-pass 1` completes the first pass and creates the log file but no output file.

`-f mp4` identifies the output format used in the second pass.

`NUL` creates the log file.

`&& \` tells FFmpeg to run a second pass if the first pass was successful.

Line 2. During this pass, FFmpeg uses the log created in the first pass to encode the file.

`-b:v 5000k` sets the overall target.

`-maxrate 5000k` sets the maximum bitrate. It's the same as the target, so this means CBR.

`-bufsize 5000k` sets the size of the VBV.

`-pass 2` finds and uses the log file for the encode.

`test_1080p_CBR.mp4` sets the output file name.

Note that all bitrate-related commands in the first pass must also be in the second pass. Figure 8-23 shows what the CBR-encoded file looks like in Bitrate Viewer. Although the file isn't a total flat line, there's much less data rate variability, and the file would be much simpler to deliver. Of course, overall quality is slightly lower than VBR, and there's a risk of transient quality problems.

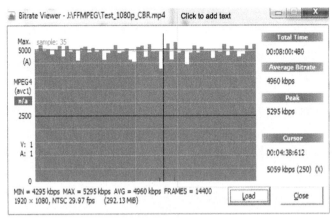

Figure 8-23. Two-pass CBR encoding with FFmpeg.

200 Percent Constrained VBR Encoding in FFmpeg

Here's what 200 percent constrained VBR would look like in FFmpeg. The first line is the same, but I've boosted `-maxrate` to `10000k`.

```
ffmpeg -y -i  test_1080p.MOV -c:v libx264  -b:v 5000k -pass 1  -f mp4
NUL && \

ffmpeg -i  test_1080p.MOV -c:v libx264  -b:v 5000k -maxrate 10000k
-bufsize 5000k -pass 2  test_1080p_200p_CVBR.mp4
```

Figure 8-25 shows what the 200 percent constrained VBR file looks like in Bitrate Viewer. Quality would be optimal, and there should be no transient quality problems. Again, with this worst-case file with mixed high- and low-motion footage, deliverability might be a real issue.

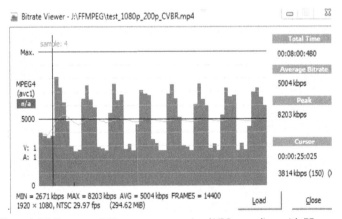

Figure 8-25. Two-pass 200 percent constrained VBR encoding with FFmpeg.

110 Percent Constrained VBR Encoding in FFmpeg

Here's what 110 percent constrained VBR would look like in FFmpeg. The first line is the same as the previous two, but -maxrate in pass two is limited to 5500k.

```
ffmpeg -y -i  test_1080p.MOV -c:v libx264  -b:v 5000k -pass 1  -f mp4
NUL && \

ffmpeg -i  test_1080p.MOV -c:v libx264  -b:v 5000k -maxrate 5500k
-bufsize 5000k -pass 2  test_1080p_110p_CVBR.mp4
```

Figure 8-26 shows what the 110 percent constrained VBR file looks like in Bitrate Viewer. The data rate is very similar to the other two, of course—although the peak bitrate is 5852 kbps compared with 5295 for CBR. While quality would be slightly less than 200 percent constrained VBR, there should be no transient quality problems, and the file should be pretty simple to deliver.

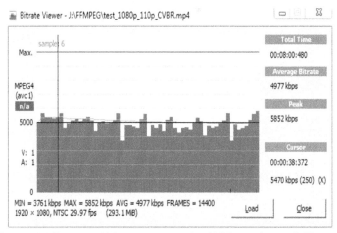

Figure 8-26. Two-pass 200 percent constrained VBR encoding with FFmpeg.

Tip: *Running multiple FFmpeg encodes simultaneously is a great way to speed up your multiple file encoding chores—particularly on a multiple-core computer. Be careful when encoding multiple files in the same folder using two-pass encoding, however, since you'll be creating multiple log files that will overwrite each other and ruin the second encode. You can separately name the log file using the* -passlogfile *switch, or simply run the different encodes from different folders, which is what I do.*

Summary and Conclusion

In this chapter, you learned that:

- Constant bitrate (CBR) encoding encodes all content to a single, consistent bitrate. Quality is slightly slower than that of variable bitrate (VBR), and severe transient quality issues can occur, but the streams are easier to deliver than VBR. Two-pass encoding is generally preferred to one-pass, because it tends to eliminate transient quality issues.

- Variable bitrate encoding matches encoding bitrate with scene complexity. Quality is slightly higher than CBR, and VBR tends to avoid transient quality issues in most files. When producing for streaming, you should always use constrained VBR, limiting the maximum data rate to no more than 200 percent of the target. Use two-pass encoding whenever you produce VBR files.

- VBR encoding impacts file deliverability. Files encoded using 200 percent constrained VBR may be harder to deliver than CBR files. Files encoded using 110 percent constrained VBR are much simpler to deliver.

- Many producers use 110 percent constrained VBR. This eliminates transient quality issues in most files, simplifies deliverability, and maintains the switching heuristics of iOS devices. Overall quality will be slightly lower than 200 percent constrained VBR, but the difference probably wouldn't be noticeable by most viewers.

- The maximum buffer size impacts both quality and data rate consistency. If you're most concerned about deliverability and compatibility with older devices, use a one- to two-second buffer. If deliverability and compatibility aren't issues, you can go as high as six seconds or more.

Chapter 9: I-, B-, P-, and Reference Frames

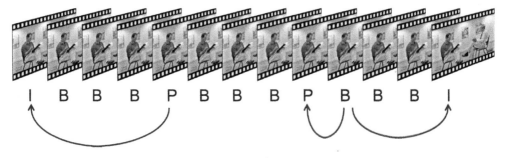

Figure 9-1. I-, B-, and P-frames illustrated.

Most codecs use different frame types during encoding. Most advanced codecs—like HEVC and H.264—use three types: I-frames (also called key frames), B-frames, and P-frames. Figure 9-1 shows all three frame types in a group of pictures (GOP), or a sequence of frames that starts with a key frame and includes all frames up to, but not including, the next key frame. In this chapter, you'll learn all about these frames types, specifically:

- what I-frames are and why they're important
- I-frame configurations for single file and adaptive streaming
- what B-frames are and why they're important
- recommended B-frame configurations
- what reference frames are and why they're important
- recommended B-frame configurations
- how to configure I-frames, B-frames, and reference frames in FFmpeg.

Frame Overview

Briefly, an I-frame is entirely self-contained and is compressed solely with intra-frame encoding techniques—typically a technology like JPEG, which is used for still images on the web and in many digital cameras. P- and B-frames reference information contained in other frames as much as possible. As you can see in Figure 9-1, P-frames, for predictive coded picture, can look backward for these redundancies, while B-frames, for bipredictive coded picture, can look backward and forward. This doubles the chance that the B-frame will find redundancies, making it the most efficient frame in the GOP.

The Hunt for Redundant Blocks

Let's take a deeper look at this search for redundant information. During encoding, each consecutive frame is divided into multiple blocks. When encoding the first frame in the video, which always is an I-frame, the encoder doesn't reference any other frames, and stores the complete frame. You see this in Figure 9-2.

Assume the next frame, frame 2, is a P-frame. When compressing the P-frame, the encoder can compare blocks in frame 2 with those in frame 1. If the content in a block is the same, the encoder can reference this block during encoding, and tell the decoder to simply display this block during playback. This is the redundant information the encoder searches for. The reference frame for frame 2 is frame 1.

Any information that's unique to frame 2 is encoded separately, again using a JPEG-like still image compression technique. You see this on the second frame in the bottom row in Figure 9-2. Intuitively, storing redundant blocks is very efficient—say a byte or two will do it. Encoding the residual information is much less efficient. That's why videos with high degrees of redundant information, like talking head videos, compress more efficiently than soccer games.

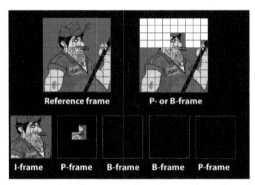

Figure 9-2. B- and P-frames store the information that changes from the reference frame or frames.

Assuming frame 3 is a B-frame, the encoder can search backwards and forwards for these redundant blocks of pixels. When you hear about a particular codec's "search" mechanism, it's the technique used to search for these redundancies. Again, the frames that the encoder searches are called reference frames, since during encoding and decoding the codec references these frames. Overall, this technique is called inter-frame compression. Depending upon the content in the video, this can be much more effective than the intra-frame used in I-frames.

Working with I-frames

How do you use these frame types to your advantage? With I-frames, recognize that these are the largest frames, which makes them the least efficient from a compression standpoint. Basically, you only want I-frames where they enhance either quality or interactivity, or where they're mandated by your adaptive streaming segment size. This means that you deploy I-frames differently depending upon whether you're encoding for a single file or adaptive streaming.

I-frames and Single Files

In all cases, video playback must start on an I-frame, since that's the only complete frame. When encoding a single file, as opposed to multiple files for adaptive streaming, often this file is stored on the viewer's hard drive and watched interactively, so the viewer can drag the play head slider to various points in the video. To make sure playback is responsive, when encoding a single file, you should insert an I-frame every 10 seconds, or every 300 frames in a 29.97 fps file.

How much difference in quality does I-frame interval make? Table 9-1 shows the peak signal-to-noise ratio (PSNR) ratings for 720p files, with the highest values in green and lowest in red. For the record, I produced these files with a B-frame interval of three, and 16 reference frames, with scene change detection disabled. Data rates vary from clip to clip, and were those calculated in Chapter 7 after performing constant rate factor (CRF) testing. Bitrate control techniques were those listed in Table 8-6.

	.5 Sec	1 Sec	2 Sec	3 Sec	5 Sec	10 Sec	Max Delta
Tears of Steel	38.22	39.05	39.49	39.64	39.74	39.87	4.32%
Sintel	37.09	38.06	38.57	38.75	38.97	39.08	5.37%
Big Buck Bunny	37.03	37.93	38.52	38.68	38.64	39.09	5.57%
Talking Head	43.63	44.10	44.40	44.51	44.61	44.68	2.42%
Freedom	40.33	40.67	40.88	40.96	40.99	41.03	1.72%
Haunted	41.89	42.20	42.35	42.39	42.45	42.49	1.44%
Average	**39.26**	**39.96**	**40.37**	**40.51**	**40.59**	**40.75**	**3.88%**
Screencam	35.35	38.13	37.68	38.86	40.78	41.26	16.71%
Tutorial	38.26	43.06	43.61	44.65	46.15	47.89	25.17%

Table 9-1. The impact of I-frame interval on video quality.

As the color coding shows, the longest key frame interval produced the highest quality in all test clips, although the difference was much more significant in the Screencam and Tutorial clips than in any other.

Figure 9-3 graphically presents the data from the table. As you can see, with real-world clips and animations, the quality difference between a key frame interval of 10 seconds and even two seconds is pretty small. With the synthetic Screencam and Tutorial clips, lower key frame values dramatically impact quality, probably because at the aggressive data rate of 600 kbps, key frame size meaningfully detracts from the bandwidth available for B-and P-frames.

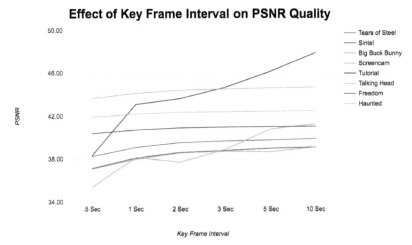

Figure 9-3. Key frame interval and PSNR quality in graphic form.

What does all this tell you? When encoding files for single file playback, use a key frame interval of 10 or even 20 seconds, particularly for synthetic files. If you're using a key frame interval of .5 seconds, or even 1 second, you're definitely leaving some quality on the table.

I-frames and Scene Change Detection

I-frames also improve quality when inserted at a scene change, because all subsequent P- and B-frames can reference this high-quality frame. So, when encoding for single-file delivery, you also want an I-frame at scene changes. Most applications use a checkbox or similar control labeled "key frames at scene changes" or something intuitive like that.

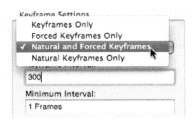

Figure 9-4. Choosing a key frame interval of 300 and natural key frames, which means key frames at scene changes.

As you can see in Figure 9-4, Telestream Episode Pro uses the term "Natural Keyframes" to enable key frames at scene changes and "Forced Keyframes" to enable key frames at regular intervals. For single files, you want both.

> **Tip:** *Some tools let you choose the key frame interval with either seconds or frames. If you'll be encoding files with different frame rates, like 23.976/24 fps clips and 29.997/30 fps clips, use the seconds value to create your presets. That way, you can use the same preset for all files, irrespective of frame rate.*

I-frames and Adaptive Streaming

The rules change completely when choosing an I-frame interval for adaptive streaming. Briefly, adaptive bitrate (ABR) technologies produce multiple streams with different quality levels to distribute to devices with varying connection speeds and CPU power. Then each stream is divided into multiple segments (also called chunks or fragments) of identical duration. During playback, the player will often choose segments from different streams to adjust to changing playback conditions, which is shown in Figure 9-5. To enable playback of each segment, you need an I-frame at the start.

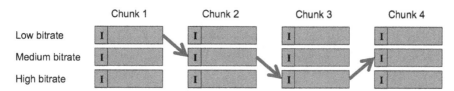

Figure 9-5. With ABR streaming, you need an I-frame at the start of each segment.

When producing ABR streams, follow these rules.

- ***I-frame interval must divide evenly into the segment size.*** Segment sizes range from two to 10 seconds. If your segment is four seconds, your I-frame interval can be 1, 2, or 4. If your segment is 10 seconds, your I-frame interval can be 1, 2, 5, or 10. Typically smaller segment sizes allow the ABR system to respond more quickly to changing conditions, so expect your I-frame interval to be 1 or 2. Sorenson Squeeze has a highly usable and logical interface that assigns the I-frame interval to all streams in the ABR group, and chooses the segment size (Figure 9-6).

- ***Disable scene change detection unless you're sure the encoder will also insert key frames at specified intervals.*** Otherwise, the encoder will restart the key frame interval at the new key frame, and may not produce key frames at the required locations.

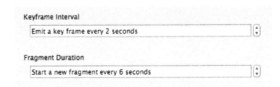

Figure 9-6. Make sure the key frame interval divides evenly into the fragment (or segment size).

Instantaneous Decode Refresh (IDR) Frames

One other I-frame-related configuration option that you'll see in Telestream Episode and some higher-end encoders is the instantaneous decode refresh (IDR) frame (Figure 9-7). Briefly, the H.264-specification enables two types of I-frames: normal I-frames and IDR frames. If an I-frame is an IDR frame, no frame after it can refer back to any frame before it. In contrast, with regular I-frames, B- and P-frames located after the I-frame can refer back to reference frames located before it.

Figure 9-7. Choosing the number of IDR frames. You'll learn about Slices later in this chapter.

In terms of random access within the video stream, playback can always start on an IDR frame because no frame refers to any frames behind it. However, playback cannot always start on a non-IDR I-frame because subsequent frames may reference previous frames. Here's a blurb from the Telestream Episode help file:

> An IDR frame is an I-frame whose preceding frames cannot be used by predictive frames. More distant IDR frames may allow more efficient compression but limits the ability of a player to move to arbitrary points in the video. In particular, QuickTime Player may show image artifacts when you scrub the timeline unless every I-frame is an IDR frame.

Since one of the key reasons to insert I-frames into your video is to enable interactivity, I use whatever setting results in every I-frame being an IDR frame. With Telestream Episode, I would choose Every as shown in Figure 9-7. If your streaming encoder doesn't offer this option, it's safe to assume that every I-frame is an IDR frame.

Tip: *For more on IDR frames, check out the article "Everything You Ever Wanted to Know About IDR Frames but Were Afraid to Ask" at* bit.ly/IDR_frames.

Quick Summary: I-Frames

1. When encoding for single-file delivery, use an I-frame interval of between 10 and 20 seconds, with scene detection enabled.

2. When encoding for adaptive streaming:

- make sure the I-frame interval divides evenly into your segment size. Most producers use a key frame interval of between two and three seconds.

- disable scene change detection unless you're absolutely sure that the encoder will insert I-frames at the specified interval even if there's an intervening I-frame caused by a scene change.

3. In all cases, every I-frame should be an IDR frame.

Working with B-frames

Now let's turn our attention to B-frames. As mentioned, B-frames are the most efficient frame, so they help improve compressed quality. However, files with B-frames are harder to decode because the player has to buffer all referenced frames in memory while playing back the file, and display them in their proper order. As you'll see in Chapter 10, that's why B-frames aren't enabled in the Baseline profile, which is the least complex H.264 profile used on low-power devices.

Otherwise, when producing for general computer and OTT playback, always use B-frames when available in the selected profile. Most encoding tools will let you choose the maximum number of B-frames to insert sequentially between I- and P-frames (or between P- and P-frames). Looking back at Figure 9-1, you can see that the file has three B-frames between each I and/or P-frames, which means a B-frame interval of 3.

Before exploring the magic number for B-frame interval, let's review some common B-frame related parameters, as shown in Figure 9-8, which is taken from Sorenson Squeeze when encoding with the MainConcept H.264 codec. Note that I copied the Reference Frames control from another section of the preset screen to create one neat screen for you. If you're looking for that setting in MainConcept Squeeze preset, it's on the upper right.

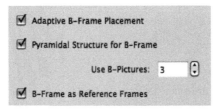

Figure 9-8. Common B-frame related options from Sorenson Squeeze.

Figure 9-8 presents three new concepts: Adaptive B-Frame Placement, Pyramidal Structure for B-Frame, and B-Frame as Reference Frames. Here are definitions and recommendations from a white paper produced by a company named Rhozet, which has since been acquired by Harmonic, so the white paper is no longer available online.

- **Adaptive B-Frame Placement.** Allows the encoder to adaptively change the B-frame pattern based on the source content. This is very useful when you are using a longer GOP and trying to hit low bit rates. In general, this increases the encoder's efficiency and should always be checked.

- **B-Frame as Reference Frames.** Allows the encoder to use B-frames as a reference to build other frames. This also increases the efficiency of the encoder and should always be checked. Not available in Baseline profile.

- **Pyramidal Structure for B-Frame.** Allows the encoder to compress B-frames based on other B-frames. Like the above two settings, this increases the efficiency of the encoder and should always be checked. Not available in Baseline profile.

By way of background, in MPEG-2 encoding, B-frames can't be used as reference frames. With H.264, they can, and most authorities agree that this improves overall quality. Note that when a program has two separate controls—one for reference B-frames, the other for pyramidal B-frames—the first enables B-frames to be used as reference for P-frames, while the second enables B-frames to be used as reference for other B-frames. I know, I know. Take a deep breath and read the line again, and it will start to make sense.

I want to emphasize the first control, Adaptive B-Frame Placement, which you should always enable because it gives the encoder permission not to use a B-frame if another frame type will improve quality. As a practical matter, this means that you seldom consistently achieve the B-frame interval that you select—especially if you choose an interval of 6 or higher.

You see this in Figure 9-9, a screenshot of Telestream Switch showing the animated video Big Buck Bunny encoded with a B-frame interval of 15. In the timeline, white frames are I-frames, purple frames are P-frames, and blue frames are B-frames. Height reflects frame size. The longest sequence of consecutive B-frames in the entire file is the group of 11 a bit in front of the I-frame on the right. This is dwarfed by the sequence of 20 P-frames in the center of the figure. Most other B-frames are deployed in groups of two or three.

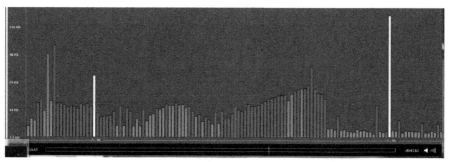

Figure 9-9. I-, B-, and P-frames in the video Big Buck Bunny shown in Telestream Switch.

On the upper right in Figure 9-9, you may be able to see percentage numbers for each frame type (there's a B-frame percentage of 71 percent in the figure). Using this output, I created Table 9-2, which shows the B-frame percentage for files created with the different B-frame values shown. Two of the files, Haunted and Big Buck Bunny, we've worked with before. El Ultimo is a very simple cartoon-type animation that I wanted to test to see how the x264 codec would actually deploy B-frames in such a simple file.

B-frame Percentage	1B	2B	3B	5B	8B	15B
Haunted	47%	64%	71%	77%	77%	77%
Big Buck Bunny	44%	58%	67%	70%	71%	71%
El Ultimo	46%	62%	68%	73%	74%	74%

Table 9-2. B-frame deployments for three video files at the requested B-frames shown.

Figure 9-10 graphically displays the data in Table 9-2, showing that actual deployments of B-frames tend to peak at about 5, with very small gains thereafter. This is why typically there's very little quality difference between files encoded with a B-frame interval of 5 or so and those encoded with higher values.

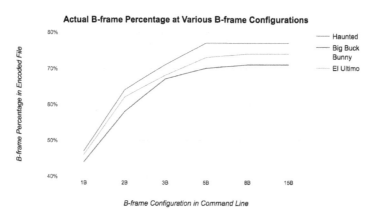

Figure 9-10. Basically, actual B-frame deployments peak at a B-frame interval setting of about 5.

Speaking of that, Table 9-3 shows how B-frame interval affects video quality. I'm showing the Screencam and Tutorial files separately because they behaved differently, although it's unclear whether this is characteristic of these files as a group, or idiosyncratic to the two test files.

	0B	1B	2B	3B	4B	5B	10B	15B	Max Delta
Tears of Steel	38.95	39.41	39.56	39.65	39.62	39.61	39.60	39.63	1.75%
Sintel	38.34	38.71	38.74	38.76	38.76	38.75	38.75	38.75	1.07%
Big Buck Bunny	39.96	40.34	40.41	40.40	40.38	40.41	40.40	40.39	1.13%
Talking Head	44.21	44.44	44.50	44.52	44.51	44.51	44.50	44.50	0.68%
Freedom	40.76	40.93	40.93	40.96	40.93	40.93	40.91	40.91	0.49%
Haunted	42.19	42.33	42.39	42.41	42.36	42.38	42.36	42.36	0.50%
Average	**40.74**	**41.03**	**41.09**	**41.11**	**41.09**	**41.10**	**41.09**	**41.09**	**0.94%**
Screencam	44.46	44.20	43.85	43.73	43.60	43.57	43.26	43.35	2.69%
Tutorial	48.35	48.57	48.71	48.72	48.74	48.72	48.72	48.72	0.81%

Table 9-3. The impact of B-frame configurations on quality as measured by PSNR.

With all other files, adding more B-frames translates to higher quality, but only to a degree. That is, after excluding the screencam and tutorial files, the overall highest quality was achieved at a B-frame interval of 3. To restate and emphasize, on average, values beyond 3 actually reduced quality, however slightly, and B-frame intervals of 10 and 15 never produced the highest value.

The data in Table 9-3 is graphically presented in Figure 9-11, which excludes the screencam and tutorial file. As you can see, the overall difference is minor, with no improvement beyond 3 and often a slight decline after 5 or 10.

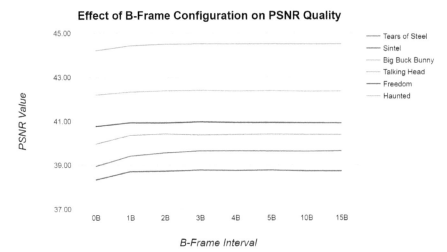

Figure 9-11. The Effect of B-frame configuration on PSNR values.

Beyond average values, we also care about lowest-quality frame, which is presented in Table 9-4. For perspective, you probably wouldn't notice a drop in quality unless it strayed below 30 dB or so, particularly in a synthetic screencam or animated file. Using this as a guide, you see three potential problem videos, Sintel (27.45), Big Buck Bunny (24.37), and Screencam (27.79). Looking at the individual frames, however, the quality drop is noticeable in the Big Buck Bunny and the Screencam videos, but not Sintel. We'll see if reference frame adjustments cure these problems.

	0B	1B	2B	3B	4B	5B	10B	15B	Max Delta
Tears of Steel	32.45	32.19	32.52	31.96	31.83	30.81	30.86	31.64	5.23%
Sintel	29.15	28.87	28.72	29.12	27.45	27.53	27.54	27.46	5.86%
Big Buck Bunny	24.66	24.70	24.59	24.38	24.37	24.64	24.47	24.43	1.35%
Talking Head	39.16	39.12	39.52	39.20	39.31	39.25	39.20	39.40	1.02%
Freedom	35.34	35.45	35.14	35.17	35.41	35.29	35.44	35.12	0.94%
Haunted	37.02	37.16	36.57	36.84	36.28	36.55	36.24	36.36	2.47%
Average	**32.96**	**32.91**	**32.84**	**32.78**	**32.44**	**32.35**	**32.29**	**32.40**	**2.03%**
Screencam	31.45	31.35	31.43	29.97	29.74	32.09	31.01	27.79	13.42%
Tutorial	43.94	44.61	45.01	45.42	45.45	45.52	45.35	45.32	3.47%

Table 9-4. Which B-frame interval produced the lowest-quality frame?

Tip: *In the next chapter we'll discuss H.264, and I'll recommend choosing an x264 preset to control a large group of encoding parameters to achieve a certain balance between encoding time and quality. All presets include values for B-frames and reference frames, but not I-frames, which are always set separately. Certainly you can override the B-frame and reference frame values in the preset, but you should know that absent the override, the preset would set these values.*

B-Frames and Compatibility

There are many urban legends surrounding B-frames and compatibility. For years, I recommended a B-frame interval of 3, primarily to reduce any compatibility risk. As a confirming example, cloud-encoding service Zencoder says the following in its encoding help files (bit.ly/Zen_B). "The default is 0 for widest compatibility. We recommend a value of 3 for compression/quality improvements. Values higher than 5 or 6 rarely provide much benefit, and greatly increase encoding time."

Beyond this, there's not much detail available from reputable sources about which B-frame setting to use. For example, in its "Technical Note TN2224" (http://bit.ly/appletn2224), Apple recommends using B-frames "as needed." Maybe it's just me, but I find that tough to translate into an integer. In its "HLS Authoring Specification for Apple Devices" (bit.ly/A_Devices_Spec), Apple doesn't mention B-frames at all.

In the tip just before this section, I note that the x264 presets contain fixed configurations for B-frames and reference frames. Jason Garrett-Glaser, the lead developer of x264, reports that he chose those settings because they represented "roughly optimal positions on the speed-compression curve based on testing" (bit.ly/JGGonB). When pressed about compatibility issues, he commented, "You'll be better off not basing your encoding settings on weird urban legends." It'd definitely hard to argue with that, particularly based upon the lack of guidance from Apple, which doesn't seem to know which B-frame setting is best (or at least isn't telling us).

What we absolutely know, however, is that B-frame settings in excess of 5 typically don't result in significantly more B-frames in the file (Table 9-2), and that B-frame intervals beyond 3 don't enhance the quality of most files (Table 9-3). We know that B-frame intervals of 10 and 15 deliver the worst-quality frames (Table 9-4) though the quality difference is minor.

To be fair, tests not included in the book did show that higher B-frame values do improve quality when encoding with other bitrate control techniques, like 200 percent constrained VBR. However, the improvement beyond three B-frames is incredibly slight, like an improvement from 41.07 to 41.09 dB. All of this is a long way of saying that for most real-world videos, you should specify a B-frame interval of 3, which strikes a good balance between optimum overall quality and avoiding ugly frames.

Quick Summary: B-Frames

1. Always enable adaptive B-frames when available.

2. Always enable B-frames as reference frames when available.

3. Always enable pyramid B-frames when available.

4. When encoding real-world videos and animations, a B-frame interval of 3 presents a good mix of optimum quality and avoiding ugly frames.

5. Regarding screencams and PowerPoint-based videos, I didn't see enough evidence to warrant a different recommendation for B-frames, so I'm going with 3 for these files too.

Reference Frames

Briefly, a reference frame is a frame that the frame being encoded can use for redundant information. You have two basic controls over reference frames: first, setting the number, and second, enabling B-frames to be used as reference frames.

The first question is the optimal number of reference frames. Intuitively, increasing the number of reference frames will increase encoding time, because the encoder has to search through more frames for redundancies. For example, set reference frames at 1, and once the encoder searches a single frame with redundancies, it's done. Set it at 16, and the encoder has to search through 16 frames. The hoped-for benefit is an increase in quality, as more redundancies should translate to higher quality.

Let's look at the quality side first. Table 9-5 explores this question, with 720p files encoded using a B-frame interval of 3 and other parameters as designated in previous chapters. I separated the

Screencam and Tutorial files again, though unlike with B-frames, there was little variation from the other files.

Average Quality	1 Ref	5 Ref	10 Ref	16 Ref	Max Delta	10 - 16 Delta	16 - 5 Delta
Tears of Steel	39.34	38.99	39.47	39.49	1.28%	-0.04%	-1.26%
Sintel	38.45	38.54	38.58	38.59	0.35%	-0.02%	-0.12%
Big Buck Bunny	39.99	40.09	40.11	40.11	0.31%	0.00%	-0.05%
Talking Head	44.27	44.36	44.39	44.40	0.29%	-0.03%	-0.10%
Freedom	40.68	40.80	40.85	40.87	0.47%	-0.06%	-0.19%
Haunted	42.24	42.32	42.35	42.36	0.26%	-0.02%	-0.08%
Average - 720p	40.83	40.85	40.96	40.97	0.34%	-0.03%	-0.29%
Screencam	43.59	43.73	43.76	43.70	0.38%	0.14%	0.07%
Tutorial	48.58	48.65	48.68	48.68	0.22%	-0.01%	-0.07%

Table 9-5. Impact of the number of reference frames on PSNR quality.

As always, the red columns mean the lowest value, the green value the highest. As you can see, with all videos except Tears of Steel, 1 was always the lowest score, while 16 averaged the highest score, though the Max Delta quality differences were very minor. Note that the difference between 10 and 16 reference frames in the top six videos averaged a minuscule 0.03 percentage points, which is significant given that 10 reference frames produced the best low frame quality (Table 9-6) and shaved 21 percent from encoding time. Figure 9-12 presents the results graphically, where the slight upward slope from 1 reference frame to 16 reference frames shows only a very slight improvement on most files.

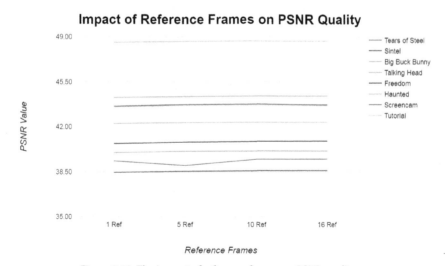

Figure 9-12. The impact of reference frames on PSNR quality.

Digging into the numbers, these results seems to indicate that most reference blocks come from frames proximate to the frame being encoded, and that adding to the search quickly brings diminishing returns.

> **Note:** *The sharp-eyed reader will check if the 5 Ref column in Table 9-5 is identical to the 3B value in Table 9-3 since they were encoded using identical parameters. As you'll see, the results are very, very close, but not identical. I wish I had an explanation, but I don't. Sometimes encoding different output files using the exact same parameters in FFmpeg delivers a slightly different result. Perhaps it's load on the machine, or something else. Whatever the cause, the differences are insignificant, and I just wanted you to know that I checked too!*

Reference Frames and Transient Quality

Table 9-6 tells which reference frame value avoids transient quality issues. With the B-frame interval of 3 used in these tests, the only file with a value below 25 was Big Buck Bunny. With the total variation of 0.72 percent in the Big Buck Bunny file, it's clear that changing the reference frame setting won't be a big help.

The bottom line for most files appears to be that high reference frame values don't significantly impact either overall or transient quality. This makes the reference frame decision more related to encoding time than output quality.

Low Frame	1 Ref	5 Ref	10 Ref	16 Ref	Max Delta	10 - 16 Delta	16 - 5 Delta
Tears of Steel	31.78	31.58	31.95	31.93	1.18%	0.08%	-1.09%
Sintel	28.77	28.60	29.00	28.90	1.39%	0.34%	-1.04%
Big Buck Bunny	24.76	24.81	24.63	24.71	0.72%	-0.30%	0.41%
Talking Head	39.36	39.57	39.55	39.62	0.67%	-0.17%	-0.12%
Freedom	35.36	35.17	35.38	35.12	0.73%	0.73%	0.12%
Haunted	36.30	36.25	36.27	36.22	0.23%	0.14%	0.10%
Average - 720p	**32.72**	**32.66**	**32.80**	**32.75**	**0.41%**	**0.15%**	**-0.26%**
Screencam	30.99	31.48	30.95	30.47	3.32%	1.59%	3.32%
Tutorial	45.06	45.46	45.25	44.96	1.11%	0.65%	1.11%

Table 9-6. Lowest frame quality for each reference frame value.

Reference Frames and Encoding Time

Regarding encoding time, Table 9-7 tells the tale. As you can see, the average encoding time delta between real-world and animated videos with 1 or 16 reference frames was 136 percent. Dropping down to 10 reference frames shaved 21 percent off encoding time, while dropping to 5 reference frames reduced encoding time by 43 percent. On the other hand, the encoding time difference for the Screencam file was less overall, while it was insignificant for the PowerPoint-based Tutorial file.

Encoding Time	1 Ref	5 Ref	10 Ref	16 Ref	Max Delta	10 - 16 Delta	16 - 5 Delta
Tears of Steel	39	49	72	91	133%	-21%	-46%
Sintel	40	53	71	76	90%	-7%	-30%
Big Buck Bunny	41	53	68	85	107%	-20%	-38%
Talking Head	37	47	61	77	108%	-21%	-39%
Freedom	99	142	200	263	166%	-24%	-46%
Haunted	47	65	93	123	162%	-24%	-47%
Average - 720p	**51**	**68**	**94**	**119**	**136%**	**-21%**	**-43%**
Screencam	56	90	100	111	98%	-10%	-19%
Tutorial	23	23	24	26	13%	**-8%**	**-12%**

Table 9-7. Reference frames and encoding times.

To put this all in perspective, say you're encoding real-world videos and animations in-house and you're at capacity. You're about to spend another $25,000 on a workstation with an enterprise encoding program like Capella Systems Cambria FTC or Telestream Vantage. If you're currently encoding using 16 reference frames, you can cut your encoding time roughly in half by switching to 5 reference frames (from 119 seconds to 68). The toll on quality? A drop from 40.70 to 40.58 dB, or about 0.3 percent. If you're really in a financial bind, you can drop your reference frames to 1 and lose only about 0.41 percent in PSNR quality.

Quick Summary: Reference Frames

1. The qualitative difference in both overall and low frame quality is very minor with all reference frame values. For most users, this makes reference frame setting an encoding time issue rather than a quality issue. I'll use a setting of 10 going forward.

2. If you're operating at capacity, and are about to buy new gear, you can cut encoding time significantly by dropping the number of reference frames down to 1. The total quality delta will be less than 0.5 percent.

Note: *After trying all the bitrate control and frame-related alternatives to potentially improve the quality of the screencam files, I'm still not happy with the low frame quality. For this reason, going forward, I'm going to bump the Screencam data rates to 1600 kbps for 1080p, 1000 kbps for 720p and 400 kbps for 360p. I'm really close to doing the same for Big Buck Bunny, but the lowest-quality frames in the Screencam files are just a bit more obvious to the viewer.*

Encoding Slices

Some encoding tools offer the option of choosing the number of slices. What are these?

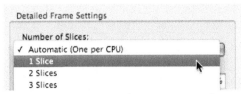

Figure 9-13. Use 1 Slice for maximum quality.

Slices are a concept in H.264 and HEVC. Briefly, when you use multiple slices, the encoder divides each frame into multiple regions and searches for redundancies in other frames only within the respective region. This can accelerate encoding on multi-core computers, because the encoder can assign the regions to different cores. However, since redundant information may have moved to a different region between frames—say, in a panning or tilting motion—encoding with multiple slices may miss some redundancies, decreasing the overall quality of the video.

Here's a snippet from the Telestream Episode help file:

> Speed up processing by transcoding parts, slices, of the same frame in parallel. Using more slices may decrease image quality somewhat as redundancies between parts of the frame cannot be fully utilized.

This is illustrated in Figure 3-18. If this video were encoded in a single slice, movement within the quadrants would be irrelevant, and the encoder could find inter-frame redundancies irrespective of where the content is (or was) in the frame. If that distinguished rider on the left (then Governor, now Senator Mark Warner from Virginia) started on the left and moved through the video toward the right in a sequence of five or six frames, there would be significant inter-frame redundancies, which translates to very good quality.

Figure 9-14. This video frame cut into four slices.

With slices, however, the encoder can't refer to information in previous or subsequent frames that wasn't in that slice, so as the rider moves from left to right, significant inter-frame redundancies may go unrealized. For this reason, unless you're in a significant hurry, I recommend setting slices to the lowest value. The default value for FFmpeg and x264 is 0, so no worries there.

Applying These Findings

Table 9-8 shows our encoding parameters to this point. You'll learn about B-frame strategy shortly.

| | Chapter 7 | | | Chapter 8 | | | Chapter 9 | | | |
	1080p	720p	360p	Target	Max	VBV	I-Frm	B-Frm	Strategy	Refs
Tears of Steel	5000	2000	900	100%	110%	1 sec	2-3	3	2	10
Sintel	5000	2000	900	100%	110%	1 sec	2-3	3	2	10
Freedom	6000	2500	900	100%	110%	1 sec	2-3	3	2	10
Haunted	6000	2500	900	100%	110%	1 sec	2-3	3	2	10
Big Buck Bunny	3000	1500	600	100%	200%	1 sec	2-3	3	2	10
Talking Head	3000	1500	600	100%	110%	1 sec	2-3	3	2	10
Screencam	1600	1000	400	100%	200%	2 sec	2-3	3	2	10
Tutorial	1000	600	200	100%	200%	1 sec	2-3	3	2	10

Table 9-8. Recommended encoding parameters for the different file types.

I-, B-, and Reference Frames in FFmpeg

Let's change our focus to controlling these parameters in FFmpeg, starting with the I-frame.

I-frame Controls in FFmpeg

As you learned earlier, the I-frame controls the group of pictures (GOP) size of the video file, so an I-frame setting of 90 means a GOP size of 90. I bring this up because the easiest way to remember FFmpeg's I-frame switch is to think G for GOP size. When setting the I-frame interval in FFmpeg, you have the following three controls to consider.

-g 72 sets the maximum key frame interval at 72, or three seconds for a 24 fps file. If not set, FFmpeg will insert an I-frame every 250 frames. For single files, you can use an interval of five to 10 seconds, or just don't set this option. For files produced for adaptive streaming, use an interval that divides evenly into your segment size, usually either two or three seconds.

-keyint_min 72 is the minimum distance between I-frames. If not set, FFmpeg will use a minimum interval of 25. When encoding a single file, you can simply not set this option. When producing for adaptive streaming, you should set the minimum to the same value as the GOP size to ensure I-frames at the specified interval.

`-sc_threshold 0` sets the threshold for scene detection. If not set, the threshold is 40. This is fine for single files, but not adaptive. When producing for adaptive streaming, you should disable scene change detection with the setting of 0 as shown in the string.

These commands deliver the key frame interval shown in Figure 9-13.

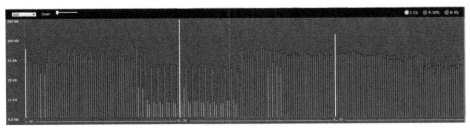

Figure 9-13. Key frames at regular intervals, but not at scene changes.

I-frames at Specified Interval and Scene Changes

If you want I-frames at the specified interval and at scene changes, use the following switches.

```
-force_key_frames expr:gte(t,n_forced*3) -keyint_min 25
-sc_threshold 40
```

`-force_key_frames expr:gte(t,n_forced*3)` forces the I-frame at the key frame interval of three seconds. Substitute the desired I-frame interval for the 3 in the string.

`-keyint_min 25` sets the minimum I-frame interval at 25, which is the default. If the default value is acceptable, you don't have to include this switch.

`-sc_threshold 40` sets the threshold for scene detection at 40, which is the default. Again, if the default value is acceptable, you don't have to include this switch.

This produces the key frame cadence shown in Figure 9-14. With a key frame interval of 2 or 3, my tests reveal that key frames at scene changes add very little extra quality. For example, the file shown in Figure 9-13 had a PSNR value of 41.22207 dB, while the file in Figure 9-14 had a PSNR value of 41.25565 dB, about 0.08 percent higher. So I tend to keep it simple and not use key frames at scene changes, but it's your choice.

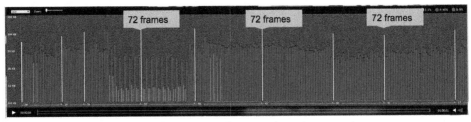

Figure 9-14. Key frames at regular intervals, and at scene changes.

Tip: *There's a lengthy discussion of the best option for achieving consistent key frame intervals for Dynamic Adaptive Streaming over HTTP (DASH) encoding at* bit.ly/Iframes_DASH. *The recommendations shown in Table 9-8 follow the recommendation there, but it's not the only way to skin this particular cat.*

B-frames in FFmpeg

When you set B-frames with FFmpeg, you should set these two values.

`-bf 3` sets the desired value for B-frames, in this case the recommended interval of 3. Note that if you don't manually insert a B-frame interval, but do insert a preset (like Very Slow), the preset controls the B-frame interval. If you don't insert an interval or choose a preset, I believe FFmpeg uses 16 but I was unable to confirm this.

`-b_strategy 2` enables adaptive B-frame placement, and there are three option. 0 is very fast, but not recommended. 1 is the faster and default mode, and 2 is the slower mode that I recommend. You can read about why at bit.ly/OptimizeBs. To make a long story short, choosing 2 instead of 1 roughly doubled the number of B-frames inserted into the file. If you don't choose a setting, but choose a preset, the setting in the preset controls this setting. If you don't choose a preset or a specific setting, FFmpeg uses a value of 1.

Figure 9-15 shows how much difference the second switch makes in terms of B-frames actually inserted into the file. On top, with a setting of 1, only 9 percent of the frames are B-frames. With a setting of 2, 58 percent of the frames are B-frames.

-b_strategy 1 9% B frames PSNR 36.62

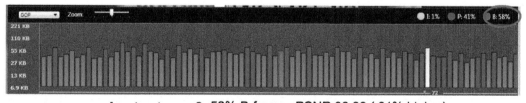

-b_strategy 2 58% B-frames PSNR 36.69 (.01% higher)

Figure 9-15. A setting of 2 inserts many more B-frames into the file, but doesn't significantly improve quality.

Interestingly, despite the second file having more than six times the number of B-frames, the quality improvement was negligible.

Reference Frames in FFmpeg

When you set B-frames with FFmpeg, you should set the value shown below.

> `-refs 10` inserts that input value, in this case 10, for reference frames. Note that if you don't manually insert the number of reference frames, but do insert a preset (like Very Slow), the preset controls the number of reference frames. If you don't insert an interval or choose a preset, I believe FFmpeg uses 16 but I was unable to confirm this.

Pulling this all together, a simple one-pass encode might look like this.

```
ffmpeg -i TOS_720p.mp4 -c:v libx264 -g 72 -keyint_min 72 -sc_threshold 0
-bf 3 -b_strategy 2 -refs 10 -b:v 2000k TOS_output.mp4
```

This produces an MP4 file with a keyframe interval of three seconds, with no keyframes at scene changes. FFmpeg will insert 3 B-frames using the second strategy, and will search ten reference frames for each encoded frame. Audio would pass through unchanged from the source.

That's it for frame types. In the next chapter, you'll learn all about the H.264 standard and codec, the closest we have to a one-size-fits-all codec.

Chapter 10: Encoding H.264

ITU –		ISO –	
International Telecommunications Union		International Standardization Organization	
Telephone, Radio, TV		Photography, Computer, Consumer Electronics	
1984	H.120		
1990	H.261 – Video Conferencing		
1993		MPEG-1 – Video CD	
1994	(H.262)	MPEG-2 – Digital Cable and Satellite TV	
1995	H.263 – Improved Video Conferencing		
1997		ATSC – U.S. HDTV	
1999		MPEG-4	
2002	AVC (H.264)	AVC (MPEG-4 Part 10)	

Figure 10-1. The evolution of H.264 (from a presentation by Streamcrest Associates).

In previous chapters, we performed all tests using the H.264 codec. Most of those lessons were generic, and apply equally to other codecs. In this chapter, we'll discuss H.264-specific configurations and information.

Figure 10-1 provides a historical perspective of H.264. First, as I'll detail in a moment, it was a joint standard from two powerful standards bodies. Second, H.264 is well established, released for deployment more than 14 years ago. Not shown in the chart is that it was broadly embraced for computer playback (QuickTime, Flash, and Silverlight); in adaptive streaming technologies (HLS, DASH, Smooth Streaming, HDS); on mobile devices (iOS, Android, Windows); on OTT devices (Roku, Apple TV); and for smart TVs (all of them). While getting long in the tooth, H.264 is still the closest we have to a one-size-fits-all codec. That's what makes it so important, and that's why the earlier chapters showed examples using H.264.

In this chapter, we'll start with a high-level look at H.264, covering issues like container formats and potential royalty obligations. Then you'll learn how to configure the most commonly presented H.264 encoding options.

Next, you'll see how the quality produced by the different H.264 codecs can vary, and also learn how to work with Advanced Audio Coding (AAC) audio compression. You'll walk away familiar with the most common H.264 encoding parameters and ready to tackle your own encoding

Specifically, you will learn:

- which container formats you can use with the H.264 codec

- which activities result in an obligation to pay royalties

- what profiles and levels are and how they affect quality and playback compatibility

- what context-adaptive binary arithmetic coding (CABAC) and context-adaptive variable-length coding (CAVLC) are and when to choose one over the other

- how and why quality differs among the various H.264 codecs, and which deliver the best (and worst) quality

- how x264 presets and tuning mechanisms operate and how to use them

- which audio codecs you can use with H.264 and how to configure them

- how to encode x264/AAC files in FFmpeg

What Is H.264?

H.264 is a video compression technology, or codec. As shown in Figure 10-1, H.264 was jointly developed by the International Telecommunication Union (as H.264) and International Organization for Standardization/International Electrotechnical Commission Moving Picture Experts Group (as MPEG-4 Part 10, Advanced Video Coding, or AVC). Thus, the terms "H.264" and "AVC" mean the same thing and are interchangeable.

Architecturally, H.264 is a codec defined in the MPEG-4 specification. Of the specification's 28 parts, four are most relevant to streaming. These are:

- *Part 2—MPEG video (the MPEG-4 codec).* This was the first video codec incorporated into the MPEG-4 specification. Although it was adopted by Apple, the MPEG-4 codec delivered lower quality than other codecs available at that time, like the RealVideo and Windows Media Video codecs, so the MPEG-4 codec never achieved much mindshare or market share in the streaming media marketplace.

- *Part 3—MPEG-4 audio (AAC, etc).* These are the audio compression technologies that can be included in the MP4 container format defined in Part 14. More on these below.

- *Part 10—Advanced Video Coding (AVC/H.264).* This is the H.264 video codec. Note that while the H.264 codec is a part of the MPEG-4 specification, the codec can be used in container formats other than that defined in Part 14. For this reason, it's common to see the H.264 codec included in files using the Flash container format (.flv or .f4v) or the QuickTime container format (.mov); in MPEG-2 transport streams (.ts); or in the proprietary container formats used by adaptive streaming formats like Adobe's HTTP Dynamic Streaming (.f4f) or Microsoft's Smooth Streaming (.ismv).

- **Part 14—Container Format (MP4).** This is the container format defined by the MPEG-4 spec. You learned about container formats back in Chapter 1; for now, recognize that whenever you see the file extension .mp4, the file is produced using the MPEG-4 container format.

When it launched, MPEG-4 was billed as the unifying standard for broadcasters with advanced features like object orientation and two multiplex layers enabling compatibility with broadcast and streaming architectures. For more on this, check out "Will MPEG-4 Fly?" at bit.ly/MPEG-4_fly. The MPEG-4 codec itself was so bad that in 2004, I wrote a column proclaiming "MPEG-4 is Dead" (bit.ly/MPEG4_dead). I still get grief about that column, but it applied to the MPEG-4 codec, not the standard (he said a bit defensively), so turned out to be accurate.

In the streaming media space, the MPEG-4 specification gained very little traction until implementations of the H.264 codec started to produce better quality than competitive codecs like VP6 and Windows Media Video, and the average computer became powerful enough to play H.264 video. Of course, it didn't hurt when Apple built H.264 playback into its little device called the iPod, which morphed into the iPhone and iPad and created several huge new markets along the way. Then Adobe integrated H.264 into Flash, and Microsoft did the same with Silverlight, and the strength of the H.264 codec pulled the MPEG-4 spec into the forefront of streaming.

Outside the streaming media marketplace, H.264 was widely used by all the devices that typically use the technology recommended by their standards body—which is the ITU for TV, radio, and mobile phones, and the ISO for photography, consumer electronics, and computers. This widespread adoption and usage gives H.264 significant momentum going forward. For example, its inclusion in multiple devices like mobile phones and iPods dramatically reduces the cost of chips and other components that enable H.264 playback, creating a natural barrier to entry for competitive formats.

The first challenger to H.264, Google's VP8 (via Google's acquisition of On2 Technologies), never saw much success. Although it displayed about the same performance as H.264 (see bit.ly/vp8vh264), VP8 arrived to the market much later than H.264. It was royalty free, but royalty rates for H.264, which I'll cover in a moment, were reasonable. So VP8's royalty-free status proved largely irrelevant.

Over the past two years, two codecs have begun to challenge H.264. HEVC, which I'll cover in Chapter 11, has achieved great success in 4K delivery to smart TVs, set-top boxes, and some OTT devices. Google's VP9 has been deployed by YouTube and some other vendors, like JW Player, to replace H.264 for 1080p and lower-resolution delivery. Both HEVC and VP9 deliver quality similar to H.264 at about half the data rate, although this varies significantly by content and configuration.

Container Formats

Again, we covered container formats back in Chapter 1. Briefly, to recount, a container format, according to Wikipedia, is "a meta-file format whose specification describes how data and metadata are stored" (bit.ly/containerformat).

When encoding with the H.264 codec, you must choose the correct container format for your target player; otherwise, the file won't play. For example, even though iPhones can play .ts files containing video encoded with the H.264 codec, they can't play .ismv files encoded with H.264 but packaged into the Smooth Streaming container format. I'll cover the container formats you should use for each target player and platform in Chapters 13 through 15.

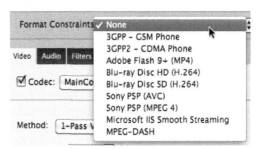

Figure 10-2. You can encode H.264 video into a number of container formats,
as shown in this screenshot from Sorenson Squeeze.

If you had to choose one container format to produce a single file that plays almost everywhere, use the MPEG-4 container format and produce an .mp4 file. That's because all players—whether Flash, Silverlight, iPad, iPod, Android, or Windows Phone—play .mp4 files. As covered in more detail in Chapters 13 through 14, most adaptive streaming formats use different containers, which you'll have to customize for each target.

Note that the H.264-specific encoding options you'll learn about in this chapter apply to all H.264-encoded files, irrespective of the intended container. So while you'll have to change your container for each target, the H.264-specific encoding parameters themselves remain the same.

Other H.264 Details

Like most video coding standards, H.264 actually standardizes only the "central decoder ... such that every decoder conforming to the standard will produce similar output when given an encoded bit stream that conforms to the constraints of the standard," according to the "Overview of the H.264/AVC Video Coding Standard" published in IEEE Transactions on Circuits and Systems for Video Technology (bit.ly/h264_spec). Basically, this means that there's no standard H.264 encoder. In fact, H.264 encoding vendors can utilize a range of different techniques to optimize video quality, as long as the bitstream is compatible with H.264 decoders. This is one of the key reasons that H.264 encoding interfaces vary so significantly among the various tools.

It's also one of the key reasons that the quality of H.264-encoded files varies so significantly among the different codec vendors. Unlike VP6 and Windows Media, which come from a single vendor and are relatively uniform in terms of quality irrespective of encoding tool, there are multiple H.264 codec developers. Quality fluctuates markedly among them, as you'll see at the end of this chapter.

H.264 Royalties

H.264 was developed by a consortium of companies that (gasp!) want to get paid for their efforts. To promote this goal, they patented many of the underlying technologies and contracted with a company called MPEG LA to set up and administer licensing and royalty collection. Typical customers of MPEG LA include consumer equipment manufacturers (Blu-ray Disc players and recorders); software developers (encoding programs, streaming players); and content developers.

To explain, companies like Adobe, Apple, and Microsoft, as well as Samsung, Sony, and Panasonic, pay MPEG LA by the unit to include H.264 decoders in their respective players. There's a maximum annual fee that started at $3.5 million per year in 2005 and 2006, but cost $8.125 million in 2016, and increases to $9.75 million per year in 2017 through 2020. This number was generally thought to be reasonable, and enabled multiple vendors to include H.264 playback in hundreds of millions of hardware and software players, including multiple browsers and operating systems.

MPEG LA has a licensing FAQ at mpegla.com/main/programs/AVC/Pages/FAQ.aspx, and you can download the "AVC Portfolio License Briefing" at bit.ly/h264royalties. Here's a brief overview of those terms, primarily focused on content producers.

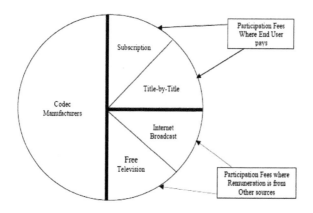

Figure 10-3. H.264 royalty categories per MPEG LA's license summary.

Figure 10-3 presents a chart MPEG LA. Codec manufacturers on the left of the wheel are subject to royalties after shipping more than 100,000 units. On the top right, if you're selling H.264-encoded content—on either a subscription or pay-per-view basis—you owe the following, according to the license briefing:

- **Subscription:** Royalties start at 100,001 subscribers; for 100,000 and under, there is no fee. For 100,000 to 250,000 subscribers, the annual royalty is $25,000, increasing to $50,000 for 250,001 to 500,000 subscribers. Between 500,001 and 1 million subscribers, the annual royalty is $75,000, while services with more than 1 million subscribers owe $100,000 annually.

- **Title-by-Title (pay-per-view):** There is no royalty for videos that are 12 minutes or shorter. For videos longer than 12 minutes, the price is the lower of 2 percent of the price or $0.02 per title.

For those producing H.264 video for free distribution, in August 2010, MPEG LA announced that its "AVC Patent Portfolio License will continue not to charge royalties for Internet video that is free to end users (known as 'Internet Broadcast AVC Video') during the entire life of this license." In essence, if the video is free, there is no royalty.

> **Note:** *In December, 2016, Nokia sued Apple for infringing upon eight H.264 patents with products including "the iPhone, iPad, iPod, Apple Watch, Mac computer products, and Apple digital media players such as Apple TV." It appears from the complaint that Nokia is claiming that virtually any use of H.264 encoding or decoding is royalty bearing. It is also clear that Nokia is shooting for far more than the $0.20/unit charged by MPEG LA. If Nokia wins, this means that any companies who distribute H.264 encoders or decoders who aren't currently paying royalties to Nokia can expect the proverbial bill in the mail, amount, as of yet, undetermined. Eleven years after MPEG LA issued their first H.264 rate card, the cost structure could be completely revamped. For example, Nokia is asserting a legal argument that would allow them to charge much more for encoders than decoders. The result of this lawsuit, which may take years to play out, might dramatically impact pricing for H.264 and HEVC.*

Comparing H.264 with Other Codecs

H.264 sucked all the oxygen out of the room as it related to previous codecs, including WMV, VP6, VP8, and the MPEG-4 codec, which all pretty much ceased to exist once H.264 was available in Flash. Looking ahead, the most critical short-term competition will come from the aforementioned HEVC and VP9.

In terms of quality comparisons, check out what Netflix had to say in a blog post from August 2016 (bit.ly/netflix_codecs). To reach its conclusions, Netflix tested 5,000 12-second clips from its catalog at 1080p, 720p, and 480p, at eight quality levels per configuration. The team applied six quality metrics resulting in more than 500,000 bitrate quality curves. Here's what they found:

Here's a snapshot: x265 and libvpx [VP9] demonstrate superior compression performance compared to x264, with bitrate savings reaching up to 50% especially at the higher resolutions. x265 outperforms libvpx for almost all resolutions and quality metrics, but the performance gap narrows (or even reverses) at 1080p.

So x265 and VP9 can shave 50 percent from your bandwidth costs, which is pretty impressive. The problem, of course, is that changing codecs is a bit more complicated than changing your shirt. Most problematical, particularly for HEVC, is the playback side. That's because HEVC playback isn't available in any desktop or iOS browsers, although it is available on later Android devices. VP9 playback is available in the latest versions of all browsers except Safari, as well as Android, but not iOS.

Back when producers made the switch from VP6 to H.264, playback for both was available in Flash, so the transition was seamless. Today, particularly for HEVC, it's quite painful, and as far as I know, HEVC hasn't been deployed by video distributor for browser-based playback. Despite the fact that HEVC and VP9 are both better performers, most producers will continue with H.264 for their mainstream browser-based deliveries, as well as mobile.

Also on the horizon is the AV1 codec from the Alliance for Open Media, which is scheduled to supplant VP9 as early as December of 2016. AV1 was a bit too unbaked to include in this book, but you can get a feel for the history and design goals of the new codec at bit.ly/whatisav1.

With this behind us, let's jump into the basics of H.264 encoding.

Basic H.264 Encoding Parameters

Let's start with the basics—profiles and levels—which are the most fundamental configuration options you can access from almost all encoding programs, and of course, FFmpeg.

Profiles and Levels

Profiles and levels are the most basic H.264 encoding parameters, and are available in one form or another in most H.264 encoding tools. According to now changed (but less descriptive) Wikipedia definitions, (en.wikipedia.org/wiki/H264), a profile "defines a set of coding tools or algorithms that can be used in generating a conforming bit stream," whereas a level "places constraints on certain key parameters of the bit stream." In other words, a profile defines specific encoding techniques that you can or can't use when encoding a file (such as B-frames), while the level defines details such as the maximum resolutions and data rates within each profile.

Take a look at Figure 10-4, which is an edited screenshot from Wikipedia's H.264 article. On top are H.264 profiles, including the Baseline, Main and High, which are the profiles most frequently supported in computer- and device-oriented players. On the left are the different encoding techniques available, with the table detailing which are supported by the respective profiles.

Feature	Baseline	Main	High
Bit depth (per sample)	8	8	8
Chroma formats	4:2:0	4:2:0	4:2:0
Flexible macroblock ordering (FMO)	Yes	No	No
Arbitrary slice ordering (ASO)	Yes	No	No
Redundant slices (RS)	Yes	No	No
Data Partitioning	No	No	No
SI and SP slices	No	No	No
Interlaced coding (PicAFF, MBAFF)	No	Yes	Yes
B slices	No	Yes	Yes
CABAC entropy coding	No	Yes	Yes
4:0:0 (Monochrome)	No	No	Yes
8x8 vs. 4x4 transform adaptivity	No	No	Yes
Quantization scaling matrices	No	No	Yes
Separate C_b and C_r QP control	No	No	Yes
Separate color plane coding	No	No	No
Predictive lossless coding	No	No	No

Figure 10-4. Encoding techniques enabled by profile, from Wikipedia.

In theory, as you apply more advanced encoding algorithms, your quality should improve. What's the trade-off? Either increased encoding time, increased decoding complexity, or both. To complete the picture, you typically select the profile in your encoding tool via a drop-down box like that shown in Figure 10-5 or via the FFmpeg switch you'll learn shortly.

Figure 10-5. Choosing your profile in Capella Systems Cambria FTC.

Why do profiles exist? To define different grades of H.264 that can be used by different devices depending upon the power of their CPU. For example, the original iPods and iPhones could only play the Baseline profile, so video encoded using the Main or High profiles won't play on these devices. In contrast, most computers and all over-the-top (OTT) devices like Apple TV and Roku boxes can play video encoded using the High profile, as well as video encoded using the Baseline or Main profile.

Life would be easiest for all streaming professionals if they could produce one set of files that played everywhere, but that would have to use the Baseline profile. How much quality would you leave on the table? And, for those concerned with playback on older computers and mobile devices, how much easier are Baseline-encoded files to playback? Well, let's have a look.

Comparative Quality—Baseline, Main and High Profiles

Table 10-1 shows the comparative quality of 720p videos encoded using the Baseline, Main, and High profiles. As you can see, the Baseline profile delivers the lowest quality in all cases, and the High profile the best. What might be surprising is how little difference there is; only an average of 2.84 percent for all clips, with about 80 percent of that between the Baseline and Main profiles. The difference between Main and High is only half a percent.

Average Quality	Baseline	Main	High	Delta - Baseline/Main	Delta - Main/High	Total Delta
Tears of Steel	37.52	39.11	39.46	4.26%	0.88%	5.19%
Sintel	37.13	38.27	38.58	3.08%	0.78%	3.90%
Big Buck Bunny	38.45	39.82	40.11	3.56%	0.72%	4.31%
Talking Head	43.69	44.34	44.39	1.48%	0.12%	1.60%
Freedom	39.60	40.62	40.85	2.57%	0.58%	3.17%
Haunted	41.55	42.22	42.35	1.60%	0.31%	1.91%
Screencam	46.43	46.74	46.87	0.67%	0.28%	0.95%
Tutorial	43.44	44.04	44.18	1.38%	0.32%	1.71%
Average	**40.98**	**41.89**	**42.10**	**2.32%**	**0.50%**	**2.84%**

Table 10-1. Comparative quality of the different profiles at 720p. The data.

Figure 10-6 shows the data in Table 10-1 graphically. While all scores improve from Baseline to High, the steepest part of the slope is between Baseline and Main.

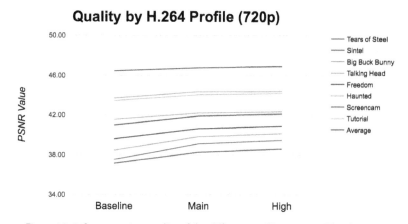

Figure 10-6. Comparative quality of the different profiles at 720p. The chart.

We'll look at how this applies over a complete adaptive bitrate (ABR) ladder in Chapter 14. For now, understand that in most instances—particularly at higher quality levels, like our 720p files—the difference in overall quality between the Baseline, Main, and High profiles likely wouldn't be distinguishable by the average viewer.

Which profile produces the best low-quality frames? This is shown in Table 10-2. Again, while the Baseline profile was overall the worst, the total delta of 2.73 percent is unimpressive. In the files with values below 30 dB that would prove most concerning—Tears of Steel, Sintel, and Big Buck Bunny—switching to the High profile likely would only visibly improve quality in the Tears of Steel video.

Low Frame	Baseline	Main	High	Delta - Baseline/Main	Delta - Main/High	Total Delta
Tears of Steel	29.81	30.96	31.53	3.89%	1.79%	5.78%
Sintel	28.40	28.61	29.00	0.73%	1.35%	2.12%
Big Buck Bunny	23.82	24.52	24.61	2.96%	0.36%	3.33%
Talking Head	38.11	39.35	39.59	3.27%	0.60%	3.89%
Freedom	33.24	34.87	35.39	4.91%	1.47%	6.48%
Haunted	36.45	36.43	36.24	-0.06%	-0.52%	-0.57%
Screencam	34.61	33.64	34.15	-2.81%	1.50%	-1.33%
Tutorial	36.59	37.45	37.39	2.34%	-0.17%	2.17%
Average	**32.63**	**33.23**	**33.49**	**1.90%**	**0.80%**	**2.73%**

Table 10-2. Lowest-quality frames by profile.

Given all the techniques shown in Table 10-4 that are available in the Main and High profiles, but not Baseline, you probably were expecting a more significant difference. Why is this significant? Because you'll have to use the Baseline profile for older iOS devices and Android devices. If the quality difference between the profiles were significant, it might make sense to encode different adaptive groups for targets that can play the High profile and those limited to the Baseline profile. Here the difference is relatively modest, so you could save encoding and storage dollars by encoding all files using the Baseline profile without noticeable quality loss.

Now let's look at the playback side.

CPU Required for Playback—Baseline, Main, and High Profiles

One of the early concerns about playing H.264 on computers was the CPU required to play back the files. For this reason, many producers encoded using the Baseline profile, rather than Main or High. Figure 10-7 tends to indicate that this isn't necessary for computers acquired in the past 10 years or so. Specifically, the figure shows CPU utilization from Windows Device Manager during the playback of 720p files encoded using the three profiles on a circa 2006 Dell Precision Workstation driven by a 2.93 GHz Intel Core 2 Extreme X6800.

Utilization while playing back Baseline-encoded files is fractionally lower, perhaps 3.3 to 6.6 percent (there are 30 lines, so each is around 3.3 percent). However, the overall burden on the computer is well under 50 percent in all cases, and the computer played all files without dropping any frames.

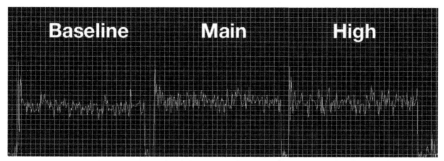

Figure 10-7. CPU required to playback 720p files encoded using the Baseline, Main, and High profiles on a Dell Precision workstation.

Figure 10-8 shows CPU utilization during playback of the same files on the Samsung Nexus 10 tablet captured via an app called CPU Monitor Advanced Pro. The tablet is driven by a 1.7 GHz dual-core Cortex-A15 from ARM that's in the lower end of Cortex family (now up to A73). Perhaps the Baseline-encoded file used a bit less CPU, but it wasn't significant.

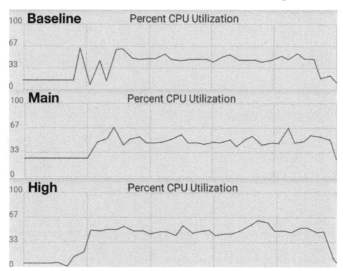

Figure 10-8. CPU utilization during playback of Baseline, Main, and High-encoded files on a Samsung Nexus 10 tablet.

What's the takeaway on profiles? Here's the quick summary.

Quick Summary: Profiles

    1. In general, use the highest-quality profile your target device will support.

2. That said, the quality difference between the profiles isn't as much as you might think. When encoding for multiple platforms, it may make sense to encode with the Baseline profile to create one file (or one set of files) that you can deliver to all targets. We'll explore that in more detail in Chapter 14.

3. The CPU required to play back files encoded using the Baseline, Main, and High profiles is very similar. In the absence of other data to the contrary, you shouldn't choose a lower-quality profile over concerns about playability.

H.264 Levels

What about H.264 levels? As mentioned earlier, levels provide bitrate, frame rate and resolution constraints within the different profiles, which is shown in Figure 10-9. Note that whenever you encode a file, the encoder inserts a level into the file metadata. Before attempting to play the file, devices will check the metadata to make sure the level doesn't exceed its capabilities. You can see a level indication in MediaInfo in Figure 10-21.

Level	Max decoding speed		Max frame size		Max video bit rate for video coding layer (VCL) kbit/s			Examples for high resolution @ highest frame rate (max stored frames)
	Luma samples/s	Macroblocks/s	Luma samples	Macroblocks	Baseline, Extended and Main Profiles	High Profile	High 10 Profile	Toggle additional details
4	62,914,560	245,760	2,097,152	8,192	20,000	25,000	60,000	1,280×720@68.3 (9) 1,920×1,080@30.1 (4) 2,048×1,024@30.0 (4)
4.1	62,914,560	245,760	2,097,152	8,192	50,000	62,500	150,000	1,280×720@68.3 (9) 1,920×1,080@30.1 (4) 2,048×1,024@30.0 (4)
4.2	133,693,440	522,240	2,228,224	8,704	50,000	62,500	150,000	1,280×720@145.1 (9) 1,920×1,080@64.0 (4) 2,048×1,080@60.0 (4)
5	150,994,944	589,824	5,652,480	22,080	135,000	168,750	405,000	1,920×1,080@72.3 (13) 2,048×1,024@72.0 (13) 2,048×1,080@67.8 (12) 2,560×1,920@30.7 (5) 3,672×1,536@26.7 (5)
5.1	251,658,240	983,040	9,437,184	36,864	240,000	300,000	720,000	1,920×1,080@120.5 (16) 2,560×1,920@51.2 (9) 3,840×2,160@31.7 (5) 4,096×2,048@30.0 (5) 4,096×2,160@28.5 (5) 4,096×2,304@26.7 (5)

Figure 10-9. Levels constrain bitrate, frame rate and resolution for the different profiles. From Wikipedia.

In this role, levels enable primarily device vendors to further specify the types of streams that will play on their devices. For example, the iPhone SE Apple released in the summer of 2016 will play, "H.264 video up to 4K, 30 fps, High Profile level 4.2 with AAC-LC audio up to 160 kbps, 48 kHz, stereo audio in .m4v, .mp4, and .mov file formats."

If you check the chart in Figure 10-9, you'll see that High profile level 4.2 means that the bitrate can't exceed 62.5 Mbps. You'll also see that the device should be limited to 2048x1080@60 fps playback, and that you need to support level 5.1 for 4096x2048@30 fps playback. In this case I would assume that Apple knows what it's doing, and simply limit 4K video produced for this device to 62.5 Mbps. Beyond that, and either the file won't load on the device (iTunes typically won't load non-conforming files on any iDevice) or it will load but won't play.

Accordingly, when you're producing for devices, you need to ensure that your encoding parameters don't exceed the specified level, which again should be designated by the device manufacturer. Otherwise, the file may not play smoothly, or even load.

Levels and Computers/OTT

In contrast, levels are irrelevant when encoding for computer playback because software-based streaming players, like Adobe Flash and the key browsers for HTML5 playback, can play H.264 video encoded using any profile or any level.

Back in the early days of producing H.264, like 2007, it was important to configure your streams carefully so that they played back smoothly on older computers of the day. To be clear, this wasn't technically a levels-related issue, it was the fact that a single-CPU computer couldn't play a 1080p H.264 stream encoded at 10 Mbps. Unlike iTunes, Flash didn't check the file's level and reject the file; the computer attempted to play the file and simply couldn't.

Today, most desktops and notebooks still in service can play any 1080p stream. However, if you attempt to play a 4K stream on a Core2Duo computer like the Dell Precision 390 workstation discussed around Figure 10-7, it won't be pretty. Again, however, this isn't a levels-related issue. It's simply the fact that the computer isn't powerful enough to play the file. Delivering via adaptive streaming typically takes care of this issue; if the computer can't play the file smoothly, it will simply check down to a lower-quality file.

Levels and Encoding Tools

When producing H.264 files, some encoding tools let you specify a level, and present an error message if you encode using parameters that exceed the selected level. This is shown in Figure 10-10, a screenshot of Adobe Media Encoder. If you were producing for a device with this encoder, compatibility with the selected level is key, so you'd have to dial back your encoding parameters to those specified in the required level. If you were producing for computer playback, you would simply choose a higher level that lets you produce the file at the selected parameters, and restart encoding.

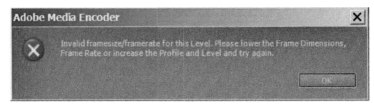

Figure 10-10. Oops, the selected frame size exceeds the parameters allowed for the selected level.

Other encoders take the approach of Telestream Episode Pro, which Telestream end-of-lifed in late 2016. Specifically, as shown in Figure 10-11, you can set the level to Auto, and Episode won't check for level-based conformity during the encode. Obviously, this is appropriate for computer playback, but not when encoding for older mobile devices.

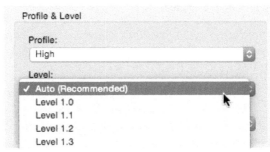

Figure 10-11. Most tools let you select Auto for level, so it doesn't
constrain your encoding settings when not needed.

Some encoding tools don't let you specify a level. When you're producing for devices with such encoders, you'll need to manually ensure that the resolution, frame rate and data rate don't exceed those supported in the specified level.

Quick Summary: Levels

1. It's critical to ensure that streams bound for older mobile devices don't exceed the specified levels.

2. Levels are typically not relevant when encoding for computers, where the resolution and data rate of your video are the most important considerations.

Entropy Coding

When you select the Main or High profiles, you'll have two options for entropy coding, which controls how the frame-related compressed data is packed before storage. The options are CAVLC, for context-based adaptive variable length coding, and CABAC, for context-based adaptive binary arithmetic coding. Of the two, CAVLC is the lower-quality, easier-to-decode option, while CABAC is the higher-quality, harder-to-decode option. The two options are shown in Figure 10-12 from Sorenson Squeeze. Looking ahead to Chapter 11, CABAC is the only entropy encoding option available for HEVC.

Figure 10-12. Your Entropy Coding choices: CAVLC and CABAC.

The short story is that you should always enable CABAC when encoding with the Main and High profiles; it does deliver a small quality improvement and the increased CPU for playback is negligible. The longer story is complicated by posts like this one from the Linux "x264 FFmpeg Options Guide" (bit.ly/ffmpeg_lin).

> CABAC is the default entropy encoder used by x264. Though somewhat slower on both the decoding and encoding end, it offers 10-15% improved compression on live-action sources and considerably higher improvements on animated sources, especially at low bitrates. It is also required for the use of trellis quantization. Disabling CABAC may somewhat improve decoding performance, especially at high bitrates. CABAC is not allowed in Baseline profile. Recommended default: -coder 1 (CABAC enabled)

When I ran the profile comparisons shown in Table 10-1, I enabled CABAC for the Main and High profiles and used CAVLC with the Baseline encoded files. The total quality difference between the Baseline and High profile files was 2.73 percent, and the largest single difference at 5.23 percent for the Tears of Steel file. So if you're looking for 15 percent, you may be looking for a while.

	Main - CABAC	Main - CAVLC	Delta	High - CABAC	High - CAVLC	Delta
Tears of Steel	39.13	38.52	1.57%	39.48	38.71	1.95%
Sintel	38.27	37.69	1.54%	38.58	37.89	1.80%
Big Buck Bunny	39.29	38.64	1.65%	39.64	38.84	2.00%
Talking Head	44.34	44.10	0.53%	44.39	44.11	0.64%
Freedom	40.62	40.18	1.09%	40.85	40.25	1.48%
Haunted	42.22	41.91	0.72%	42.35	41.93	0.98%
Screencam	46.68	46.10	1.23%	46.90	46.26	1.37%
Tutorial	44.10	42.96	2.57%	44.08	43.02	2.39%
Average	**41.83**	**41.26**	**1.36%**	**42.03**	**41.38**	**1.58%**

Table 10-3. The impact of CABAC on PSNR quality for files encoded with the Main and High profiles.

Of course, that doesn't mean you shouldn't enable CABAC whenever it's available. Table 10-3 shows the peak signal-to-noise ratio (PSNR) values of files encoded using the Main and High profiles with and without CABAC. As you can see, with the Main encoded files, CABAC improved quality by 1.36 percent, which improved slightly to 1.58 percent with files encoded using the High profile. Not a jackpot by any means, but not worth leaving on the table, either.

What about the CPU hit? Figure 10-13 shows the CPU utilization on the old Dell Precision 390 workstation driven by a 2.93 GHz Intel Core 2 Extreme X6800 playing back a 720p files encoded with the High profile with CABAC and CAVLC. As you can see, CABAC playback required a discernable but slight increase in CPU requirements, but not enough to make a difference either way. On any more modern computer or notebook, the difference would be irrelevant.

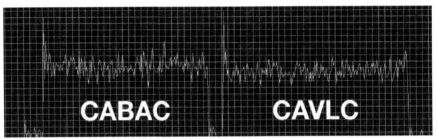

Figure 10-13. CPU required to play 720p files encoded using the High profile with CABAC and CAVLC on a circa 2006 Dell Precision Workstation.

What about on mobile? Figure 10-14 shows CPU utilization on the Samsung Nexus 10 tablet playing the same two files. Again, perhaps the CAVLC file is slightly lower, but the difference isn't meaningful in any way.

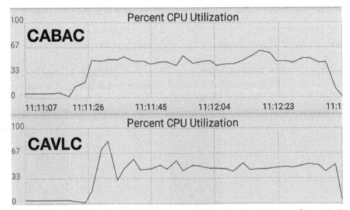

Figure 10-14. CPU required to play 720p files encoded using the High profile with CABAC and CAVLC on Samsung Nexus 10 tablet.

The bottom line is that CABAC delivers a small quality improvement with very little increased CPU requirements upon playback. Which gets us back to the short story I told at the start, when available, you should always use CABAC. To make it skimmable, chunkable, and otherwise easily digestible, here's the same thing with more white space around it.

Quick Summary: Entropy Coding

1. CABAC delivers a small quality improvement with very little increased CPU requirements upon playback

2. CABAC should be enabled whenever encoding with the Main and High profiles (it's not available with the Baseline profile).

All H.264 Encoders are Not Created Equal

I made this point earlier, but let's reiterate and explore further. Since H.264 is a standard, there can be many different H.264 codecs. This is very much like MPEG-1, MPEG-2, and HEVC, and very much unlike VP6 and the WMV codecs, which each came from one developer. Since there are multiple developers of H.264 codecs, there are bound to be quality differences.

The ultimate arbiter of H.264 quality is Moscow State University (MSU), which released eight H.264 quality comparisons, the last of which in 2012. Since then, the team has issued two reports on HEVC quality that we'll touch on in the following chapter. You can download the free version of the 2012 report at bit.ly/um_h264_2012. The CliffsNotes version is shown in Figure 10-15. As you can see, the x264 codec is the clear leader, with MainConcept about 20 percent behind.

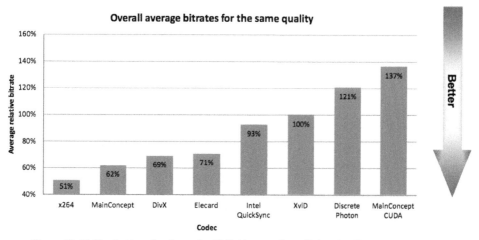

Figure 10-15. The bottom line from the 2012 Moscow State University H.264 comparison.

Over the past four years or so, x264 has overtaken MainConcept in terms of application support, probably as a result of x264's performance advantage and MSU consistently reporting it. Whatever the cause, x264 enjoys by far the most application support, and is available in FFmpeg, so I'll focus the rest of the chapter on x264.

x264 Presets and Tuning

So far, in previous chapters and this one, we've learned how to set most of the basic options available in most x264-based encoding tools. However, we're just touching the surface of the full range of options in the codec. For example, there are configuration options that control the range of the search that the encoder performs when looking for redundancies, and the precision of that search. There are literally dozens of other controls and attempting to identify their best settings for the different types of videos covered in this book would be daunting.

Fortunately, with the x264 codec, you don't have to. Rather, the developers of the codec have created presets that adjust many of the x264 configuration options to trade off encoding time with quality. These are shown on the left in Figure 10-16 (from Ultra Fast to Placebo). On the right are tuning mechanisms that enable producers to customize their encodes for certain types of videos (film, animation, still image), for low latency or fast decode, or to perform well on different quality benchmarks (SSIM, PSNR). Rather than study the individual configuration options available in x264, we'll focus on these presets and tuning mechanisms.

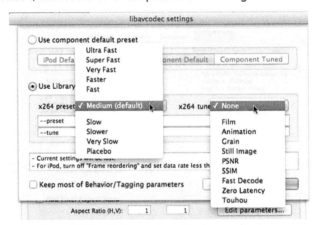

Figure 10-16. x264's presets and tuning mechanisms.

x264 Presets

There are 10 x264 presets, ranging from the low-quality/high-speed Ultrafast, to the optimum-quality/slowest-speed Placebo. These presets are available only for the x264 codec, so they won't be available if you're working with MainConcept or a different H.264 codec.

Most encoders let you choose these presets via controls like those shown in Figure 10-16, and you'll learn how to choose the presets in FFmpeg at the end of the chapter. However, not all programs that use the x264 codec enable these presets. Looking ahead, as you'll see in Chapter 11, the x265 codec also uses presets with the same names as those used in x264.

I'm not going to detail the options in each preset since they're very well defined on various websites (like bit.ly/x265_preset_details, or bit.ly/hb_presets). Rather, I'm going to focus on quality and encoding speed, starting with the quality side as shown in Table 10-4. To produce the table, I encoded all videos at the 720p configurations using the High profile.

Average Quality	Ultrafast	Superfast	Veryfast	Faster	Fast	Medium	Slow	Slower	Veryslow	Placebo	Total Delta
Tears of Steel	36.07	37.82	38.51	39.23	39.26	39.33	39.27	39.41	39.47	39.40	9.43%
Sintel	35.14	36.71	37.42	38.40	38.43	38.46	38.40	38.55	38.57	38.47	9.75%
Big Buck Bunny	36.23	38.01	38.92	39.97	40.02	40.03	40.01	40.12	40.12	40.06	10.74%
Talking Head	43.38	43.38	44.06	44.39	44.28	44.28	44.21	44.34	44.39	44.29	2.34%
Freedom	38.46	39.26	40.01	40.41	40.32	40.58	40.55	40.69	40.85	40.77	6.22%
Haunted	41.13	41.30	41.89	42.20	42.07	42.27	42.25	42.27	42.35	42.31	2.98%
Screencam	44.46	45.67	46.68	47.12	46.82	46.96	46.95	47.06	46.88	46.76	5.99%
Tutorial	38.47	41.83	43.62	44.50	44.37	44.30	43.99	44.14	44.07	43.91	15.68%
Average	38.40	39.41	40.13	40.77	40.73	40.83	40.78	40.90	40.96	40.88	7.89%

Table 10-4. Output quality in PSNR value by x264 preset.

As you can see, the fastest preset consistently produced the lowest-quality output, with the best quality strangely split between Faster and Veryslow. The difference between the best and worst values averaged only 7.89 percent, although it did range as high as 15.68 percent for PowerPoint-based tutorial footage.

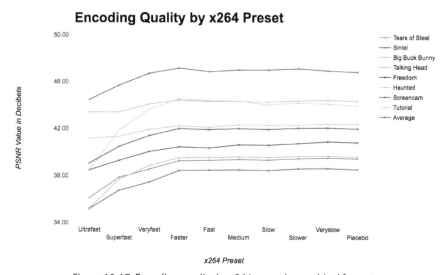

Figure 10-17. Encoding quality by x264 preset in graphical format.

Figure 10-17 puts those values into graphical format. As you can see, there's a noticeable increase in the quality of every file though the Faster preset, at which time it begins to slow or even reverse.

What about encoding time? This is shown in Figure 10-18. Note that I normalized the encoding time of the Freedom file from the 4:25 actual time to the 2:00 time of every other test file; otherwise, it would throw the entire graph out of whack.

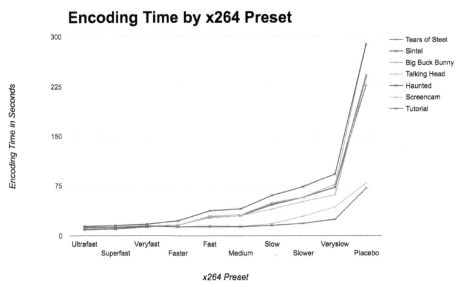

Figure 10-18. Encoding time by x264 preset.

What does Figure 10-18 show us? That encoding time stays fairly low through the Veryfast preset, then starts to extend, but doesn't really blow up until the Placebo preset. How to synthesize this data? Well, I attempt to help you do just that in Figure 10-19.

To explain, the chart:

- doesn't include the Tutorial and Screencam videos, because they perform so much differently than the others

- averages the quality of all videos, and plots the average as a percentage of the difference between the highest and lowest PSNR score, not the raw PSNR score. So the lowest score (Ultrafast) is 0 percent, while the highest score (Veryslow) is 100 percent

- averages the encoding time of all presets, and presents the average as the percentage of the difference between the fastest and slowest encoding time. Again, the fastest time is 0 percent, while the slowest time is 200 percent.

Essentially, the chart illustrates the encoding time/quality trade-off. As an example, the medium preset took 8.6 percent of the encoding time of the placebo preset, but delivered 93.8 percent of the quality. What information can we derive from this chart?

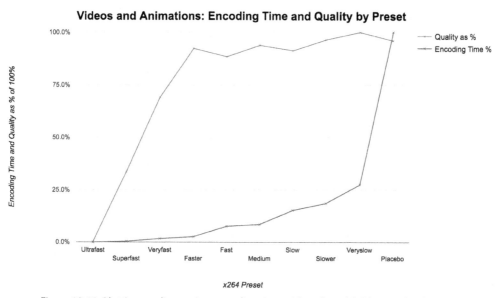

Figure 10-19. Plotting quality against encoding time with real-world videos and animations.

- First, that the Faster preset is the minimum preset that you should run for production videos, capturing 92.3 percent of the available quality in 2.6 percent of the encoding time.

- At the other end of the spectrum, if encoding time isn't an issue, you should use the Veryslow preset, which delivers 100 percent of the available quality in 27.3 percent of the time of the Placebo preset.

- Finally, you should never use the Placebo preset, since it delivers less than 100 percent of the available quality while taking three times longer than the Veryslow preset.

I tested for and recorded the lowest-quality frames output with the various presets, and the result were consistent with the findings discussed above. In fact, the chart looked like a match with Figure 10-17.

What about with synthetic videos? This is shown in Figure 10-20. Here we see that these videos peak at the faster preset, and that supposedly higher-quality presets not only extend encoding time, but reduce quality. While I wouldn't take this as gospel because the test sample is so limited, if I was charged with encoding lots of purely synthetic videos, I would definitely run my own set of experiments to identify the best preset to use with these videos.

Again, the lowest-quality frame analysis was similar to what you see in Figure 10-20. That is, the lowest-quality frames were both produced by the Ultrafast preset, with quality improving through the Faster preset. After then, the quality of the lowest frame in the video started dropping, moderately for the Tutorial video, and significantly for the Screencam.

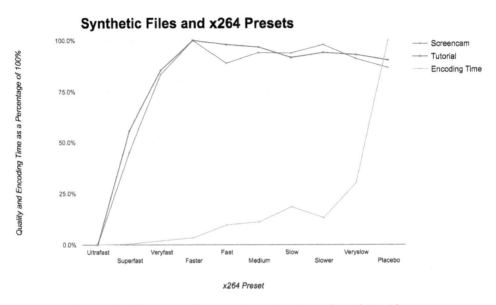

Figure 10-20. Plotting quality against encoding time with synthetic videos.

Tip: *One of the more impressive analyses of the x264 presets is available at bit.ly/xpreset. One of the observations is that the choice of preset makes a more significant difference at lower data rates. Overall, the author concludes, "if we have more time for the compression and if the sharp and detailed image are important for us, slow and slower presets are, in my opinion, the best ones (with an emphasis on the latter). ... If the speed of compression (not the image quality) is a priority, I propose to choose faster preset (surprisingly good results for SSIM and PSNR indexes) or fast."*

Quick Summary: x264 Presets

1. x264 Presets are a convenient way to choose a range of configuration options that trade off video quality against encoding time.

2. For real-world videos, the Faster preset is probably the fastest option that should be selected, since it captures 92.3 percent of the available quality in 2.6 percent of the encoding time. If encoding time isn't an issue, use the Veryslow preset, which delivers 100 percent of the available quality in 27.3 percent of the time of the Placebo preset.

3. For Screencams and PowerPoint videos, quality peaked with the Faster preset. Run your own tests to confirm, but this looks like the best bet for these types of videos.

Tuning Mechanisms

The last subject we'll cover in this chapter is tuning mechanisms, again designed for certain types of videos or to produce certain types of performance. We'll look at three tuning mechanisms: animation for animated videos, and film and grain for film-based videos (or those supposed to look like them).

Like presets, tuning options are available only with the x264 codec, not other H.264 codecs, and they aren't presented in all encoding programs that support x264. Most desktop programs that enable x264 tuning do so as shown in Figure 10-16, where you simply select the tuning mechanism in the program's user interface. You'll learn how to select tuning options in FFmpeg at the end of this chapter.

Again, I'm not going to delve into the details of each tuning mechanism as there are multiple sources that do so (see bit.ly/x264_tune for one). Rather, I encoded with and without the tuning mechanism to learn whether it increased quality, and if so, by how much.

Animation Tuning

If you produce a lot of animated videos with the x264 codec, the animation tuning mechanism looks like a winner. You can see this in Table 10-5, where I supplemented the Big Buck Bunny and Sintel animations with two *SpongeBob SquarePants* movie trailers, and short animated clip from a cartoon called El Ultimo. Specifically, the first three columns show the clips encoded with the High profile, then the High profile with animation tuning. As you can see, the clips encoded with animation tuning averaged 1.66 percent higher. These clips also performed better in the low-quality frame analysis.

Presets - Animation	PSNR			Low Frame		
	High	Anim	Delta	High	Anim	Delta
Big Buck Bunny	39.64	40.08	1.11%	24.75	25.11	1.44%
El Ultimo	45.85	46.58	1.59%	41.64	41.88	0.56%
Sintel	38.57	39.11	1.39%	28.85	29.53	2.35%
SpongeBob 1	37.46	38.21	1.99%	26.10	26.21	0.41%
SpongeBob 2	39.29	40.17	2.24%	33.41	33.53	0.34%
Averages	40.16	40.83	1.66%	30.95	31.25	1.02%

Table 10-5. The positive benefits of tuning for animation.

I've recommended the animation tuning mechanism to multiple clients who stream animated content, and you should try it as well. Interestingly, I ran the same tests with the other clips we've been working with, and animation tuning improved their quality as well, boosting the quality of the Freedom clip by 2.39 percent. I'm hesitant to recommend animation tuning for all clips because the configuration options are specifically designed for animated content. But it's worth a try if you have the time to subjectively confirm the PSNR results.

Film and Grain Tuning

The results for film and grain tuning were not as positive. To explain, the first set of columns in Table 10-6 show three movie clips encoded using the High profile, and then the High profile with film tuning. Here, film tuning dropped quality by 0.15 percent. The second set of three columns explores the grain tuning mechanism on the same three clips. Here, the benefit was minuscule at 0.12 percent.

	High	Film	Delta	High	Grain	Delta
Elektra	42.35	42.54	0.46%	42.35	42.71	0.87%
Tears of Steel	41.47	41.32	-0.37%	41.47	41.28	-0.47%
Zoolander	40.31	40.10	-0.53%	40.31	40.29	-0.05%
Average	**41.38**	**41.32**	**-0.15%**	**41.38**	**41.43**	**0.12%**

Table 10-6. Film and grain tuning produced meh benefits.

Overall, I've never been a fan of film and grain tuning options and nothing I see here reverses that trend.

Quick Summary: x264 Tuning

1. x264 tuning mechanism are designed to improve quality or performance for specific types of videos or quality metrics.

2. Animation tuning seems to improve quality of all animated videos as measured by PSNR. If you distribute a lot of animated content, you should experiment with this tuning mechanism to see if it improves the quality of your animations.

3. The film and grain tunes have not worked well for me in this and other tests.

Working in FFmpeg

Here are the FFmpeg-related commands for the configuration options covered in this chapter.

Choosing Profiles in FFmpeg

The default profile used by FFmpeg depends upon the compilation; in my tests, FFmpeg defaulted to the High profile. To change that, insert the following string:

```
-profile:v baseline or main
```

As discussed in this chapter, you should use the highest profile compatible with your target playback device.

Setting Levels in FFmpeg

I'm not sure how FFmpeg chooses the default level for its encodes. In every case I checked, the level inserted by FFmpeg exceeded the level that seemed appropriate for the actual file parameters. For example, I encoded a file at 640x360@600 kbps using the High profile, which according to my reading of Wikipedia, was within the specs for Level 3. FFmpeg injected Level 3.1 into the file metadata. I next encoded a file at 1280x720@6000 kbps using the High profile, which fits under the constraints of Level 3.1, and FFmpeg injected Level 5 into the file metadata. It's possible that there were other constraints coming into play that forced FFmpeg into the higher level, like macroblocks or luma samples, but I couldn't tell this from the files.

Of course, if FFmpeg is inserting too high a level, that may cause those files to be rejected by a target device that could play the file if the level designation was correct. So if you're using FFmpeg to create files for mobile playback, you better sort this out by manually inserting the correct level and testing playback on various target devices.

You set levels in FFmpeg using the following string.

```
-level:v <integer>
```

So, if you wanted to encode to Level 2.2, you would insert the string `-level:v 2.2` anywhere in the command line.

Note that inserting the level into the command string does not force FFmpeg to constrain the encoding parameters to those specified by the level specifications. For example, I encoded a file to 1280x720@6000 kbps using the High profile, and inserted Level 2.2 into the command string as shown above. According to Wikipedia, Level 2.2 tops out at 720x276@12.5 fps. As shown in Figure 10-21, FFmpeg produced the file at the original target parameters, which far exceed those set in the levels.

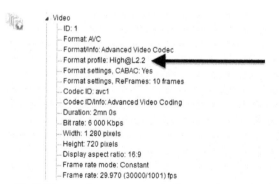

Figure 10-21. FFmpeg does not constrain file encoding to the designated level.

The bottom line is that if you're using FFmpeg to produce for mobile devices, you need to make sure that your file parameters don't exceed the level designated for each device, and that you properly insert the level into the command string.

Setting Entropy Encoding (CABAC versus CAVLC)

The default entropy encoding setting for FFmpeg is CABAC when it's available, which is the Main and High profiles. FFmpeg uses CAVLC for the Baseline profile, which is the only option. If, for some reason, you wish to use CAVLC when encoding in the Main or High profile, use the following string:

```
-coder 0
```

Substituting 1 for 0 forces CABAC (-coder 1), but you can achieve the same result by omitting the -coder command string entirely and going with the default.

Choosing an x264 Preset

If you don't choose a preset, FFmpeg essentially applies the parameters of the medium preset, which is the default in most programs that use x264. To choose a different preset, insert the following string into the command line:

```
-preset <preset name>
```

So you would choose the Fast preset with the string -preset fast.

Choosing an x264 Tuning Mechanism

By default, x264 doesn't apply a tuning mechanism. To deploy a tuning mechanism, use the following string:

```
-tune <tune name>
```

So you would choose the Animation preset with the string -tune animation.

OK, now you know all you need to know to go forth and conquer when encoding with H.264 with any application or cloud program, or FFmpeg. May the force be with you. We take a shorter look at HEVC in the next chapter.

Chapter 11: Encoding HEVC

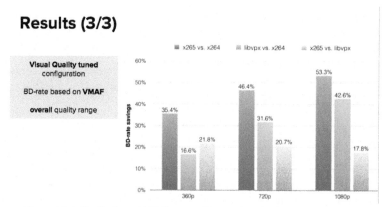

Results (3/3)

Figure 11-1. Netflix found HEVC more efficient than both VP9 and H.264.

As shown in Figure 11-1, Netflix found HEVC more efficient than both VP9 and H.264 in its August 2016 codec comparison (bit.ly/nf_codecq). This gives HEVC a slight edge over VP9 for producers seeking better compression than H.264 affords, but only on platforms that support HEVC playback. While HEVC will likely play a big role in some distribution strategies down the road, its path to enjoying the same ubiquity as H.264 is far from clear.

In this chapter, you'll learn:

- about HEVC—how it works, how much it costs, where it plays, and how it compares to H.264 and VP9 in terms of quality and encoding time

- considerations for encoding HEVC, including a look at HEVC encoding profiles and HDR

- how to encode HEVC in the Adobe Media Encoder

- how to encode in FFmpeg with the x265 HEVC codec.

Technology Background

H.265/HEVC is the successor codec to H.264. Like H.264, it was jointly developed by the International Organization for Standardization/International Electrotechnical Commission Moving Picture Experts Group (MPEG) and International Telecommunication Union Video Coding Experts Group (VCEG). The primary goal of the new codec was 50 percent better compression efficiency than H.264 and support for resolutions up to 8192x4320. HEVC development began in 2007, and the first version was released for distribution on January 25, 2013.

The current implementation includes a Main profile supporting 8-bit 4:2:0 video, a Main 10 profile with 10-bit support, and a Main Still Picture profile for digital pictures that uses the same coding tools as a video "intra" picture. HEVC will continue to advance, with work already starting on extensions for 12-bit video and 4:2:2 and 4:4:4 chroma formats—as well as incorporating scalable video coding and 3D video into the spec.

How HEVC Works

Like H.264 and MPEG-2, HEVC uses three frame types—I-, B- and P-frames—within a group of pictures (GOP), which incorporate elements of both inter-frame and intra-frame compression. HEVC incorporates numerous advances, including:

- **Coding Tree Blocks.** Where H.264 used macroblocks with a maximum size of 16x16, HEVC uses coding tree blocks, or CTBs, with a maximum size of 64x64 pixels. Larger block sizes are more efficient when encoding larger frame sizes, like 4K resolution. This is shown in Figure 11-1.

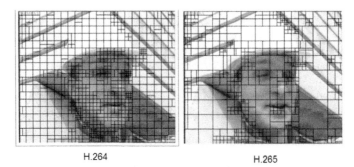

H.264

H.265

Figure 11-2. Larger blocks sizes enhance encoding efficiency. Image from Elemental Technologies.

- **More intra-prediction directions.** Where H.265 used nine intra-prediction directions, HEVC can use more than 35, adding more potential reference pixel blocks that fuel more efficient intra-frame compression (see Figure 11-3, from an Ateme presentation no longer available on the web. The obvious cost is the additional encoding time required to search in the additional directions.

- **Adaptive motion vector prediction**, which allows the codec to find more inter-frame redundancies.

- **Superior parallelization tools**, including Wavefront Parallel Processing, for more efficient encoding in a multi-core environment.

- **Entropy coding**, which is CABAC-only—no more CAVLC.

- **Deblocking improvements**, including improvements to the exiting filter and the creation of a second filter called sample adaptive offset, which further limits artifacts along block edges.

- **Luma:** 35 prediction directions (33 + Planar + DC)

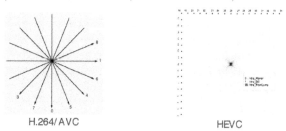

H.264/AVC

HEVC

Figure 11-3. Searching is expanded to find more reference pixel blocks.

Otherwise, there's a lot of similarity between H.264 and HEVC, just as there was between MPEG-2 and H.264. This is shown in Figure 11-4, from an Elemental Technologies white paper titled "HEVC Demystified: A Primer on the H.265 Video Codec" (bit.ly/ET_H265).

COMPONENT	MPEG-2	H.264	HEVC/H.265
General	Motion compensated predictive, residual, transformed, entropy coded	Same basics as MPEG-2	Same basics as MPEG-2
Intra prediction	DC Only	Multi-direction, multi-pattern, 9 intra modes for 4x4, 9 for 8x8, 4 for 16x16	35 modes for intra prediction, 32x32, 16x16, 8x8 and 4x4 prediction size
Coded Image Types	I, B, P	I, B, P, SI, SP	I, P, B
Transform	8x8 DCT	8x8 and 4x4 DCT-like Integer Transform	32x32, 16x16, 8x8 and 4x4 DCT-like Integer Transform
Motion Estimation Blocks	16x16	16x16, 16x8, 8x16, 8x4, 4x8, 4x4	64x64 and hierarchical quad-tree partitioning down to 32x32, 16x16, 8x8 Each size can be partitioned once more in up to 8 ways
Entropy Coding	Multiple VLC tables	Context adaptive binary arithmetic coding (CABAC) and context adaptive VLC tables (CAVLC)	Context adaptive binary arithmetic coding (CABAC)
Frame Distance for Prediction	1 past and 1 future reference frame	Up to 16 past and/or future reference frames, including long-term references	Up to 15 past and/or future reference frames, including long-term references
Fractional Motion Estimation	½ pixel bilinear interpolation	½ pixel 6-tap filter, ¼ pixel linear interpolation	¼ pixel 8-tap filter
In-Loop Filter	None	Adaptive deblocking filter	Adaptive deblocking filter and sample adaptive offset filter

Figure 11-4. The evolution of standard-based video coding, from MPEG-2 to HEVC.

As you can see, the general concepts are similar, as are the frame types and various other elements. Where H.264 has greater precision than MPEG-2, especially in the Transform and Motion Estimation Blocks components, HEVC has greater precision than H.264. Of course, some of this is "under the hood" and not configurable with either codec. You can add to this that HEVC uses profiles like H.264—although instead of Baseline, Main, and High, most HEVC encoders use (for now) Main and Main 10.

The bottom line is that most of the principles that you've learned up till now will flow seamlessly into your HEVC encodes, particularly if you migrate from the x264 codec to the x265 codec. There, as long as you use FFmpeg, you can use the same command scripts—almost argument for argument, as I'll cover in the final major section of this chapter. Other similarities between x264 and x265 include the availability of constant rate factor (CRF) encoding, and the use of presets and tuning mechanisms.

Standard versus Codec

You know this, but let's review. HEVC is a technology standard. As such, there are multiple HEVC codecs produced to be compliant with the standard. These include the x265 codec, which is the HEVC codec we'll spend the most time with. As with the available H.264 codecs, there are quality variances with HEVC codecs, which you can see in Figure 11-5, showing the overall results from the 2015 Moscow State University (MSU) HEVC codec comparison (bit.ly/um_hevc).

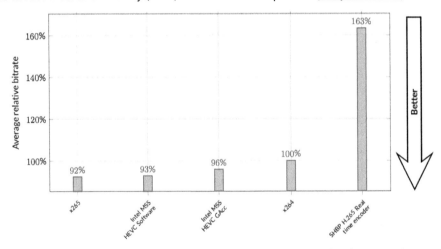

Figure 11-5. Rankings from the Moscow State University 2015 HEVC codec comparison.

As you can see, x265 is the overall quality leader. In Figure 11-6, you'll see x265's ranking in the 2016 comparison dropped to fourth (bit.ly/um_hevc_16). Why do I spend so much time with x265 given its most recent ranking? First, it's open source, so every reader can get his or her hands on it. Second, it's available in FFmpeg, so it's very accessible.

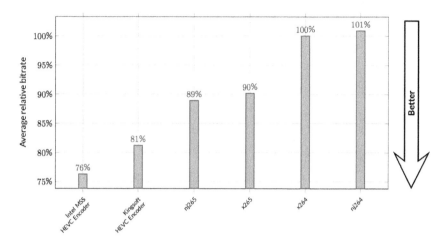

Figure 11-6. Rankings from the MSU 2016 HEVC codec comparison.

Third, it's implemented in most third-party encoders that I've reviewed, including those from Telestream and Harmonic—but not Elemental, which always develops its own codecs. Fourth, it's the HEVC codec that Netflix used for its August 2016 codec comparison (Figure 11-1), so it must have something going for it.

Packaging HEVC

HEVC is a codec, not a container format. Although you can package HEVC in multiple container formats, single files are typically encoded into the MP4 container format, while adaptive bitrate files are typically packaged in Dynamic Adaptive Streaming over HTTP (DASH) format. Much more on DASH in Chapters 13 to 15.

How Much Does HEVC Cost?

HEVC is a royalty-encumbered technology, so if you want to build an HEVC encoder or distribute an HEVC player, you'll have to pay a royalty, or multiple royalties. Today, there are three organizations with HEVC-related IP that require licensing: MPEG LA, HEVC Advance, and Technicolor. There are also multiple known organizations with HEVC-related patents that may someday claim royalties, all of which has seriously retarded HEVC commercialization.

You can download an overview of MPEG LA's HEVC royalty terms at bit.ly/mpegla_hevc. You can download a summary of HEVC Advance's terms at bit.ly/HEVCA_sum. Technicolor hasn't made its plans public. Table 11-1 summarizes what we know.

	MPEG LA	HEVC Advance	Technicolor
Encoder/Decoder	$0.20/each after 100,000 units	Mobile/Tablet/PC - $0.40 Connected Home/Other - $0.80 4K UHD+ TV - $1.20	Unknown
Content	None	Subscription and PPV	Unknown
Annual Cap	$25 million	$40 million - encode/decode $5 million - content	Unknown

Table 11-1. Known HEVC royalty rates.

The bottom line is this:

- all smart TV and set-top box manufacturers have licensed HEVC

- some retail OTT devices like Roku 4 have HEVC decode

- Google has included HEVC software decode in Android version 5+, but that's paid by the reseller of the device (e.g. Samsung)

- neither Apple nor Microsoft have included HEVC decode in their operating systems

- HEVC decode isn't available in any browser

- Apple uses HEVC for FaceTime in later devices, but it's not accessible for general-purpose video playback—although that could change at any time.

Without question, HEVC's royalty policy has severely stifled the technology's adoption. In August 2016, Tom Vaughan, Vice President and General Manager, Video of MulticoreWare, the developer of x265, published a proposal titled "It's Time to Move Forward with HEVC" in Streaming Media (bit.ly/hevc_proposal). In it, he recommended HEVC IP owners form a single pool and make software decoding free on consumer devices. He also recommended no content-related royalty. Given the actions of HEVC IP owners to date, it's tough to see any of that happening.

In late 2015, the Alliance for Open Media (AOM) formed to create a royalty-free codec (bit.ly/aom_1) with charter members Google, Amazon, Netflix, Cisco, Microsoft, Netflix, and Intel. Later, AMD, ARM, and NVIDIA joined the party (bit.ly/aom_2), and the group announced a target date of March 2017 for the AV1 codec. Apple, as always, did nothing to clarify the situation. Given the members in the group, the following conclusions seem likely.

- Google, Microsoft, and Mozilla will incorporate AV1 into their respective browsers (Chrome, Edge, Firefox) and operating systems (Android, Windows, Windows Phone) as soon as possible. As a corollary, the incentive to add HEVC to these browsers/operating systems is greatly reduced.

- Google (YouTube), Netflix, and Amazon will start publishing with AV1 once it's available. This will influence smart TV and other device manufacturers to support the new format.

- Intel, ARM, NVIDIA, and AMD will incorporate hardware-accelerated AV1 playback into the CPUs, systems on a chips (SoCs), and graphics processing units (GPUs).

Hold the presses: *In November 2016, HEVC Advance announced that it will "not seek a license or royalties on HEVC functionality implemented in application layer software downloaded to mobile devices or personal computers after the initial sale of the device, where the HEVC encoding or decoding is fully executed in software on a general purpose CPU." This excludes browsers from the royalty, but only if they're not shipped with the computer/device. So, the royalty would still apply for Microsoft Edge (shipped with Windows) and Safari (shipped with Macs and iOS devices, and Chrome (shipped with Chrome). So far, no browser vendors have announced that they will support HEVC.*

Where Will HEVC Play?

So, what does the royalty policy and the availability of AV1 mean for HEVC distribution? In my view, the streaming market divides into four markets.

Browser—Desktop and Notebook

At this point, HEVC decode is not available in any browsers, although this may change. While it's technically possible to integrate HEVC decode in a browser via a plugin, the market is moving away from plugins as part of that whole Flash is Dead movement. So I see desktop and notebook browsers dominated by VP9 initially, and later AV1—with HEVC making few inroads through 2018 or so.

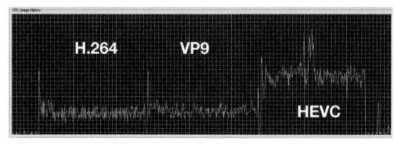

Figure 11-7. Required CPU horsepower for H.264, VP9, and HEVC 720p playback.

If and when HEVC playback does become available in a browser, it will require more CPU horsepower to play back than H.264 or VP9, as shown in Figure 11-7. These are playback tests performed a circa 2006 Dell Precision Workstation driven by a 2.93 GHz Intel Core 2 Extreme X6800. To perform these tests, I encoded the Tears of Steel file at 720p resolution in all three formats, and played them back in the VLC Player on the Dell, recording CPU utilization in Windows Task Manager.

This is an older computer, and probably outside the target range for most streaming producers. Still, the lesson is clear: on all platforms without hardware acceleration, HEVC playback will consume much more CPU (and battery power) than either other codec.

Mobile

HEVC is in Android and iOS, but not accessible in the latter. VP9 playback is available in Android and you would expect Google to add AV1 decode as soon as possible. It's tough to see HEVC playback making many inroads in mobile, but Apple could change that with one press release.

Note that most computers and notebooks have the CPU horsepower to play HEVC files, up to 1080p or so. Desktop computers, of course, are always plugged in, while notebooks have huge batteries and are typically plugged in when AC power is available. In contrast, while many newer (2015 and beyond) mobile devices have the power to play HEVC, power consumption is greatly elevated, and HEVC playback has been shown to reduce battery life by about 50 percent as compared with H.264 (see bit.ly/hevc_batlife). Figure 11-7, of course, makes this easy to believe.

Because of this reduction in battery life, some industry analysts believe that HEVC won't be popular on mobile devices until hardware decode is available to play the videos without a disproportionate hit on battery life. As of this writing (late 2016), most mobile devices still don't have HEVC decode on board, though it is definitely coming.

Smart TV/Retail OTT

This is the "voluntary" market for watching IP-based TV in the living room—as in you buy your smart TV at Wal-Mart, or your Roku 4 at Amazon, and expect them to play 4K video. My perception was that HEVC was more widely supported among these devices, but that might not be the case. Here's what one of the top VP9 evangelists at Google had to say.

> VP9 is extremely well supported in TVs and STBs. I'd say that VP9 has close to if not as broad penetration in smart TVs as HEVC does. By the time this book is published, there will be no difference in penetration in new TVs. All of the major manufacturers support VP9 8-bit in their 4K TVs. And they've either recently released VP9 10-bit (HDR-capable) support or will do so by CES next year.

> OEMs were initially slow to add either of the new codecs (VP9 or HEVC) to their 1080p TVs, because they treated that class as being in maintenance mode and didn't want to spend money to upgrade the underlying HW. But that's changing too. For instance, Samsung, LG and Sony had VP9 in their FHD sets in 2016. Again, I'd say we're at least in as good a shape in <4K TVs as HEVC is.

So, if you're thinking about publishing to these devices, start with a clean slate that includes both VP9 and HEVC. Going forward, every product manager for a smart TV or retail OTT box like Roku has to be thinking about AV1 decode—if only to play video files from YouTube, and perhaps from Netflix and Amazon. If AV1 and HEVC are both available down the road, why not use AV1 and avoid the content royalty?

Internet Protocol TV (IPTV)

This is the "involuntary" market for watching IP-based TV in the living room—as in you sign up for the service via your satellite or cable provider, and they install the box you'll use for decode. While I'm guessing many set-top boxes are starting to support VP9, I've not seen any VP9-based channels launching, with VP9 support seemingly focused on general-purpose payback. Whether this will change with AV1 remains to be seen.

What it all Means

Here's a summary of the foregoing sections.

- If you're looking to replace H.264 with a more efficient codec for computer-based playback, VP9 is the natural choice, not HEVC.

- The mobile market is cloudy as Android supports both formats, and Apple supports neither.

- If you're creating a subscription service targeting smart TVs and OTT boxes, you have to approach this on a device-by-device basis. HEVC comes with a potential content-royalty of up to $2.5 million for subscription and pay-per-view ($5 million if you support both revenue models), while VP9 is free.

- IPTV seems firmly in the HEVC camp—although if you can use VP9 you can save the content royalties.

Comparing HEVC and VP9

There have been multiple studies comparing HEVC to H.264 and VP9, most recently the Netflix study discussed earlier. As discussed in the article I wrote about the study (bit.ly/nf_codecq), there are questions about how broadly applicable Netflix's findings are,. In fact, as you can read about next chapter, in subsequent tests, Netflix adjusted their VP9 encoding parameters and achieved very close to parity with HEVC.

Overall, though, I believe that both VP9 and HEVC are sufficiently superior to H.264 to justify switching over for the associated bandwidth savings. YouTube has used VP9 since 2015, and as I write in the Netflix article, JW Player recently switched over to VP9 with great results.

In the short term, VP9 is your only option in browsers, with VP9 and HEVC equally available on OTT and smart TVs. Beyond that, VP9 is on its way out. By the time you read this, it may have already been replaced by AV1. So the real issue isn't HEVC versus VP9, it's HEVC versus AV—and then only on platforms that support both formats.

If you do decide to use HEVC, will you be able to shave 50 percent off H.264 bandwidth at the same quality? Well, that's what we study next.

Comparing HEVC and H.264

So, you're considering deploying some 1080p and lower-resolution footage in HEVC. What data rate should you use? Can you simply divide by two and achieve the same quality? We will look at this issue in two ways. The first is shown in Table 11-2. Remember back in Chapter 7 when we used CRF encoding to help choose our data rates for H.264? Well, x265 has a CRF mode as well. I applied the same factor (23) to the 1080p, 720p, and 360p source files, recorded the data rate and computed PSNR value, and compared the results with those of H.264.

CRF23 - 1080p	FPS	x265 Data Rate	PSNR	x264 Data Rate	PSNR	Analysis Data Rate	PSNR
Tears of Steel	24	2,779	41.92	4,485	41.71	38.04%	0.50%
Sintel	24	3,276	41.79	5,002	41.53	34.51%	0.63%
Big Buck Bunny	30	2,255	43.97	3,375	43.64	33.19%	0.76%
Screencam	30	459	46.85	1,200	46.85	61.75%	0.01%
Tutorial	30	448	48.43	690	47.28	35.07%	2.44%
Talking Head	30	1,417	44.17	2,638	44.09	46.29%	0.19%
Freedom	30	4,068	42.07	5,467	41.87	25.59%	0.49%
Haunted	30	3,507	42.12	6,064	42.23	42.17%	-0.26%
Average		**2,276**	**43.92**	**3,615**	**43.65**	**39.57%**	**0.59%**

Table 11-2. Data rate and output quality for x264 and x265.

Looking at the overall average numbers, at CRF 23, x265 produced a data rate of 2276 kbps, a reduction of 39.57 percent as compared with x264. At these data rates, x265 file quality was 0.59 percent higher than H.264 quality, with a peak signal-to-noise ratio (PSNR) value of 43.92 dB compared with x264 at 43.65 dB. So at 1080p, x265 won't get you a 50 percent savings, but it will deliver very close to 40 percent with slightly higher quality.

Using the same analysis, at 720p, x265 shaved 37.38 percent off the data rate produced by x264, with PSNR quality 0.45 percent higher at 43.18 dB, as compared with 42.98 dB for x264. At 360p, x265 delivered files that were 32.77 percent smaller, with quality 0.22 percent higher than x264 (41.55 dB compared with 31.47 dB). This is, as you would expect, the savings get smaller with file resolutions.

The second way to determine if x265 delivers the same quality as x264 at half the data rate is to test just that, which is how I produced the results shown in Table 11-3. That is, I encoded the x265 files at half the data rate of the x264 files, and compared PSNR values. As always, green backgrounds show the highest score. In terms of pure PSNR, x265 won by about 0.69 percent, although it took healthy contributions from the synthetic files to tip the scales in x265's favor. If you average just the real-world and animated files, and remove the synthetic files from the equation, x264 wins by almost a full percentage point (0.87 percent)—which, to be fair, wouldn't be noticeable by most viewers.

	1080p - PSNR			1080p - Low Frame Quality		
	x264	x265	Delta	x264	x265	Delta
Tears of Steel	41.47	41.29	-0.42%	34.88	35.92	2.97%
Sintel	40.46	39.92	-1.34%	30.13	31.69	5.18%
Big Buck Bunny	41.44	40.92	-1.27%	25.04	29.58	18.12%
Talking Head	44.08	44.15	0.17%	39.62	39.59	-0.07%
Freedom	41.78	40.99	-1.91%	35.52	35.34	-0.52%
Haunted	41.97	41.78	-0.45%	35.62	35.88	0.74%
Screencam	45.70	47.29	3.46%	34.18	33.18	-2.91%
Tutorial	44.91	48.19	7.31%	38.90	43.12	10.84%
Average	42.73	43.07	0.69%	34.24	35.54	4.29%

Table 11-3. Comparing x264 and x265 files encoded at half the data rate of x264.

The second set of columns measured low frame quality, and here x265 outperformed x264 by 4.29 percent, a healthy advantage. Very healthy numbers from Big Buck Bunny, our perennial low-frame-quality problem child, buoyed this result. This performance reminded me of a comment to one of my articles on Streaming Media titled "How to Encode to HEVC: A Simple Guide for H.265 First-Timers" (bit.ly/howto_hevc).

Specifically, the reader, who appears to work at Elemental Technologies (but surely can't be named Scamphunter Deepbluesea) commented:

> One thing I have noticed with HEVC, at least in our implementation, is that it very rarely macroblocks, but instead, will lose detail. Some of the testing tools flag this, but from the human eye perspective, momentary loss of detail seems to be less objectionable than macroblocking in H264, and especially MPEG-2.

This comment, and the test results, seem to indicate that not only does HEVC improve quality, it avoids artifacts in problem frames—a nice win/win.

The numbers for 720p were very similar. x265 produced the overall best quality by 0.51 percent, but if you remove the synthetic files from the equation, x264 bested x265 by about 0.74 percent. In the low frame analysis, x265 proved 5.24 percent higher than x264, with Big Buck Bunny improving from a potentially problematical 24.70 dB to a more manageable 28.10 dB.

Overall, if you decide to simply switch over your existing 1080p footage from x264 to x265, you should be able to reduce your data rates by 40 to 50 percent while retaining similar high-end quality, and boosting low-end quality.

Note: *Encoding in CRF mode with HEVC and FFmpeg uses the same exact syntax as shown back in Chapter 7 for x264, except you switch in the x265 codec as shown shortly.*

4K and 2K Results

What about going higher than 1080p? We explore that in the following tables, where we produced 4K (3840x2160) and 2K (2560x1440) files using CRF encoding with a value of 23 in x264 and x265. At CRF 23, 4K files encoded in H.264 format averaged 14.7 Mbps. Interestingly, when I checked 4K data rates for a client in mid-2016, the average data rate YouTube used for 4K videos was 14 Mbps, which is certainly in the same ballpark. As you can see in the table, x265 reduced that to just over 8 Mbps, a reduction of 45.95 percent, while increasing PSNR quality by 0.24 percent. One reality check is that it's been widely reported that Netflix encoded *House of Cards* at between 10 and 16 Mbps, which is between 25 and 100 percent higher than our numbers.

For 2K content, CRF 23 produced a data rate of 7330 kbps for x264; in the aforementioned client study, YouTube data rates for the same resolution and codec averaged 6775 kbps, though ranging as high as 7 Mbps. HEVC cut this to 4192 kbps, while again slightly increasing PSNR quality by 0.39 percent.

Overall, HEVC delivers sufficient bandwidth savings at lower resolutions to justify switching for platforms that support it, while delivering even larger savings at ultra-HD resolutions. As mentioned earlier, you should strongly consider using HEVC for every platform that supports it.

3840x2160 - CRF 23	FPS	x265 Data Rate	x265 PSNR	x264 Data Rate	x264 PSNR	Analysis Data Rate	Analysis PSNR
New	30	5,934	44.11	13,600	43.92	56.37%	0.44%
Tears of Steel	24	8,231	42.32	15,100	42.24	45.49%	0.20%
Sintel	24	9,919	43.83	15,500	43.79	36.01%	0.10%
Average		**8,028**	**43.42**	**14,733**	**43.32**	**45.95%**	**0.24%**
2560x1440 - CRF 23							
New	30	2,866	43.02	5,753	42.93	50.18%	0.22%
Tears of Steel	24	4,374	42.15	7,593	41.97	42.39%	0.44%
Sintel	24	5,336	42.52	8,644	42.31	38.27%	0.50%
Average		**4,192**	**42.56**	**7,330**	**42.40**	**43.62%**	**0.39%**

Table 11-4. CRF calculations for x264 and x265 for 2K and 4K content.

Encoding Time

Encoding time calculations are always messy. For example, suppose you encoded the same file to H.264 and HEVC on a 40-core workstation, and the encoding time was the same. Sounds good, right? But what if the HEVC encodes consumed 100 percent of all CPU resources, and

H.264 only 10 percent? The time is the same, but by designing their code to use the multiple processors more efficiently, an encoding vendor should be able to encode H.264 up to 10 times faster than HEVC.

That said, some numbers are better than no numbers. Table 11-5 compares the average encoding times of all 720p files using x264 and x265 and the encoding presets shown. As you can see, with the faster presets, the times are very similar, but as the encoding gets more complex, the difference gets pretty dramatic.

	Ultrafast	Superfast	Veryfast	Faster	Fast	Medium	Slow	Slower	Veryslow	Placebo
x265	14	19	31	35	40	52	125	352	547	2506
x264	11	12	15	16	27	28	42	48	66	213
Increase	29%	59%	115%	110%	50%	81%	199%	626%	726%	1077%

Table 11-5. Average encoding times for 720p files with x264 and x265.

Figure 11-8 shows this information graphically. As you can see, so long as you choose the Medium preset or faster, the times are in the same ballpark. Beyond that, the difference gets pretty stark. In general, count on HEVC taking at least twice as long as H.264, but this will depend upon which HEVC codec you're using—and, of course, the encoding tool.

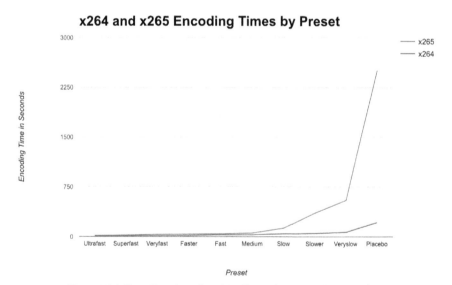

Figure 11-8. Encoding times for 720p files with x264 and x265 codecs.

Note: *The folks at MulticoreWare have advised me that for true x265 performance benchmarks, you should encode with the x265 encoder, not FFmpeg. While the output quality should be identical, FFmpeg includes other overheads, like converting the input MP4 file to YUV for encoding. In contrast, since the x265 encoder can only input YUV, you need to YUV beforehand. Of course, the same could be said for the x264 and VP9 encoders, for which I also used FFmpeg. So I'm comfortable that my results are representative, if not quite the fastest that x265 (or x264 or VP9) could produce.*

Basic HEVC Encoding Parameters

Now that we understand how H.264 and HEVC compare, let's talk basics of HEVC encoding. As you saw in Figure 11-4, HEVC is a lot like H.264 and even MPEG-2. That means all of the non-H.264 specific lessons learned in previous chapters apply here. Briefly, to produce files with x265 in this chapter, I:

- halved the data rate computed for H.264

- used the same bitrate control technique and VBR buffer controls as with H.264. This meant 110 percent constrained VBR for all files except Big Buck Bunny and Screencam, which I encoded using 200 percent constrained VBR.

- used a VBV buffer for all files of 1x the data rate—except for Screencam, where I used a 2x buffer.

- used a key frame interval of 2 seconds for all files, with 3 B-frames and 10 reference frames for all files.

Note that I didn't redo any of the testing performed earlier with H.264, though I would at least verify these assumptions if I was performing this type of work for a client. For the most part, the basics we covered in Chapters 7 through 9 should be very close to universal. I present a summary of these settings, and those gleaned from this chapter in Table 11-9.

In terms of basic operation, most HEVC encoding tools also encode to H.264 format, and the interfaces are typically very similar. The three areas we'll focus on related to HEVC operation are shown in Figure 11-9, a screenshot from MulticoreWare's x265 Encoder application, which is a GUI front end for the company's x265 command-line encoder. You should see three pretty familiar concepts: profiles (1), presets (2), and tuning mechanisms (3).

Remember, of course, that different encoding tools use different HEVC codecs, so they will present different options. MulticoreWare is the developer of x265, so you would expect its encoder to provide access to and leverage all of its features. Some encoding vendors show far fewer options—like Adobe Media Encoder, which lets you choose a profile and a quality level, and that's it.

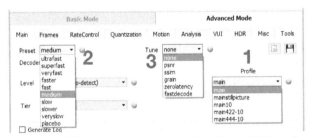

Figure 11-9. x265 encoding basics in MulticoreWare x265 Encoder.

There is no animation preset with x265, and given the poor results achieved with the grain tune with x264, I won't address tuning at all.

HEVC Profiles

Most HEVC encoding tools let you select the Main or Main 10 profile. The Main profile supports 8 bits per sample, which allows 256 shades per primary color, or 16.7 million colors in the video. In contrast, the Main 10 profile supports up to 10 bits per sample, which allows up to 1024 shades and over 1 billion colors. Of course, you'll need a 10-bit display to see the extra colors, which most potential viewers don't have at this point. That's because the real target of Main 10 are high-dynamic-range (HDR) displays, which are in the works, but somewhat stifled by the industry's inability to agree on a single standard.

In addition, if your video has an 8-bit color depth, which most videos do, encoding in 10-bit won't add the colors and improve video quality. On the other hand, some experts argue that processing in 10-bit color may improve the encoding precision of 8-bit source videos, even if it doesn't add colors. My tests didn't quite confirm this claim, as you can see in Table 11-6.

720p - x265	Main	Main 10	Delta
Tears of Steel	37.05	37.73	1.84%
SIntel	41.37	41.25	-0.29%
Big Buck Bunny	37.21	37.16	-0.13%
Talking Head	41.15	41.15	0.00%
Freedom	39.70	39.57	-0.31%
Haunted	39.56	41.78	5.61%
Average	**39.34**	**39.77**	**1.12%**

Table 11-6. Main 10 delivered slightly higher quality than Main.

Here, I encoded using the Main and Main 10 profiles and otherwise identical features. Although the Main 10 encoded videos averaged slightly higher quality, four of the six videos were either about the same or worse quality.

I ran the same tests in Adobe Media Encoder, and the videos encoded with the Main 10 profile averaged over 36 percent higher PSNR scores than the Main profile. When I compared the videos in the Moscow State University tool, however, I noticed that the videos encoded with the Main profile had a slight cast, and looked slightly dingy. I'm guessing that this issue isn't the technical superiority of the Main 10 profile over the Main profile as much as a bug in the Adobe encoder.

Before chasing the extra quality some claim Main 10 can deliver, note that if you encode your video using the Main 10 profile, only Main 10 compatible decoders will be able to play the video. Most early HEVC players were not Main 10 compatible, so if you're distributing your HEVC videos to the general public, as opposed to specific smart TVs or set-top boxes, there is a compatibility risk (see Figure 11-10).

Figure 11-10. Only Main 10-compatible players can play Main 10 files.

So I recommend using the Main profile for general-purpose distribution, even if your video is 10-bit in origin. If you're distributing to known Main 10-compatible HEVC decoders, you should consider encoding with Main 10 even if your video is 8-bit in origin. Obviously, if you're encoding HDR video, you'll need to use Main 10.

> **Note:** *To encode to Main 10 using FFmpeg and x265, you'll have to download or compile a Main 10-specific version. You can't simply call the Main 10 x265 codec from the standard downloadable version of FFmpeg.*

Quick Summary: HEVC Profiles

> *1.* If you're encoding video for general-purpose distribution, use the Main profile for the broadest possible compatibility.

> *2.* If you're producing for a platform or platforms with known Main 10 compatibility, encode using the Main 10 profile, whether the source footage is 8-bit or 10-bit.

About High Dynamic Range (HDR)

HEVC is a codec, and HDR is a display technology. 4K refers to the number of pixels in a video file. How do these technologies and concepts interrelate? Well, it's complicated, but here's my take.

HDR refers to displays that can display an expanded range of brightness, which is shown in Figure 11-11, which is from an simulated HDR comparison from the website 4K Ultra HD Review (bit.ly/4Kultrahd). The HDR simulation on the left shows both brighter and darker pixels, allowing more detail to come through. In technical terms, this means that it has an expanded dynamic range, with brighter bright pixels, and darker dark pixels than the normal display.

HDR displays also display an expanded color space as compared to older TV sets, which you can read about at bit.ly/rec2020v709. So you get more colors, and more brightness. Unlike plain Jane 4K TV sets, the difference doesn't depend upon how close you sit to the TV, or how big the set is. The difference will be very noticeable even on similarly sized sets viewed from the same distance.

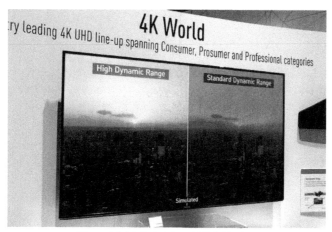

Figure 11-11. A simulated HDR display.

The Encoding Side

That's the display side. How do we encode files that leverage these extra capabilities? Briefly, the increased contrast delivered by HDR, along with the expansion of color space, means that each compressed pixel will require much more data to define. Some of that data will be included with the compressed video, and some will be in an accompanying metadata file—which, according to some estimates, will add about 20 percent in file size.

Unfortunately, there isn't a single standard for how HDR data is stored or displayed. According to discussions that I had with a contact at Elemental Technologies, the basic compressed stream for most HDR standards will be similar, but the metadata will all be different. In an encoding interface, the various standards will likely be selected via a simple checkbox or drop-down list. It's very simple from a user perspective, but the development effort required to support the different standards would be substantial.

To be clear, all HDR content must be mastered and encoded for HDR displays. Legacy content might look a bit better, but to get the complete benefit, you'll need specially mastered and encoded content, and a compatible display.

Of course, the lack of a single standard complicates more than just encoding, it complicates distribution. For example, Amazon's *Mozart in the Jungle* is available on HDR, but only on a very specific list of Samsung TVs. Other movie distributors are leaning towards supporting an industry group called the UHD Alliance, which includes TV manufacturers Sony, Panasonic, and Sharp; technology providers Dolby and Technicolor; and content producers/distributors Disney, Fox, Warner Bros., Netflix, and DirecTV. Before buying a UHD TV, identify the sources of UHD content you plan to watch and the standard they intend to use. If you're a UHD producer, make sure the encoder that you purchase supports the standard or standards you intend to support.

OK, back to our discussion about producing HEVC.

x265 Presets

The encoding presets in x265 are the same as x264, even using the same names. How do they compare? Table 11-7 shows the quality side of the equation. For the record, I produced these files using the x265 codec in FFmpeg.

As you can see, the Ultrafast preset always produced the lowest quality, and Placebo the highest. Interestingly, quality actually dropped after the Superfast preset, and didn't surpass that level until the Fast preset. Overall, the average difference between the highest and lowest scores was 6.7 percent.

	Ultrafast	Superfast	Veryfast	Faster	Fast	Medium	Slow	Slower	Veryslow	Placebo	Total Delta
Tears of Steel	37.25	38.06	38.04	38.05	38.34	38.39	38.84	38.86	38.93	39.00	4.70%
Sintel	35.87	36.89	36.66	36.67	37.11	37.25	37.74	37.79	37.90	37.97	5.86%
Big Buck Bunny	36.10	37.65	37.61	37.60	37.91	38.26	38.70	38.89	39.03	39.18	8.54%
Freedom	38.16	39.01	38.45	38.46	38.71	38.98	39.36	39.44	39.52	39.58	3.72%
Haunted	41.36	41.77	41.39	41.39	41.55	41.68	41.97	41.92	41.97	42.02	1.60%
Screencam	44.03	46.70	46.55	46.54	46.78	47.12	48.31	48.69	48.99	49.34	12.07%
Tutorial	42.46	47.14	46.46	46.42	46.52	47.19	48.35	47.65	48.02	48.53	14.31%
Average	38.64	39.51	39.30	39.31	39.58	39.74	40.13	40.18	40.27	40.35	6.70%

Table 11-7. PSNR quality by video file and encoding preset.

How does encoding time factor in? This is shown in Figure 11-12. Here I've normalized encoding time on a scale from 0 to 100, with the time of the Ultrafast encode set to 0. The quality side represents the 6.7 percent total difference on a scale of 0 to 100 percent, so you can see how each of the presets contributes or detracts from quality.

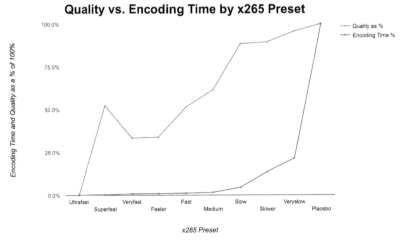

Figure 11-12. Quality versus encoding time by x265 preset.

From an encoding time perspective, the needle barely even moves until the Medium preset, and there's such a big quality jump between Medium and Slow that using the Slow preset looks like an obvious move. At Slow, you're just under 89 percent of total quality, and encoding time really starts to jump. If you're running out of capacity, it's worth experimenting with Superfast, as the bang for your encoding time buck is substantial. To put the numbers in perspective, PSNR for Superfast averaged 39.51 dB, while slow averaged 40.13 dB, which isn't a difference that most viewers would notice.

Tip: *Note that you can see the exact configuration options used for each preset at bit.ly/x265_pre, a page created by x265 developer MulticoreWare.*

Adobe Media Encoder Presets

I ran a similar set of tests with the encoding presets available with Adobe Media Encoder, although only on the Tears of Steel test clip. Table 11-8 shows the raw results, encoding time reported in seconds. As you can see in the table, the lowest-quality preset produced the lowest PSNR scores, and the highest produced the highest, with an overall quality differential of 8.15 percent.

TOS-Main10	Lowest	Lower	Good	Higher	Highest	Delta
Quality	35.78	37.03	37.75	38.36	38.70	8.15%
Encoding Time	14	21	35	167	1246	

Table 11-8. Quality versus encoding time by preset for Adobe Media Encoder.

Figure 11-13 spreads the differences in quality and encoding time from 0 to 100 percent, and shows them graphically. Based upon what I see, Good is the most logical preset since the quality difference between Good and Higher is minor, yet Higher takes almost five times longer.

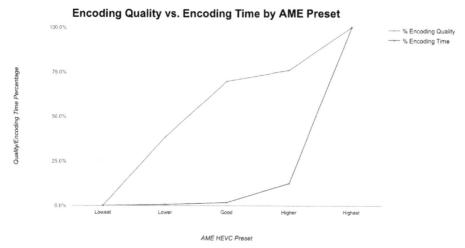

Figure 11-13. Quality versus encoding time by Adobe Media Encoder preset.

Applying These Findings

If I were producing HEVC video, here's where I would start my encoding configurations. While we had valid tests for Sintel and Tears of Steel, the rest of the numbers are just guesstimates—but you have to start somewhere.

	Data Rate					Bitrate		Frames/Ref Frames				HEVC	
	2160p	1440p	1080p	720p	360p	Max Rate	VBV	I-Frm	B-Frm	Strategy	Refs	Profile	Preset
Tears of Steel	10000	5000	2500	1000	450	110%	1 sec	2	3	2	10	Main	Slow
Sintel	10000	5000	2500	1000	450	110%	1 sec	2	3	2	10	Main	Slow
Freedom	12000	6000	3000	1250	450	110%	1 sec	2	3	2	10	Main	Slow
Haunted	12000	6000	3000	1250	450	110%	1 sec	2	3	2	10	Main	Slow
Big Buck Bunny	6000	3000	1500	750	300	200%	1 sec	2	3	2	10	Main	Slow
Talking Head	6000	3000	1500	750	300	110%	1 sec	2	3	2	10	Main	Slow
Screencam	3200	1600	800	500	200	200%	2 sec	2	3	2	10	Main	Slow
Tutorial	2000	1000	500	300	100	200%	1 sec	2	3	2	10	Main	Slow

Table 11-9. Starting points for HEVC encodes.

Note that we don't have a lot of commercial comparisons we can use because there's very little HEVC-encoded content available for testing. As mentioned above, Netflix reportedly encodes *House of Cards* at 16 Mbps, which blows my numbers out of the water. But like I said, you have to start somewhere.

Encoding x265 in FFmpeg

The majority of the basic FFmpeg file controls you learned for H.264—like GOP size, resolution, CRF encoding, key frame interval, and so on—are identical for HEVC. Here are commands for the HEVC-specific options discussed in this chapter. Note that you can find the complete command line documentation for x265 at bit.ly/x265_documentation. But these commands work with the x265 encoder, not FFmpeg.

One big change is to change to the x265 codec in the command string, which looks like this:

```
-c:v libx265
```

Since AAC is still the audio codec, no changes are necessary there.

HEVC Profiles

As mentioned, in order to create Main 10 output with FFmpeg, you need an will need an FFmpeg build with 10 bit libx265. Once you have that, you can specify the profile using this string:

```
-profile main
```

```
-profile main10
```

x265 Presets

Note that the x265 presets use the exact same names as x264, and you specify them the exact same way, using this string:

```
-preset [preset]

-preset veryslow
```

Note that if you don't specify a preset, FFmpeg will use the default Medium preset.

Other Commands

Just to be perfectly clear, as with x264, you can encode files using the x265 codec compiled into FFmpeg, or you can encode using the separate x265 encoder at x265.org. I like using FFmpeg because it's easier. For example, it allows me to encode .mp4 files rather than converting to YUV, which you have to do for the x265 encoder.

On the other hand, there really is very limited documentation for the advanced x265 controls available in FFmpeg, which is a pain. But x265 is very well documented (see bit.ly/x265_documentation). In theory, you should be able to add any x265 configuration option to an FFmpeg command script by adding `-x265-params` to the FFmpeg command string and adding the x265 parameters after that (see bit.ly/x265_ffmpeg). You can see an example of how this is used at bit.ly/2enaCWp, although I didn't use this approach in any of my testing.

x265 Sample Scripts

Here are the two-pass script used to encode the Freedom test clip to 1.25 Mbps, 110 percent constrained VBR, using the slow preset with I-frames every 2 seconds, 3 B-frames and 10 reference frames.

```
ffmpeg -y -i Freedom_720p.mp4 -c:v libx265 -preset slow -g 60
-keyint_min 60 -sc_threshold 0 -bf 3 -b_strategy 2 -refs 10
-b:v 2500k -pass 1 -f mp4 NUL && \

ffmpeg -iFreedom_720p.mp4 -c:v libx265 -preset slow -g 60
-keyint_min 60 -sc_threshold 0 -bf 3 -b_strategy 2 -refs 10
-b:v 2500k -maxrate 2750k -bufsize 2500k -pass 2
Freedom_720p_HEVC.mp4
```

So that's HEVC. In the next chapter, you'll learn the ins and outs of deploying and encoding VP9.

Chapter 12: Working with VP9

Figure 12-1. YouTube viewers watched 25 billion hours of VP9 between April 2014 and March 2015.

VP9 is an open-source codec from Google that was developed from technology acquired from On2 Technologies in February 2010. The first codec Google released from this acquisition was VP8, which was paired with the Vorbis audio codec in the WebM file structure. VP9 is the next iteration of the codec, which became available on June 17, 2013. VP9 will be the last VPx-based codec released by Google, as the company contributed all codec technology to the Alliance for Open Media in September 2015.

In this chapter, you'll learn:

- about VP9, including which container formats it's packaged in, intellectual property status, where it plays, and how it compares to H.264 and HEVC quality- and performance-wise

- the common encoding parameters for VP9, including sample scripts for FFmpeg.

Technology Background

VP9 development started in late 2011. Coding tools include multiple prediction block sizes, from 64x64 down to 4x4; up to 10 intra predictors; sub-pixel interpolation; three different transform types; and entropy encoding. The codec supports a maximum resolution of 6400x6400 at up to 120 fps, as well as multiple color spaces, including Rec 601, Rec 709, Rec 2020, SMPTE-170,

SMPTE-240, and sRGB. A technical paper detailing these codec components and operation is available at bit.ly/vp9_tec.

YouTube was the first, and is still by far the largest users of VP9. In a blog post titled "VP9: Faster, better, buffer-free YouTube video" (bit.ly/YT_vp9), published on April 6, 2015, YouTube reported, "In the last year alone, YouTube users have already watched more than 25 billion hours of VP9 video, billions of which would not have been played in HD without VP9's bandwidth benefits." Soon thereafter, I compared the data rates YouTube used for VP9 against those used for H.264, and learned that at 1080p, the VP9 files were 43 percent smaller, and at 720p, they were about 35 percent smaller (bit.ly/yt_vp9).

On September 1, 2015, the Alliance for Open Media (AOM) announced its formation (bit.ly/aom_1). AOM consolidates the efforts of open-source codec developers Google, Mozilla, Cisco, Microsoft, and Intel into one codec, AV1, which is expected to ship by the end of 2017. As with VP8 and VP9, the AV1 codec will be completely royalty- and disclosure-free. The AV1 codec is largely based upon VP10, the successor to VP9. Google has stated that it will not deploy VP10 internally or release it publicly, making VP9 the last of the VPx-based codecs to be released.

Packaging VP9

VP9 is a codec, not a container format. Although you can package VP9 in multiple container formats, single files are typically encoded into the WebM container format. Adaptive bitrate files are typically packaged in DASH format. For example, as shown in Figure 12-2, YouTube uses DASH for VP9 files (nine lines down, DASH: yes).

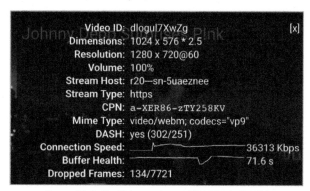

Figure 12-2. YouTube packages VP9 files in DASH.

Much more on DASH in Chapters 13 to 15.

VP9 Intellectual Property Status

Both VP8 and VP9 are available under a FreeBSD license that enables users to deploy encode or decode capabilities in both proprietary software and open-source software without disclosing their source code in either instance. So VP9 is royalty free, while HEVC is encumbered with royalties that max out at about $65 million per year as described in Chapter 11.

In the interest of completeness, I wanted to briefly address the patent risk associated with VP9. Ever since Google purchased On2, there have been rumors of patent related issues. In late 2012, MPEG LA started trying to piece together a patent pool relating to VP8, but it never coalesced.

In March 2013, MPEG LA and Google entered into agreements granting Google a license to technologies that "may" be essential to VP8 and one "next-generation VPx" codec, which turned out to be VP9. In return, MPEG LA dropped its plans to form a VP8 patent pool. Nokia— which was a member of the MPEG LA H.264 patent pool, but didn't sign the aforementioned agreement—later sued Android licensor HTC. The company claimed that VP8, as used in the Android operating system, infringed on one or more of its video compression-related patents (bit.ly/no_vp9). In August 2013, Nokia lost that suit (bit.ly/vp9_nokia).

It's possible that other IP owners will come out of the woodwork and attempt to sue Google over VP9. However, given that VP9 will be at least partially superseded by the Alliance for Open Media's AV1 codec, it's likely that any claims will be made against that codec, into which much of VP9's IP was directed. Of course, with founding members Amazon, Cisco, Google, Intel, Microsoft, Mozilla, and Netflix—and subsequent members AMD, ARM, and NVIDIA—the alliance can amass a significant war chest to dispute any IP claims.

Where Does VP9 Play?

Let's review the main playback markets that we first touched on last chapter.

Browser—Desktop and Notebook

Browser-based playback is the primary mechanism for playing back videos on computers and notebooks. Over the past few years, playback has shifted from plugins like Flash and Silverlight to browser-based playback via HTML5. This means that the decoder has to actually be in the browser for the video to play.

Under this schema, most browsers included H.264 playback almost from the start, and those that didn't (Firefox, Opera) were able to leverage H.264 decoding in the Macintosh, Windows, Android or iOS operating systems. Since VP8 and later VP9 were free, browsers like Firefox and Opera integrated them as soon as they were available. Google also integrated VP8 and VP9 playback in Chrome, for obvious reasons. After joining the Alliance for Open Media, Microsoft pledged VP9 support in Microsoft Edge (bit.ly/edge_vp9), which is the Windows 8/10 browser. Unfortunately, Microsoft didn't add VP9 playback to earlier versions of Internet Explorer. Still, the only browser holdout is Apple, which has never indicated whether it would or would not support VP9.

Browser market share varies by the different companies that provide it. For example, as of August 2016, Net Market Share (netmarketshare.com) reported that Chrome had a market share of 53.97 percent, with Internet Explorer second at 27.38 percent, and Safari at 4.28 percent. This means that more than 31 percent of the market couldn't play VP9 encoded files. In contrast, as of the same date W3Schools (w3schools.com/browsers) reported Chrome at 72.4 percent, Internet Explorer at 5.2 percent, and Safari at 3.2 percent—which would mean only 8 percent of the market couldn't play VP9 encoded videos.

As you probably know, players have the ability to interrogate browsers during the initial handshake to determine which codecs they can play. If a browser (or mobile device) doesn't support VP9 playback, you can send H.264-encoded videos instead. The key points are:

- VP9 has enough browser support to make encoding a separate set of files into VP9 worthwhile for the bandwidth savings

- HEVC is not currently available in any browser, so it's not an alternative for this use case.

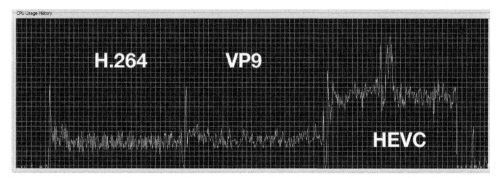

Figure 12-3. Required CPU horsepower for H.264, VP9, and HEVC 720p playback on an old Dell workstation.

Figure 12-3 is a repeat from last chapter, showing that 720p VP9 playback doesn't consume that much more CPU than H.264 playback. Again, this is on an ancient Dell Precision Workstation driven by a 2.93 GHz Intel Core 2 Extreme CPU X6800. At 720p resolution, you really can easily substitute VP9 for H.264 on virtually all relevant computers out there.

I further tested H.264 and VP9 4K playback on a much newer dual-core (four with Hyper-Threading Technology) Dell Inspiron notebook computer with an Intel i5-4210U CPU running at 1.7GHz, a $400 notebook running Intel graphics. On the Inspiron, the 4K VP9 file consumed about 50 to 60 percent of CPU, compared to 40 to 50 percent for H.264. These results, coupled with the fact that YouTube has been distributing VP9 since 2013, should provide comfort that VP9 plays well on most relatively modern computers.

Mobile

Google's Android has been able to play VP9 since version 4.4, with HEVC playback added in version 5.0. As we discussed in Chapter 11, however, most video distributors are concerned about the battery life implications of delivering a more complex codec than H.264 to devices without hardware playback. As you can see in Figure 12-4, VP9 does increase CPU utilization slightly over H.264—although it's not night and day.

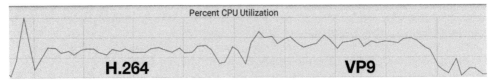

Figure 12-4. Required CPU horsepower for 720p H.264 and VP9 playback on a Samsung Nexus 10.

This is on a Samsung Nexus 10 tablet powered by a 1.7 GHz dual-core ARM Cortex-A15, which is in the lower end of Cortex family (now up to A73). Most new tablets and smartphones are powered by four-core CPUs that would play both files much more easily. Still, more complex formats mean increased battery consumption on devices without hardware support.

If you check the VP9 page on Wikipedia, you'll see that there are lots of devices with hardware support available or coming, including the MediaTek MT6795, the NVIDIA Tegra X1, Qualcomm Snapdragon 820, and two chips from Samsung. More are probably in the hardware development pipeline. It will be interesting to see whether new hardware supports VP9 and the AV1 codec once available, or whether vendors will drop VP9 support in favor of AV1. In virtually all cases, I would expect new hardware to support HEVC.

Overall, where it's easy to recommend converting from H.264 to VP9 for desktop playback, mobile devices are underpowered compared to these devices, and battery is always an issue.

Smart TV/Retail OTT

This is the "voluntary" market for watching IP-based TV in the living room—as in you buy your smart TV at Wal-Mart, or your Roku 4 at Amazon, and expect them to play 4K video. The general perception is that HEVC is more widely supported among smart TVs, but that very well might not be the case. I ran the concept of support in these segments with one of the top VP9 evangelists at Google, and he responded:

> VP9 is extremely well supported in TVs and STBs. I'd say that VP9 has close to if not as broad penetration in smart TVs as HEVC does. By the time this book is published, there will be no difference in penetration in new TVs. All of the major manufacturers support VP9 8-bit in their 4K TVs. And they've either recently released VP9 10-bit (HDR-capable) support or will do so by CES next year.

> OEMs were initially slow to add either of the new codecs (VP9 or HEVC) to their 1080p TVs, because they treated that class as being in maintenance mode and didn't want to spend money to upgrade the underlying HW. But that's changing too. For instance, Samsung, LG, and Sony had VP9 in their FHD sets in 2016. Again, I'd say we're at least in as good a shape in <4K TVs as HEVC is.

Samsung does the best job of specifying which formats its TVs play, and VP9 is supported in all 2015 and 2016 models. Netflix has publicly announced that it is experimenting with VP9, although I don't know if it has ever deployed VP9-encoded video. On the broadcast front, I've not seen any press releases about VP9-based UHD channels launching, so I would have to assume that most traditional broadcast-centric activities are likely using HEVC, not VP9. The reverse is true for web-based content. Although the vast majority of VP9 encoded video is distributed by YouTube, that single site likely has enough drawing power to make VP9 playback a required feature on most smart TVs and OTT devices.

Internet Protocol TV (IPTV)

This is the "involuntary" market for watching IP-based TV in the living room—as in you sign up for the service via your satellite or cable provider, and they install the box you'll use for decode. While I'm guessing many set-top boxes are starting to support VP9, I've not seen any VP9-based channels launching, with VP9 support seemingly focused on general-purpose payback. Whether this will change with AV1 remains to be seen.

What it all Means

Here's a summary of the foregoing sections.

- If you're looking to replace H.264 with a more efficient codec for computer-based playback, VP9 is the natural choice.

- On the other hand, the mobile market is cloudy as Android supports both formats, and Apple supports neither.

- If you're creating a subscription service targeting smart TVs and OTT boxes, you have to approach this on a device by device basis. HEVC comes with a potential content-royalty of up to $2.5 million for subscription and pay-per-view ($5 million if you support both revenue models), while VP9 is free.

- IPTV seems firmly in the HEVC camp—although if you can use VP9 you can save the content royalties.

Comparing VP9 and H.264

The promise of VP9 and HEVC was supposed to be the same quality as H.264 at half the data rate. To test this, I compared H.264 encoded using the very slow preset with VP9 encoded at half the target data rate used for H.264, but the highest possible quality. I tested both 720p and 1080p files. The results are in Table 12-1. Again, VP9 is encoded at half the data rate of the H.264 files, not the same. Note that I excluded the Tutorial files from all analyses in this chapter because the files couldn't reach the target bitrate in VP9.

Overall, at 1080p, the H.264 files at twice the data rate averaged 1.43 percent higher peak signal-to-noise ratio (PSNR) scores than VP9, which increased to 3.36 percent at 720p. While this means that you probably won't achieve the same quality at 50 percent the data rate, you'll come close. Note that when Netflix compared H.264 with VP9 for its August presentation (bit.ly/nf_codecq), the team found that at 720p, VP9 delivered quality equal to H.264 at a 36.4 percent lower data rate, which increased to a savings of 43.5 percent at 1080p. So my results are right in line with Netflix's, if not slightly more optimistic. So if you're converting over from H.264 to VP9, you should be able to reduce your data rates by 40 percent or so without any noticeable quality differential.

	1080p			720p		
	H.264	VP9	Delta - x264/VP9	x264	VP9	Delta - x264/VP9
Tears of Steel	41.47	41.12	-0.85%	39.47	38.34	-2.96%
Sintel	40.46	39.62	-2.11%	38.57	37.37	-3.21%
Big Buck Bunny	41.44	39.93	-3.79%	39.64	38.34	-3.38%
Talking Head	44.08	44.30	0.51%	44.39	44.21	-0.42%
Freedom	41.78	41.74	-0.12%	40.85	39.95	-2.24%
Haunted	41.97	42.05	0.20%	42.35	42.10	-0.59%
Screencam	45.70	44.02	-3.82%	46.88	42.35	-10.71%
Average	42.41	41.83	-1.43%	41.74	40.38	-3.36%

Table 12-1. PSNR quality of VP9 files encoded at half the target data rate of H.264.

Comparing VP9 and HEVC

Table 12-2 shows how VP9 compares with HEVC. To create this table, I encoded both sets of files to 50 percent of the target data rate used for H.264 and computed the PSNR value.

Basically, at 1080p, the PSNR values for x265 were 1.18 percent higher than VP9, which increased to 3.21 percent at 720p. Better is always better, no doubt, but scanning the scores for the individual files, it's doubtful that even the most golden eye viewer could tell the videos apart. To achieve equivalent quality, you'd have to boost the data rate of your VP9 files slightly, but certainly no more than 5 to 10 percent.

Interestingly, in PSNR-based comparisons, Netflix found that x265 was roughly 4.3 percent more efficient than VP9 at 720p resolution, which dropped to a slight edge for VP9 at 1080p. In its initial report with Netflix's own benchmark, Video Multimethod Assessment Fusion (VMAF), HEVC enjoyed a substantial advantage over VP9—although later retests found the results much closer (bit.ly/nf_vp9). I discussed my concerns about Netflix's encoding procedures and benchmark in my Streaming Media article about the presentation (bit.ly/nf_codecq), and I won't repeat them here.

	1080p			720p		
	x265	**VP9**	**Delta x265/VP9**	**x265**	**VP9**	**Delta x265/VP9**
Tears of Steel	41.29	41.12	-0.43%	39.25	38.34	-2.38%
Sintel	39.92	39.62	-0.75%	38.29	37.37	-2.44%
Big Buck Bunny	40.92	39.93	-2.47%	39.27	38.34	-2.42%
Freedom	40.99	41.74	1.79%	39.87	39.95	0.21%
Haunted	41.78	42.05	0.65%	42.22	42.10	-0.28%
Screencam	47.29	44.02	-7.42%	48.34	42.35	-14.17%
Average	42.33	41.83	-1.18%	41.70	40.38	-3.21%

Table 12-2. PSNR quality of VP9 files compared to HEVC at the same data rate.

By any measure, if you decide to deploy VP9, you should be able to achieve a substantial data rate reduction as compared with that of H.264. If and when you're faced with a choice between VP9 and HEVC, you can perform your own tests or research for more recent findings.

4K and 2K Results

I also ran some tests with 2K and 4K files to match those performed last chapter for HEVC.

		x265		**VP9**		**Analysis**	
3840x2160	**FPS**	**Data Rate**	**PSNR**	**Data Rate**	**PSNR**	**Data Rate**	**PSNR**
New	30	5,934	44.11	5,946	42.56	0.20%	-3.66%
Tears of Steel	24	8,231	42.32	8,160	42.15	-0.87%	-0.42%
Sintel	24	9,919	43.83	10,053	43.11	1.33%	-1.67%
Average		8,028	43.42	8,053	42.61	0.22%	-1.92%
2560x1440							
New	30	2,866	43.02	2,830	40.80	-1.27%	-5.46%
Tears of Steel	24	4,374	42.15	4,316	41.69	-1.34%	-1.10%
Sintel	24	5,336	42.52	5,263	41.58	-1.39%	-2.26%
Average		4,192	42.56	4,136	41.36	-1.33%	-2.92%

Table 12-3. VP9 and x265 comparisons for 2K and 4K content.

Note that while VP9 has a constant rate factor (CRF) mode, the result don't map as closely as x264 and x265, which delivered very similar quality at the same CRF levels. What I did here was encode VP9 at the same data rates used to encode HEVC in the previous chapter. Unlike the previous comparisons, where I encoded VP9 at speed 0, I encoded these files at a more reasonable setting of 1 (more on this in a moment). You can see the results in Table 12-3.

Again, although HEVC won every comparison, the 4K scores were about 2 percent apart, and the 2K scores just under 3 percent. Both formats should be able to shave close to 50 percent the bitrate from H.264 streams, although HEVC appears to be slightly more efficient. Note that Netflix's comparisons peaked at 1080p, so they have no data to add to this comparison.

Basic VP9 Encoding Parameters

Now that we understand how VP9 compares with H.264 and HEVC, let's talk basics of VP9 encoding. While many of the basic concepts are similar, VP9 encoding has multiple options that are totally unique, and Google has done a generally poor job documenting what many of them do and how they work. Until recently, few websites have used VP9, so application support among encoding tools is weak and each application seems to implement different features in different ways.

There's also a bit of a disconnect between the command line parameters available for Google's own encoder (vpxenc.exe) and VP9-specific encoding parameters for FFmpeg. Specifically, Google did an adequate job detailing the command line parameters for its own encoder, but hasn't really documented which configuration options work with FFmpeg and the appropriate command string. Meanwhile, most producers want to use FFmpeg rather than Google's own executable because it's easier to work with and more functional. As with HEVC, there's also a dearth of tools for analyzing your encoded files to verify that the selected encoding options are working as you want them to.

As a result, most of the sample scripts that Google has provided are pretty basic, which seems to be the approach that most developers are taking.

To create the VP9 files that I used in this chapter, I:

- halved the data rate used for H.264

- targeted the average bitrate without constraints (no 110 percent constrained VBR)

- used a key frame interval of 2 seconds for all files, and default alt-ref frame placement settings. Note that you can use the `-g` option for setting the key frame interval (`-g 60` for a key frame interval of 60), as well as the `-keyint_min` option to make sure that there's a key frame when you need it (`-keyint_min 60`).

Like I said, simple. Let's start by looking at the bitrate control options, and then transition to some of the more specific VP9 encoding parameters. Note that I'm going to demonstrate how to choose these options within several applications, and illustrate FFmpeg operation as part of this discussion as well.

Bitrate Control

A great place to start is with bitrate control. According to the FFmpeg wiki (bit.ly/vp9_brcontrol), VP9 supports at least five data rate control mechanisms—including variable bitrate, constant quality, constrained quality, constant bitrate, and lossless mode. Note that all of these modes are accessible from FFmpeg, but that different applications will provide access to some or all. For example, Sorenson Squeeze supports only two-pass CBR and VBR, while the free fnord WebM plugin for VP9 (fnordware.com/WebM) supports the four shown in Figure 12-5.

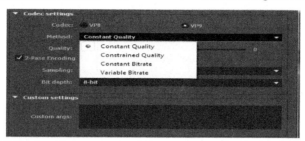

Figure 12-5. The four bitrate control techniques supported by the fnord WebM plugin.

Here's how the controls differ by technique.

Constant quality. Here you set a quality slider from 1 to 100. Note that according to the aforementioned wiki, the actual controls in FFmpeg range from 0 to 63, with lower values delivering higher quality. In FFmpeg, you would insert the desired CRF value, and then make sure to specify that the target bitrate is 0 (-b:v 0). Check the wiki (bit.ly/vp9_brcontrol) for other details. Here's the example from the wiki:

```
ffmpeg -i input.mp4 -c:v libvpx-vp9 -crf 10 -b:v 0
-c:a libvorbis output.webm
```

Most of the moving parts in the command line should be familiar to anyone with any FFmpeg experience. Specifically, you're calling ffmpeg, then identifying the input file (-i), telling FFmpeg to convert to VP9 (-c:v libvpx-vp9) for video and Vorbis for audio (-c:a libvorbis), and to output a .webm file. The critical parts of this operation is setting the CRF level (-crf 10) and setting the bitrate at 0 (-b:v 0).

Constrained quality. Here you set a quality level in the plugin as before, again on a scale from 1 to 100, but you also set a data rate that "caps" the data rate. This technique is also called Capped CRF, which we detail in Chapter 16. Interestingly, it's the technique that JW Player uses to encode VP9 delivered via its online video platform. Here's the relevant component of the example from the wiki:

```
-crf 10 -b:v 1000k
```

Obviously, you're telling FFmpeg to deliver quality at CRF level 10 without exceeding a video data rate of 1 Mbps. If the video is very simple, the data rate might be much lower than 1 Mbps. If it's complex, the encoding will likely be limited more by the bitrate control than the CRF level.

Constant bitrate. In the plugin, you choose a bitrate. Presumably behind the scenes, the encoder sets minimum and maximum settings at or near the target to minimize bitrate fluctuations. You learned how to do this in FFmpeg back in Chapter 8. Here's the wiki example:

```
-minrate 1M -maxrate 1M -b:v 1M
```

Here you're telling FFmpeg to target 1 Mbps, and to go no higher than 1 Mbps, or no lower than 1 Mbps. In other words, as close to CBR as possible.

Variable bitrate. In the plugin, you again set the target bitrate, with no minimum or maximum controls. As per the wiki, you simply set a target as follows:

```
-b:v 1M
```

FFmpeg will try to match this. The wiki doesn't say that you can set higher and lower limits with the `-minrate` and `-maxrate` commands, although it seems unlikely that you can't, given what we learned from the wiki in the constant bitrate section. Note that Google's VP9 executable does enable multiple quality and data rate controls, as you can see effectuated in the Sorenson Squeeze VP9 encoding interface in Figure 11-6.

I did experiment with the using the `-minrate` and `-maxrate` commands, and they definitely affected file quality. For example, these three experiments produced the noted PSNR scores.

- **Strict CBR.** `-minrate 1M -maxrate 1M -b:v 1M` PSNR: 37.96

- **Variable bitrate.** `-b:v 1M` PSNR: 37.99

- **200 percent constrained VBR.** `-minrate 500k -maxrate 2M -b:v 1M` PSNR: 38.03

While the PSNR differences are small, they are what you would expect: strict CBR the lowest, average data rate in the middle, and 200 percent constrained VBR the highest. The strict CBR file also had the lowest low—again, what you would expect. So it's very likely that these controls work as you would expect them to, although it's frustrating not being able to visualize the bitstream like you can with H.264 files in Bitrate Viewer or Telestream Switch.

Figure 11-6. Data rate/quality controls in Sorenson Squeeze.

The bottom line is that if you're concerned about the smooth delivery of your adaptive bitrate streams, and you're encoding your video with FFmpeg or even Google's encoder, you should experiment with the `-minrate` and especially `-maxrate` switches to limit stream variability.

Other Configuration Options

Table 12-4 shows the other options typically recommended by VP9 documentation or from other source. The first two sets of options, VOD Recommended and Best Quality (Slowest) are from the VP9 Encoding Guide available at bit.ly/vp9_guide1. The DASH column is available in a wiki page titled "Instructions to Playback Adaptive WebM Using DASH" (bit.ly/vp9_dash). The final column are the configuration options used by JW Player, which shared its encoding configuration with me in early 2016 for a Streaming Media article about VP9 (bit.ly/vp9_age1).

As you'll see, I spent most of my time testing the speed option, which controls the classic encoding time/encoding quality trade-off—with 0 being the longest, highest-quality option, and 4 being the fastest, lowest-quality option. Otherwise, I pretty much went with the options JW Player used, since I knew they had been rigorously tested before implementation.

	VOD Recommended	Best Quality (slowest)	DASH	JWPlayer
Threads	8	1	default	8
Speed (1rst/2nd pass)	4/1	4/0	default	4/2
Tile-Columns	6	0	4	6
Frame Parallel	1	0	1	1
Auto-Alt-Ref	1	1	default	1
Lag-In-Frames	25	25	default	25

Table 12-4. Other VP9 configuration options.

As mentioned previously, Google does not do a great job identifying when and where you should use the various options. Here's what I've been able to glean from different documents and encoding formulas.

- **Threads.** This allows the encoder to use multiple cores. While there's a minor quality hit, VP9 encoding is glacial without it.

- **Speed.** All encoders that specified speed used 4 for the first pass, and a lower value for the second pass. You'll see the quality/encoding time trade-off curve in a moment.

- **Tiles/columns.** With the threads command, this allows the encoder to use more than a single CPU core.

- **Frame parallel.** Here's what the VP9 Encoding Guide (bit.ly/vp9_guide) says about tile-column and frame parallel: "Turning off tile-columns and frame-parallel should give a small bump in quality."

- **-auto-alt-ref and -lag-in-frames.** These win my award for the most obtuse encoding configuration options ever (and I've seen a few). Here's the description from the VP8 Encode Parameter Guide (bit.ly/vp8_guide). "When `-auto-alt-ref` is enabled the default mode of operation is to either populate the buffer with a copy of the previous golden frame when this frame is updated, or with a copy of a frame derived from some point of time in the future (the choice is made automatically by the encoder). The `-lag-in-frames` parameter defines an upper limit on the number of frames into the future that the encoder can look.

Let's look at each encoding parameter in turn.

Threads

To test the impact of threads, I encoded twice—once with threads set at 1, once with threads set at 8. The output files were identical, with identical PSNR scores, but encoding with 8 threads cut encoding time by about 50 percent. I asked my contacts at Google about this and they replied:

> Currently our multi-threaded encoder does not compromise on quality and results are identical. For multi-core machines, definitely you should use multiple threads.

> However, when we encode on the Google cloud for YouTube, accounting is often done by cores, and if you are to optimize for the encode_cores x encode_time product, then using single threads would be the best.

So, if you're running a single encode on a multiple-core computer, always set threads to 8. If you're creating your own encoder that will run multiple encodes simultaneously, you should experiment with different settings to determine which produces the best performance.

Here's the syntax for setting threads:

```
-threads 8
```

Speed

Table 12-5 shows the PSNR values for our set of test files (less the Tutorial file, which failed to meet encoding targets) encoded at 1080p resolution. As you can see, 0 always delivered the best quality and 4 the worst, but the average difference was only 2.54 percent. Not a huge deal. The average difference was 2.96 percent at 720p—slightly higher but still pretty minor.

Speed - 1080p	4	3	2	1	0	Delta
Tears of Steel	39.85	40.01	40.73	40.86	41.12	3.19%
Sintel	38.45	38.69	39.25	39.37	39.62	3.06%
Big Buck Bunny	38.83	39.09	39.66	39.80	39.93	2.83%
Talking Head	43.36	43.48	44.08	44.22	44.30	2.17%
Freedom	40.55	40.79	41.26	41.49	41.74	2.92%
Haunted	41.33	41.45	41.86	41.98	42.05	1.75%
Screencam	43.20	43.76	43.79	43.94	44.02	1.88%
Average	40.80	41.04	41.52	41.66	41.83	2.54%

Table 12-5. Output quality by speed option.

Table 12-6 shows the encoding time to VP9 format at 1080p resolution.

	4	3	2	1	0
Tears of Steel	307	332	457	712	3422
Sintel	300	327	468	708	3535
Big Buck Bunny	231	257	416	604	2926
Talking Head	315	339	509	796	2703
Freedom	408	465	585	886	3796
Haunted	413	449	615	1038	4442
Screencam	120	106	218	290	1052
Average	299	325	467	719	3125

Table 12-6. Encoding time in seconds.

Figure 12-7 shows the encoding time/quality trade-off—although remember that from a quality perspective, the entire difference between 0 and 1 is the average quality difference of 2.54 percent shown in Table 12-5. This chart tells us that using a setting of 2 captures close to 75 percent of that qualitative difference, while adding about 50 percent to the encoding time from option 4 (467 average compared to 299). Option 1 takes you over the 75 percent threshold while more than doubling the encoding time from option 4 (719 average compared with 299). Option 0 looks like a bad investment unless encoding time is irrelevant.

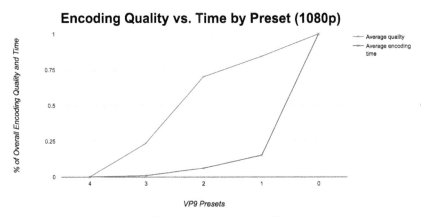

Figure 11-7. Encoding time/quality trade-off by VP9 preset.

To wrap this in a shiny bow for you, I would probably default to 2, but if I reached encoding capacity at that setting, and was forced to either buy another workstation or change to 3 or 4, I would change to 4. Even a "golden eye" viewer would have a hard time telling the difference between video with a PSNR of 40.80 compared to 41.83.

Note that most of the command strings that I reviewed used two pass encoding, with a speed setting of 4 for the first pass, and 0 to 2 for the second. Thus it appears pretty certain that scanning the file with a speed setting of 4 for the first pass doesn't degrade quality.

Here's how you set speed in the FFmpeg command string:

```
-speed 2
```

In a two-pass string, you would use a setting of 4 in the first pass, and 0 to 2 in the second.

Frame Parallel

I didn't experiment with this parameter because literally until the day before I shipped the book, the VP9 documents said, "Turning off tile-columns and frame-parallel should give a small bump in quality, but will most likely hamper decode performance severely." Google's corrections to its own documents just came too late for me to test this parameter.

Note that the default for frame parallel is enabled, so if you don't refer to this option in your command line script, it will be enabled. If you're the type who likes to wear a belt and suspenders (figuratively, of course), you would enable this in your command script using the following command:

```
-frame-parallel 1
```

To disable this option:

```
-frame-parallel 0
```

Tiles/Columns

Again, tiles/columns is another command that lets the encoder divide up the image and encode with multiple cores. Technically, you should customize this option by output resolution using this formula supplied by my Google contact.

> The way to figure this out is to take the width of the video, divide by 256, and see what power of 2 is at least as large as that. Mathematically, the effective parameter is: `tile_width = floor(log2(width/256)).`

> So:
> 320x180: 0
> 480x270: 0
> 640x360: 1
> 848x480: 1
> 960x540: 1
> 1280x720: 2
> 1920x1080: 2
> 2560x1440: 3
> 3840x2160: 3
> 8K: 4

Saving us all some spreadsheet time, he also noted, "Yes, it does not matter if the tile columns parameter is larger than what can be supported by the format. So using 4 will work for all."

So the bottom line is to use 4, and the encoder will step it down as needed. Given that the maximum setting appears to be 4, I have no idea why JW Player and the recommended VOD settings use 6, though it appears that you could use the US national deficit and the encoder would step it down to 4.

Here's the FFmpeg syntax:

```
-tile-columns 4
```

-auto-alt-ref

If you have no entry for `-auto-alt-ref`, the encoder defaults to a setting of 1, which delivered slightly higher quality than a setting of 0 in my tests. For example, with the Freedom video encoded at 720p, a setting of 1 delivered a PSNR of 39.44, while a setting of 0 delivered a PSNR of 39.17, a difference of 0.69 percent. Not a huge deal by any means, but unless you know something that I don't, I would always use a setting of 1. Again, you can do this directly by including the following in your command string:

```
-auto-alt-ref 1
```

Or, you can just leave the configuration option out. If you want to disable this configuration option—and again, I'm not sure why you would—include this in your command string.

```
-auto-alt-ref 0
```

-lag-in-frames

For `-lag-in-frames`, I asked my contact, "What is the default `-lag-in-frames` value? Does this make any difference? What are the trade-offs with values here (0 to 25)? All the recommendations in the VP9 encoding guide use 25. Should I just recommend using that?"

He replied:

> `-lag-in-frames` default is 25 if the parameter is not explicitly specified. We can reduce it to up to 16 with very little change in coding efficiency. Beyond that it starts affecting efficiency more since alt-ref frames cannot to used to their fullest potential. Note that `-lag-in-frames` needs memory to store lookahead frames. So for 4K or 8K, one can use smaller values to prevent memory issues.

So, I recommend going with 25 for all encodes up to 4K, then switching to 16. Here's how you configure this in your command string.

```
-lag-in-frames 25
```

Advice from the Stars

While writing the Streaming Media article "VP9 Comes of Age, But Is it Right for Everyone?", I spoke with JW Player's lead compression engineer, Pooja Madan (bit.ly/vp9_age1). Madan designed and implemented JW's VP9 encoding facility, after spending many, many hours experimenting and testing. In the article, she shared her top four VP9 encoding takeaways, which were:

1. Use two-pass encoding; one pass does not perform well.

2. With two-pass encoding, generate the first pass log for the largest resolution and then reuse it for the other resolutions. VP9 handles this gracefully.

3. While VP9 allows much larger CRF values, we noticed that CRF <33 speeds up the encoding process considerably without significant losses in file size savings.

4. You must use the "tile-columns" parameter in the second pass. This provides multi-threaded encoding and decoding at minor costs to quality.

Sample Scripts

Here are some sample two-pass encoding scripts. The top script was my all-inclusive, belts-and-suspenders script, which set all default configuration options at their default.

```
ffmpeg -y -iTOS_720p.mp4 -c:v libvpx-vp9 -pass 1 -b:v 1000K
-keyint_min 60 -g 60 -threads 8 -speed 4 -tile-columns 4
-auto-alt-ref 1 -frame-parallel 1 -f webm NUL && \

ffmpeg -iTOS_720p.mp4 -c:v libvpx-vp9 -pass 2 -b:v 1000K
-keyint_min 60 -g 60 -threads 8 -speed 2 -tile-columns 4
-auto-alt-ref 1 -lag-in-frames 25 -frame-parallel 1
-c:a libopus -b:a 128k -f webm TOS_720p_all.webm
```

In this script, I left out all references to default values (-auto-alt-ref, frame parallel) just to see if FFmpeg would apply the default settings. It did, and the two files were identical.

```
ffmpeg -y -i TOS_720p.mp4 -c:v libvpx-vp9 -pass 1
-b:v 1000K -keyint_min 60 -g 60 -threads 8 -speed 4
-tile-columns 4 -f webm NUL && \

ffmpeg -i TOS_720p.mp4 -c:v libvpx-vp9 -pass 2 -b:v 1000K
-keyint_min 60 -g 60 -threads 8 -speed 4 -tile-columns 4
-c:a libopus -b:a 128k -f webm TOS_720p_none.webm
```

Author's note: *I would like to thank Google's Matt Frost, Debargha Mukherjee, and Jai Krishnan for their tech read of this chapter, and for consistent support for this and other editorial efforts. I know you're busy guys, and I appreciate the bandwidth.*

Chapter 13: Choosing an ABR Technology

Figure 13-1. The transition from Flash to HTML5 is almost complete.

Up until now, we've learned all about encoding, but very little about actually delivering our encoded files. That's all about to change. In this chapter, you'll learn to how to choose the right technology to deliver to computers and notebooks, iOS and Android devices, OTT devices and smart TVs. This is an overview chapter, designed to help you understand the environment for each target device and the options available for adaptive bitrate (ABR) streaming to each. In Chapter 14, you'll learn how to configure your adaptive groups for the various ABR technologies. Then, in Chapter 15, you'll learn how to encode your files.

Specifically, in this chapter, you will learn:

- the fundamentals of HTML5 delivery, including Media Source Extensions (MSE), Encrypted Media Extensions (EME), and Dynamic Adaptive Streaming over HTTP (DASH)

- technology alternatives for creating browser-based players

- technology options for iOS and Android platforms

- technology options for some OTT devices (Roku, Apple TV, Chromecast), and some smart TVs.

Delivering to Computers via HTML5

We've been hearing that Flash is dead since Apple introduced the iPad back in 2010. Yet even today, as I write this in December 2016, Flash is still the predominant technology used by advertising-supported premium websites. This is largely because most ad servers that supply these advertisements are still using Flash—although by mid-2017, almost all will have cut over to HTML5. If you're not advertising supported, all the plumbing necessary to deliver ABR video via HTML5 is now largely in place.

What is HTML5?

To understand the transition from Flash to HTML5, it's worth discussing the two generations of HTML5 support. First, though, let's describe what HTML5 actually is.

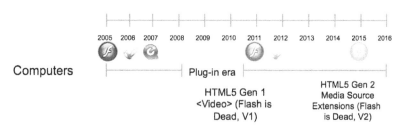

Figure 13-2. The transition from plugin-based technologies to HTML5.

Figure 13-2 shows the transition from plugin-based technologies like Flash, Silverlight, and QuickTime to HTML5. You see the plugins on the left, in full force and color, and slowly fading in 2011-12, and almost gone in 2015-16. Yeah, I did that all by myself! Pretty neat, huh?

Anyway (excuse the lame attempt at humor; writing a technical book is about as much fun as it looks), in the plugin-based world, the plugins supplied the necessary decoder and player to decode and play the video file. For example, Flash has included H.264 playback since 2007, so any browser with Flash installed could play H.264 video. Since H.264 is royalty encumbered, Adobe could pay the royalty once a year, and everyone with Flash could play H.264 videos.

The downside of plugins is that you have to install and update them, and they often may present security risks. They often crash as well.

The key benefit of plugins is instant reach. H.264 has dominated the codec landscape since 2007 because once Adobe added it to Flash, H.264 was playable in more than 98 percent of computers within six months or so. Conversely, reach is the main problem with HTML5. The browser has to supply both the player and the decoder. And all browsers have to supply playback and associated services in a sufficiently consistent way to allow developers deploying HTML5 to use one codebase for all browsers. Also complicating reach is the fact that while users typically update plugins like Flash pretty frequently, many users in locked-down environments like government, educational, and large corporates can't update to the latest browser, in which case your HTML5 delivery strategy flat-out doesn't work.

Beyond these issues, instead of one company to point your finger at if your video doesn't play (Adobe), it could be any of five or six different browser developers. Instead of technology advancement in one fell swoop, HTML5 means it's advancement according to the priorities set by each browser developer. As a prominent example, Mozilla Firefox and the Opera browser never licensed H.264 playback—although Apple, Google, and Microsoft all did. Ultimately, both Firefox and Opera found a way to use H.264 playback from the Windows/Mac/iOS/Android operating systems. But for a while, developers had to produce both WebM and H.264 files to support all browsers via HTML5. More recently, Microsoft added new features to Internet Explorer 11 to support HTML5—but only for Windows 8 users, leaving the vastly higher number of those using Windows 7 out in the cold.

Even today, the reality of HTML5 means that not all target users can or have updated to a browser that fully supports the latest HTML5 features. For this reason, any HTML5 deployment should plan for Flash fallback, or the ability to revert to Flash if the target viewer's browser doesn't support the required HTML5 features. Fortunately, this isn't difficult.

With this background, let's look at the two generations of HTML5.

HTML5 Generation 1

When Apple launched the iPad, it didn't support Flash. It depended upon HTML5 for H.264 video playback, which Apple supplied in the Safari browser. This first generation of HTML5 support was based upon the video tag shown in Figure 13-3.

```
<!DOCTYPE html>
<html>
  <head>
    <meta http-equiv="Content-Type" content="text/html; charset=UTF-8">
    <!--<meta http-equiv="X-UA-Compatible" content="IE=Edge"/>-->
    <title>Disney</title>
  </head>
  <body>
    <video preload="auto" width="640"
           height="360" poster="Disney_html.vs-1.jpg" controls>
      <!-- mp4 is for I E 9, I E 10, S a f a r i -->
      <source src="Disney.html.mp4" type="video/mp4"/>
      <!-- webm for F i r e f o x, C h r o m e -->
      <source src="Disney.html.webm" type="video/webm"/>
      <!-- swf and mp4 is for older browsers that support F l a s h 9 -->
```

Figure 13-3. The video tag that largely comprised HTML5 Gen 1.

In the HTML shown in the figure, the video tag tells the browser that it's in charge of playing the video. This particular deployment included both MP4 and WebM files, and Flash fallback. As indicated by the comments in the figure, the MP4 file is for Internet Explorer 9 and 10 and Safari, the WebM file for Chrome and Firefox, and Flash for all older browsers. Note that Chrome could play the H.264 file as well, and that the notations don't dictate which file each browser plays. Rather, the browser reads the code top to bottom. If it can play the H.264 file, it will; if not, it will read down a line. If it can play the WebM file, it will; if not, it will read down another line and fall back to Flash.

This is a simple and elegant approach, and it worked well for single-file playback. However, this first generation of HTML5 didn't support live streaming, adaptive streaming, digital rights management (DRM), captioning, or advertising. For this reason, advertising-supported sites couldn't use this first version of HTML5 or those that required DRM, like Netflix and other premium content distributors.

Of course, of all websites that deliver video over the Internet, networks and premium content distributors are but a very small percentage. So despite these deficits, this version of HTML5 was very widely deployed by sites that could do so.

In April 2015, Streaming Media surveyed its readership for an article titled "Encoding 2020: Experts Predict the Future of Video Encoding" (bit.ly/encode2020). In the survey, we asked readers to designate the percentage of streams played back on computers via HTML5, and what they expected that percentage to be in 2020. We segmented the responses based upon those spending more than $500,000 on encoding each year, and those spending less than $50,000 per year. We color-coded the Change column. Any negative change up to and including -50 percent is colored in yellow; beyond that, it's colored in red. All positive changes up to and including 100 percent are colored in blue, while those exceeding 100 percent are colored in green.

Flash vs. HTML5	2015			2020			Change		
	All	$500K+	$50K-	All	$500K+	$50K-	All	$500K+	$50K-
Flash	53%	52%	52%	19%	22%	19%	-63%	-58%	-64%
HTML5	47%	48%	48%	81%	78%	81%	71%	63%	70%

Figure 13-4. HTML5 adoption in 2015 and 2020.

It's a long introduction, but what was startling to me was that in 2015, 47 percent of desktop-targeted streams were being delivered via HTML5, which is before the advancements in HTML5 Generation 2 became pervasive. Given the constraints—no adaptive, DRM, captions, or advertising—that was a surprisingly large number. Before you uninstall Flash, however, note that our respondents predicted that they would still deliver 19 percent of their streams via Flash in 2020. Obviously our readers believed that the necessity for Flash fallback would remain a reality for some time to come.

> **Note:** *I'm spending most of my time in this book on ABR delivery. If you're interested in learning how to support HTML5 via a single file, you can check out my tutorial "Supporting HTML5 with Flash Fallback in Sorenson Squeeze 9" at bit.ly/HTML5Gen1. This includes an embedded video showing how Sorenson Squeeze can produce the files and HTML code to simplify this process.*

HTML5 Generation 2

Starting in 2015 or so, the components of HTML5 Generation 2 started to become available. These new components promised feature parity with Flash, including adaptive streaming, live streaming, DRM, captioning, and advertising support. To understand HTML5 Gen 2, you have to understand the five components discussed next. It's a bit of a deep dive, but once you understand what these components do and how they fit into the bigger picture, everything will start to make sense. Let's start with Media Source Extensions.

Media Source Extensions (MSE)

MSE is a World Wide Web Consortium (W3C) HTML Working Group specification for a JavaScript interface to play back media data within a browser. It's more functional than the video tag. Browsers and devices that support MSE can play chunks of video (or byte-range requests within a single file), which enables the adaptive delivery of live and video-on-demand (VOD) content.

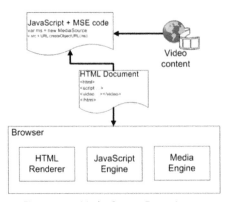

Figure 13-5. Media Source Extensions.

As you can see in Figure 13-5, MSE receives the video data and parses it for playback by the browser's media playback engine. MSE isn't a codec or playback engine; it's more of a converter of incoming live and adaptive streams for the browser's media engine to play. If you remember "MSE lets browsers play live and VOD video with captions and DRM," you've got the key takeaway.

> **Note:** *I'm not going to go into detail about DRM technologies in this book. For an introduction to DRM, check out the web article titled "What Is DRM?" (bit.ly/whatisDRM).*

Dynamic Adaptive Streaming over HTTP (DASH)

DASH is an MPEG standard that defines how to stream adaptively over HTTP. Like all HTTP-based ABR technologies, the standard includes both a file format for packing the files and specifications for the metadata file (.mpd) used by DASH players to choose and retrieve the ABR segments. Note that DASH is codec agnostic. You can encode H.264, HEVC, VP9 and other codecs into a DASH container.

DASH is one of the formats commonly recognized by MSE-based video players, but not the only ABR format. For example, multiple technologies allow MSE to play back HTTP Live Streaming (HLS) content as well as DASH. You'll learn how DASH and HLS work in the next chapter. To get the gold star for this acronym, you just have to remember "DASH is a standards-based ABR format that works with MSE."

Tip: *To learn more about the DASH standard, check out "What is MPEG DASH?" (bit.ly/WhatisDASH).*

To avoid irritating the finance types in your company, note that in November 2016, patent licensing agency MPEG LA announced that DASH would come with a price tag of $0.05 per decoder or initiator (essentially an app), but only after you ship 100,000 of either. In addition, for the first year of the license, players loaded temporarily during playback (like JW Player) are excluded. You can read more about this at bit.ly/cash4dash (hey, I do what I can to make these easy to remember).

If your videos are getting more than 100,000 views a year, this cost might be a factor in pushing you towards HLS or other non-royalty-bearing alternative. This is a fast-developing story with far-reaching significance. If you're on the fence with DASH, check streamingmedia.com for the latest news and interpretations.

Encrypted Media Extensions (EME)

EME is another JavaScript API that enables HTML5-based DRM by allowing the browser to communicate directly with DRM licensing servers, a function that previously was performed by the plugin. EME works by incorporating what's called a content decryption module (CDM) into the browser, device, or mobile operating system, which allows the browser or device to communicate directly with the license server.

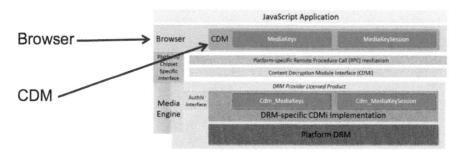

Figure 13-6. The CDM is baked into the browser.

As shown in Figure 13-6, the CDM is actually baked into the browser. It's not a component that can be downloaded or updated after the browser or operating system is installed (except in Firefox). The key takeaway here is that "EME lets browsers handle DRM."

As we'll discuss in a moment, each browser or operating system supports, at most, two DRMs. For example, Microsoft Edge and Internet Explorer support Microsoft PlayReady (and not Widevine), while Google Chrome supports Widevine (and not PlayReady). Safari and iOS devices support only FairPlay. This means that if you want your DRM-protected video to play on more than one browser or platform in a single HTML5 package, that package must support multiple DRMs. So that's where Common Encryption comes in.

Common Encryption (CENC)

CENC is an MPEG standard that specifies encryption and key mapping methods used inside one of two formats: the ISO base media file format (ISOBMFF), discussed next, and MPEG transport streams. Essentially, CENC is the standard that enables multiple DRM technologies to be stored and deployed inside of a single file to decrypt the same content. CENC is absolutely essential for supporting multiple DRM technologies with the same content, which is essential to the HTML5 delivery scheme where each target platform supports a different DRM technology. In short, "CENC lets a single HTML5 package support multiple DRMs."

ISO base media file format (ISOBMFF)

ISOBMFF is another MPEG standard that defines how various components—including audio, video, captions, and DRM—are packed into a single file. So, "ISOBMFF is the standard format for packaging and delivering all this stuff together."

Pulling It All Together

Figure 13-7 pulls these concepts together into a neat little bow. On the left, you can see the media content is packed into an ISOBMFF file, which contains DASH-formatted content and multiple DRM technologies stored using CENC. These ISOBMFF files are delivered to the browser via the content delivery network. Once there, EME communicates with the various license servers necessary to decrypt and play the content. Not shown is that the audio/video content stored in DASH format are parsed in MSE for decoding in the browser's media engine.

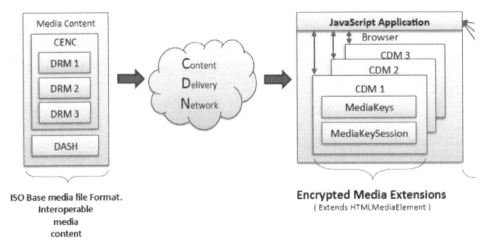

Figure 13-7. How HTML5 works with multiple DRM technologies with CENC and EME.

So, those are the components and how they all fit together. Now let's look at how many of these are currently supported.

MSE/EME: Where Do We Stand?

Table 13-1 shows the current status of browser support for HTML5 Gen 1, plus the two main components of Gen 2, MSE and EME. I grabbed these browser share numbers from netmarketshare.com in October 2016, including all browsers with a share above 0.3 percent or so. This accounts for about 91 percent of all browsers, and it's tough to tell what to assume about the remaining 9 percent.

BROWSER VERSION	Browser Share (1)	HTML5 Gen 1 (video tag)	Media Source Extensions (2)	Encrypted Media Extensions (2)	DRM - DASH
Chrome 23-41	1.88%	1.88%	1.88%	No	Plug-in
Chrome 42+	48.81%	48.81%	48.81%	48.81%	Widevine
Firefox 42+	6.77%	6.77%	No	No	Primetime/ Widevine
Microsoft Edge 12	5.16%	5.16%	5.16%	5.16%	PlayReady
Microsoft Internet Explorer 10.0	1.48%	1.48%	No	No	Plug-in
Microsoft Internet Explorer 11.0	17.73%	17.73%	17.73%	3.55%	PlayReady
Microsoft Internet Explorer 8.0 and earlier	4.22%	No	No	No	Plug-in
Microsoft Internet Explorer 9.0	4.83%	4.83%	No	No	Plug-in
Total	**90.88%**	**86.66%**	**73.58%**	**57.52%**	

Table 13-1. Support for HTML5 Gen 1, MSE, and EME.

Regarding HTML5 Gen 1 support, all browsers except Internet Explorer version 8 and earlier versions support the video tag, or 86.66 percent. The Media Source Extensions has a greater share than the Encrypted Media Extensions because Internet Explorer 11 only supports MSE in Windows 8.1, which has about a 20 percent share of non-Windows Edge users. In addition, Chrome versions prior to version 23 don't support EME.

What does this tell you? Two things. First, as mentioned previously, you'll have to support multiple DRMs to deploy with HTML5—at the very least PlayReady and Widevine, plus FairPlay for iOS and Safari. Second, as MSE/EME support are nowhere near pervasive, once again, you shouldn't plot an HTML5-based delivery approach without fallback to Flash.

> **Note:** *One of the best sources for identifying which platforms and browsers support MSE/EME is "Optimal Adaptive Streaming Formats MPEG-DASH & HLS Segment Length" at bit.ly/bitm_HTML5.*

Working with EME and Multiple DRMs

In a plugin-based world, most premium content distributors used a single DRM. To successfully distribute via HTML5 you'll have to support multiple DRMs. As you've read, multiple DRMs are technically supported in EME/CENC, so the issue becomes finding a supplier. Table 13-2 includes multiple companies that supply multiple DRMs, so hopefully provides a good starting point.

Company	Microsoft PlayReady	Google Widevine	Adobe Access	Apple FairPlay	Marlin	Other
Adobe Primetime DRM (Q4 2016)	Yes	Yes	Yes	Yes	No	No
Azure	Yes	Modular	No	No	No	NA
BuyDRM	Yes	Modular	No	Yes	Yes	Verimatrix, Windows Media
Cisco VideoGuard Everywhere	Yes	Yes	No	Yes	No	
DRMToday	Yes	Modular/ Classic	Yes	Yes	Yes	CMLA-OMA
EZDRM	Yes	Modular/ Classic	Yes	Yes	No	Windows Media
ExpressPlay	Yes	Yes	No	Yes	Yes	NA
Verimatrix	Yes	Yes	Yes	Yes	Yes	VCAS
Vualto DRM	Yes	Yes	Yes	Yes	Yes	NA

Table 13-2. Suppliers of multiple DRM technologies.

Going Forward with HTML5

OK, you get it; it's time to embrace HTML5 with Flash fallback. Now what?

The first step is to choose a development path for your HTML5 player. Unless you've got a huge budget, I recommend using an off-the-shelf player as a starting point. The usual suspects in this product category include JW Player, Bitmovin, castLabs, OpenTelly, Squadeo, Viblast, and several others. There are also some open-source alternatives like Video.js and dash.js.

I am not a programmer so can't offer much insight into which alternative is best. In the article "HTML5 Comes of Age: It's Finally Time to Tell Flash Good-bye" (bit.ly/FlashGoodbye), I present three mini case studies from Bitmovin, castLabs, and OpenTelly, which might be a good starting point if you're unfamiliar with the options.

This section ends with this brief list of factors to consider when choosing an off-the-shelf player:

- whether you have to transcode your library to support the player

- the number of required output formats

- the ability to fall back to Flash or Silverlight on unsupported browsers (and whether the player can transmux)

- supported DRM technologies

- breadth of support for browsers, mobile platforms, OTT boxes and appliances, and smart TVs—whether direct or via software development kits

- support for advertising insertion and other required features.

Your choice of off-the-shelf player will dictate which ABR format you use. This will likely be DASH or HLS, but it could also be Smooth Streaming if your existing files are encoded into that format. As you can see in Figure 13-8, as of the end of 2016, HLS is by far the most widely deployed ABR format, with Smooth Streaming second, and DASH third.

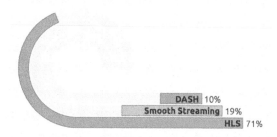

Figure 13-8. ABR format market share for 2015.

This data comes from Encoding.com's "2016 Global Media Format Report," which summarizes all encodes performed in 2015 (bit.ly/ecmf2016). In the document, encoding.com reports that most Smooth Streaming content is produced for Xbox and other gaming consoles.

Although DASH gets all the hype, HLS gets most of the play—primarily because it's the only format that can play on both iOS and Android devices, as well as in the browser via MSE. Otherwise, if you encode in DASH format for the desktop, you'll either have to deliver your iOS videos with a DASH-compatible app, or you'll have to supply HLS-encoded video as well as DASH—doubling your encoding costs. We'll talk more about strategies for supporting multiple formats in the next chapter. Again, a pretty stiff royalty on DASH announced by MPEG LA in November 2016 may convince many high-volume users to switch to or keep using HLS.

Choosing a Codec for Browser-based Delivery

This is an interesting subject. As of late 2016, I know of exactly two producers that are distributing VP9 adaptively to their viewers: YouTube (Figure 13-9) and JW Player. I know that Netflix is looking at doing the same thing, but am not sure if it actually pulled the trigger.

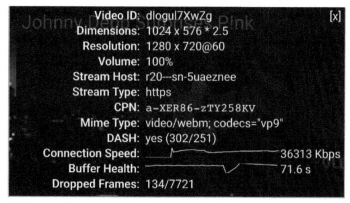

Figure 13-9. YouTube distributes VP9 encoded video in a DASH container. That `DASH: yes` *indicator could cost YouTube $30 million per year thanks to the new DASH royalty.*

Although H.264 is the knee-jerk choice for multiple-screen ABR delivery, as we learned last chapter, VP9 can produce the same quality at a much lower data rate. VP9 playback is available in Chrome, Firefox, Edge, and Opera—or about 60 percent of all browsers—as well as Android. You'd have to encode streams in H.264 format for older versions of Internet Explorer and Safari, but if you're pushing sufficient volumes, the bandwidth savings might be well worth the cost. That said, if you're looking for one codec for multiple-screen delivery, H.264 is it.

Encoding for Browser-based Playback

In the next section, we'll discuss encoding for mobile, where you'll have to pay attention to configuration options like profile and level. When encoding for computers, these aren't concerns, since browsers can playback any profile or level of H.264 video. Of course, if you want to create one set of streams for all target devices, you'll need to consider the profiles and levels used for your mobile devices.

As far as I know, there's no VP9-related browser playback limitation akin to profiles and levels, so you're OK there if you go with VP9. If and when browsers start to support HEVC, you'll have to worry about whether the browser supports the Main or Main 10 profile, but that's an issue for another day.

Quick Summary: HTML5

1. Generation 2 gives HTML5 parity with Flash, but you'll need Flash fallback to support the full universe of target users.

2. Media Source Extensions are compatible with DASH- and HLS-formatted video. Your choice will probably be dictated by the off-the-shelf player that you select.

3. If you're protecting your content with DRM, you'll need to support multiple DRM technologies to reach your targets. Fortunately, you'll have multiple suppliers to choose from.

4. Although you can use VP9 or HEVC in your DASH-formatted streams, H.264 is the only codec that plays on all relevant platforms.

5. When encoding H.264 for computer-based playback, you can use any profile and any level.

You've conquered browser-based videos; now let's move to mobile.

Distributing to Mobile

There are two ways to deliver to mobile: browser or app. When you deliver via an app, you can use pretty much any ABR technology you would like. When you deliver in the browser, you have to use a technology supported by the browser.

On the iOS platform, your only browser option is HTTP Live Streaming (HLS) using H.264. Android has a much more confusing mix of options, as shown in Figure 13-10. As you can see, different Android versions support different codecs and ABR technologies.

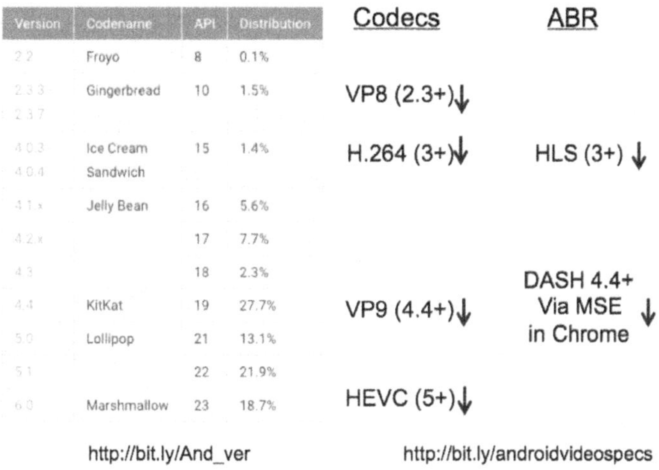

Version	Codename	API	Distribution	Codecs	ABR
2.2	Froyo	8	0.1%		
2.3.3	Gingerbread	10	1.5%	VP8 (2.3+)↓	
2.3.7					
4.0.3	Ice Cream	15	1.4%	H.264 (3+)↘	HLS (3+) ↓
4.0.4	Sandwich				
4.1.x	Jelly Bean	16	5.6%		
4.2.x		17	7.7%		
4.3		18	2.3%		DASH 4.4+
4.4	KitKat	19	27.7%	VP9 (4.4+)↓	Via MSE ↓
5.0	Lollipop	21	13.1%		in Chrome
5.1		22	21.9%		
6.0	Marshmallow	23	18.7%	HEVC (5+)↓	

http://bit.ly/And_ver   http://bit.ly/androidvideospecs

Figure 13-10. Codec and ABR options for Android.

Although Android has supported HLS since version 3.0, the quality of that support was initially quite poor, with a range of issues that included crashing, full-screen videos causing a restart, aspect ratio problems, and seeking issues. Encoding.com does a great job cataloguing these issues at bit.ly/droid_hls_probs. Because of these problems, DASH is quickly becoming the preferred format to distribute to Android clients, although the penetration of DASH-compatible versions is only 81.4 percent as of late 2016.

Note that you can also distribute VP9 and HEVC to Android clients via DASH, although I'm not aware of any publishers actually doing this. YouTube might be distributing VP9 to Android, but they haven't said. I know that JW Player has looked at this issue, but I don't know if it's decided one way or the other.

The bottom line for mobile is that HLS is your only option for a single format that will play on iOS and Android devices in the browser—although you may experience playback problems on older Android versions. DASH will not play in Safari, and is compatible with just more than 80 percent of Android devices as of December 2016. If you distribute to an app, you can use HLS or DASH.

Common Media Application Format (CMAF)

As you'll learn more about in the next chapter, there are two container formats used by ABR technologies: MPEG-2 transport streams, which is what is used in HLS, and the fragmented MP4 container format (fMP4), which is used by DASH, Smooth Streaming, and Adobe's HTTP Dynamic Streaming (HDS). A single package in fMP4 can serve DASH, Smooth Streaming, and HDS clients with separate manifest files. These are very small text files, so it creates little additional storage costs. However, you can't deliver files stored in fMP4 to HLS clients, you have to transmux them to MPEG-2 transport streams first.

At its Worldwide Developers Conference 2016, Apple announced that HLS would support fMP4 files in iOS 10 as well as tvOS and macOS. Specifically, Apple agreed to support CMAF, which is an MPEG standard for segmented media delivery formalized as MPEG-A Part 19, or ISO/IEC 23000-19. CMAF uses the ISOBMFF container with CENC. It supports H.264, HEVC, and other codecs, as well as WebVTT and IMSC-1 captioning. For compatibility, CMAF can be called by both HLS playlists (.m3u8 files) and DASH manifest files (.mpd files).

For HLS delivery, CMAF will replace files currently packaged in the MPEG-2 container format. For DASH, CMAF will supplant files currently packaged as vanilla ISOBMFF files, a relatively minor change. If you're distributing files to computers, Android, and HLS devices, you should be able to standardize on the CMAF format and use different manifest files for the different target clients. But only if you're distributing without DRM.

That's because CMAF enables two incompatible common encryption modes: cipher block chaining (CBC) for Apple's FairPlay DRM technology, and counter (CTR) mode for PlayReady, Widevine, and other DRMs. Content encrypted with CBC can't be decrypted by PlayReady and Widevine-compatible clients, while content encrypted with CTR can't be decrypted by FairPlay clients. So if you want to use CMAF to deliver protected content to iOS and everywhere else, you'll need two separate sets of files—just like now.

Even if DRM isn't an issue, if you've standardized on HLS for all of your streams, it's probably too early to change over. Not all HLS-compatible devices, or even iOS devices, will be field upgradeable, so you'll have to assess how many of these clients you'll strand when you switch over. Plus, in many cases, converting over to CMAF will require a complete library transmux from HLS to fMP4. This should be relatively simple if you saved the .mp4 files before converting them to HLS. If not, you'll need to find an HLS-to-CMAF converter. While I'm sure one is out there, I haven't run across it yet. In short, converting from HLS to CMAF will be a hassle, and you should probably wait for a good reason to do so.

Adaptive Streaming to OTT Devices

By OTT devices, I mean devices that you buy and install yourself in your living room, not the set-top boxes supplied by cable or satellite vendors. Figure 13-11 shows the US market share of the major players, with Roku in the lead with 49 percent, followed by Chromecast (22 percent), Amazon Fire TV (16 percent), and Apple TV (12 percent).

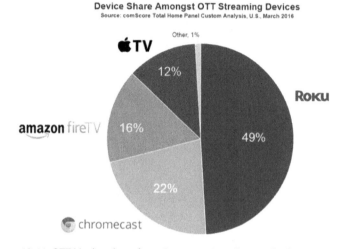

Figure 13-11. OTT Market share from Comscore, March 2016 (bit.ly/mar_16_ott).

Table 13-3 shows ABR support among the top four devices, with Apple the most restrictive. You can track down details like captioning and DRM support at the bit.ly URLs shown next to the platform name. Interestingly, Apple has already updated its Apple TV spec to include CMAF.

Platform	Smooth Streaming	HLS	DASH
OTT Platforms			
Roku (bit.ly/encode_roku)	Yes	Yes	Yes
Apple TV (bit.ly/AppleTV_recs)	No	Yes	No
ChromeCast (bit.ly/Chromecast_media)	Yes	Yes	Yes
Amazon Fire TV (bit.ly/Firetv_media)	Yes	Yes	Yes

Table 13-3. ABR format support by OTT device.

H.264 is the universal format for these devices, although the Roku 4 and Roku 4 TV units support both HEVC and VP9.

Adaptive Streaming to Smart TVs

The most recent market share stats I could find for smart TVs were BI Intelligence's numbers for 2015, grabbed from a SlideShare presentation (Figure 13-13). Unfortunately, all the companies don't do an equal job of documenting which ABR formats they support.

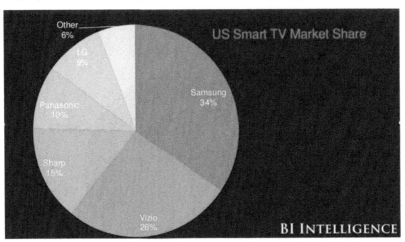

Figure 13-12. 2015 US market share for smart TVs (bit.ly/2015_STV_MS).

Samsung does a fabulous job in this regard—a model for the other companies, which may be why Samsung leads the market. As you can see in Table 13-4, Samsung supports all three major ABR technologies via Tizen, its smart TV OS. Despite searching for details on Vizio and Sharp multiple times, I've never been able to unearth details regarding their media support.

Platform	Smooth Streaming	HLS	DASH
Smart TVs			
Samsung (bit.ly/Tizen_spec)	Yes	Yes	Yes
Panasonic, LG, Toshiba (bit.ly/STA_spec)	Yes	Yes	Yes
Hybrid TV (bit.ly/HbbTV_201)	No	No	Yes

Table 13-4. ABR format support by smart TV platform.

Panasonic, LG, and Toshiba are all members of the Smart TV Alliance, which means their TVs support HLS, DASH, and Smooth Streaming (bit.ly/STA_spec). For completeness, I've included the European spec for the Hybrid Broadcast Broadband TV (HbbTV), which tends to control the features of smart TVs in Europe. As you can see, the standard only supports DASH.

> **Note:** The three top gaming platforms are the Sony PlayStation, Microsoft Xbox, and Nintendo Wii. I couldn't find ABR compatibility specs for any of them, but Wowza recommends distributing HLS to PlayStation devices, and Smooth Streaming to Xbox devices (bit.ly/wowza_game).

Summary

Here are the key takeaways regarding which ABR technology to use.

- **Computers/Notebooks.** Can be either HLS or DASH. Your choice of off-the-shelf player will likely control this decision.

- **Mobile.** HLS can play in the browser on iOS and Android devices, however imperfectly on the latter. DASH plays in Chrome on about 80 percent of Android devices (as of December 2016), but won't play in Safari. If you create an app for either platform, you can use either technology.

- **OTT.** Apple TV plays HLS only. Most others play HLS/DASH/Smooth Streaming.

- **Smart TVs.** Varies by platform.

- **Game Consoles.** Varies by platform.

OK, now you know which ABR format plays on the various platforms. Next chapter you learn how to formulate and configure your ABR group.

Chapter 14: Configuring Your Encoding Ladder

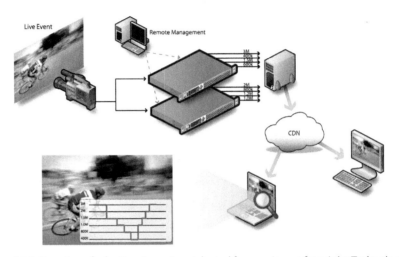

Figure 14-1. Overview of adaptive streaming. Adapted from an image from Inlet Technologies.

In the last chapter, you learned how to choose the right adaptive bitrate (ABR) technology for your target playback devices. In this chapter, you'll learn how ABR technologies work, and how to configure the streams in your encoding ladder, or the group of files you prepare to distribute adaptively to the various clients that you serve with your video. Specifically, in this chapter, you will learn:

- how ABR technologies work

- whether it's best to have a single encoding ladder for all targets, or a target-specific ladder for each target

- how to choose the number of streams, and their resolutions and data rates

- ABR-specific options to consider like bitrate control, key frame interval, and audio parameters.

Next chapter you'll learn how to actually encode the ABR streams using both static and dynamic packaging.

How ABR Technologies Work

At a high level, adaptive streaming technologies work as shown in Figure 14-1. A live or video-on-demand (VOD) source is encoded into multiple streams. These streams are distributed to different clients based upon available bandwidth, compatibility, and playback horsepower. In the early days of adaptive streaming, a dedicated server was required to communicate with the player, change streams, and dole out the necessary bits when required. These servers cost money, which increased costs, and had limited capacity, which limited audience size.

Since then, the market has transitioned to HTTP-based technologies like Apple's HTTP Live Streaming (HLS), Microsoft's Smooth Streaming, Adobe's HTTP Dynamic Streaming (HDS), and the Dynamic Adaptive Streaming over HTTP (DASH) standard. All these technologies can be deployed from standard HTTP origin servers.

All these technologies work similarly. During encoding, you produce media files and manifest files. As shown in Figure 14-2, the .ts MPEG-2 transport stream files are the media files. As you see, they're segmented into small, individual files—usually between two and 10 seconds long.

The .m3u8 files are the manifest files. Note that there are three streams in our example, and four manifest files. The master manifest file, on the left in the figure, points to the locations of the manifest files for each stream, which point to the location of each chunk on the HTTP server. You link to the master manifest file on your server, and the player takes it from there.

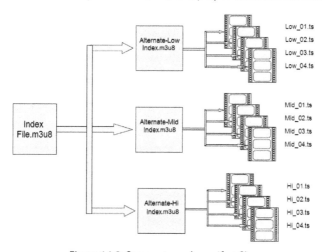

Figure 14-2. Segments and manifest files.

During playback, the player retrieves the master manifest file, and then the first segment from the first stream listed in the manifest file. The player monitors a number of heuristics including buffer condition, dropped frames, and the like, and determines when a stream change, up or down, is required. When a stream change is necessary, the player checks back with the master manifest file, finds the location of the appropriate stream, and retrieves the next segment.

Since the player is in charge of all operation, HTTP-based adaptive streaming technologies can operate on standard web servers, eliminating both the cost and the capacity issues of dedicated streaming servers. In addition, because they distribute standard HTTP segments, these can be stored in the caching mechanism used by many organizations and content delivery networks (CDNs), reducing bandwidth costs and improving quality of service. For all these reasons, the market has almost completely transitioned to HTTP-based adaptive technologies.

From Segments to Byte-range Requests

Note that when HTTP-based adaptive streaming originated, each file in the encoding ladder had to be broken into separate chunks, usually two to 10 seconds long, which created an administrative and storage nightmare. Since then, all ABR technologies have incorporated the ability to work with a single source video file in the correct ABR format, retrieving segments from that file via byte-range requests from the player. Instead of retrieving a specific chunk, the player retrieves a specific segment from the single file, simplifying file creation and distribution.

File	Size	Type
OutFile_2014-09-09_171205_DASH-264-HD_FhG_AVC_3000k.mpd	742	mpd-file
OutFile_2014-09-09_171205_DASH-264-HD_FhG_AVC_3000k.mp4	269,548,878	mp4-file
OutFile_2014-09-09_171205_DASH-264-HD_FhG_AVC_2500k.mpd	742	mpd-file
OutFile_2014-09-09_171205_DASH-264-HD_FhG_AVC_2500k.mp4	225,052,199	mp4-file
OutFile_2014-09-09_171205_DASH-264-HD_FhG_AVC_2000k.mpd	742	mpd-file
OutFile_2014-09-09_171205_DASH-264-HD_FhG_AVC_2000k.mp4	180,555,202	mp4-file
OutFile_2014-09-09_171205_DASH-264-HD_FhG_AVC_1500k.mpd	742	mpd-file
OutFile_2014-09-09_171205_DASH-264-HD_FhG_AVC_1500k.mp4	135,846,805	mp4-file
OutFile_2014-09-09_171205_DASH-264-HD_FhG_AAC_2ch_96k.mpd	725	mpd-file
OutFile_2014-09-09_171205_DASH-264-HD_FhG_AAC_2ch_96k.mp4	10,836,315	mp4-file
OutFile_2014-09-09_171205_DASH-264-HD_FhG_AAC_2ch_64K.mpd	725	mpd-file
OutFile_2014-09-09_171205_DASH-264-HD_FhG_AAC_2ch_64K.mp4	7,899,482	mp4-file
OutFile_2014-09-09_171205_DASH-264-HD_FhG_AAC_2ch_48K.mpd	725	mpd-file
OutFile_2014-09-09_171205_DASH-264-HD_FhG_AAC_2ch_48K.mp4	6,431,067	mp4-file
OutFile_2014-09-09_171205_DASH-264-HD_FhG_AAC_2ch_32K.mpd	725	mpd-file
OutFile_2014-09-09_171205_DASH-264-HD_FhG_AAC_2ch_32K.mp4	4,962,650	mp4-file
DASH-264.mpd	2,656	mpd-file

Figure 14-3. DASH manifest and video files.

You can see this in Figure 14-3, which shows a group of files prepared for delivery via DASH. The master manifest file linked to the web page is on the very bottom. Each MP4 stream is a complete stream, rather than individual segments, and the individual MPD files use byte-range requests to point to individual segments within the file.

Again, all HTTP-based technologies operate similarly. You have to create the format specific media files, and the manifest files. From a workflow perspective, most people distinguish between encoding and packaging. During encoding, the individual MP4 streams are encoded. During packaging, the segments are created from this stream, if required, along with the necessary manifest files.

The packaging process is also referred to as transmuxing, which is a "lightweight" operation that many servers can perform on the fly. As we discussed back in Chapter 1, transmuxing occurs when you change the container format of the file, but don't transcode. That's what you're seeing in Figure 14-4. A single set of files is going into the Wowza Streaming Cloud, where they are transmuxed on the fly for compatibility with the various target devices shown on the right. For example, the TV and computer might be getting DASH-packaged files, the game platform Smooth Streaming, the mobile devices HLS. The Wowza Streaming Cloud creates these packages dynamically, which we'll discuss in more detail in Chapter 15.

Figure 14-4. Dynamically packaging (transmuxing) with the Wowza Streaming Cloud.

For now, just remember that to create files for ABR delivery, you have to encode the individual streams, and then package or transmux to the necessary ABR packaging. But first, of course, you have to build the encoding ladder itself.

Building Your Encoding Ladder

Now that we know the high-level procedure for producing content for adaptive delivery, let's start to explore how to build your encoding ladder, or the files that you'll use to deliver adaptively to your viewers.

Per-title, Per-category, or One-size-fits-all?

Before the start of 2016, virtually all streaming producers used a single encoding ladder for all content. Then, Netflix started the per-title encoding revolution in December 2015. You can read Netflix's original blog post on the topic, "Per-Title Encode Optimization," at bit.ly/NF_pertitle, or my description, "How Netflix Pioneered Per-Title Optimization," at bit.ly/nf_pertitle.

The rationale for per-title encoding is clear. All videos are different, so fixed encoding ladders are inherently inefficient or inadequate, depending on the complexity of the video. Today, Netflix analyzes each video separately, and creates a unique ladder for that video. We performed a similar operation in Chapter 7 when we used CRF to create a unique target for the eight video files discussed in this book.

Soon after Netflix, YouTube announced its own per-title encoding scheme, which you can read about at bit.ly/YTpertitle. More recently Capella Systems announced the latest version of its VOD encoder Cambria FTC, with a source-adaptive bitrate ladder (SABL) that "automatically adjusts the bitrate ladder used for DASH, HLS, or Smooth Streaming based on the encoding complexity of the source video." I recently wrote a review of Cambria FTC that you can read at bit.ly/PTcambria, but the bottom line is that SABL works, and it works well. In Chapter 16, I explore all these approaches to per-title encoding, and some that you can deploy yourself.

In the next major section of this chapter, we discuss creating your encoding ladder. How does this change if you're going per-title, per-category, or one-size-fits-all? Well, it really doesn't—or at least not much. When creating one ladder for all content, you have to set values that you think work best for all of your content. When creating category-specific ladders, you set values that you think work best for all content in that category. For per-title, it's the configurations that work best for that video. Beyond that, all the same rules should apply.

One Ladder for All, or Target-specific Ladders?

The most fundamental decision facing producers targeting multiple devices is whether to encode individual packages for each target, or to encode one set of streams for all targets and (if necessary) package that for each target. In other words, if you're targeting computers, mobile, and OTT, should you encode three sets of streams each customized for the target, or one set of streams that you distribute to all. Table 14-1 shows that back in 2012, Turner Broadcasting choose the individual stream approach for its NBA League Pass offering, producing a separate set of streams for each target platform.

Web	Type	Format	Resolution	Vid BR	Frame Rate	Aud Codec	Sample Rate	Aud BR	Channels
mosaic	Flash	h264	480×270	452 kbps	29.97	HE-AAC	44.1 kHz	48 kbps	Stereo
low	Flash	h264	768×432	836 kbps	29.97	HE-AAC	44.1 kHz	64 kbps	Stereo
med	Flash	h264	896×504	1436 kbps	29.97	HE-AAC	44.1 kHz	64 kbps	Stereo
high	Flash	h264	960×540	2436 kbps	29.97	HE-AAC	44.1 kHz	64 kbps	Stereo
full	Flash	h264	1280×720	3436 kbps	29.97	HE-AAC	44.1 kHz	64 kbps	Stereo
Mobile	Type	Format	Resolution	Vid BR	Frame Rate	Aud Codec	Sample Rate	Aud BR	Channels
Audio	HLS	---	---	---	---	HE-AAC	44.1 kHz	40 kbps	Stereo
iPhone	HLS	h264	416×234	110 kbps	10	HE-AAC	44.1 kHz	40 kbps	Stereo
iPhone	HLS	h264	416×234	200 kbps	15	HE-AAC	44.1 kHz	40 kbps	Stereo
iPhone	HLS	h264	416×234	400 kbps	29.97	HE-AAC	44.1 kHz	40 kbps	Stereo
iPhone	HLS	h264	640×360	600 kbps	29.97	HE-AAC	44.1 kHz	40 kbps	Stereo
iPad	HLS	h264	640×360	1200 kbps	29.97	HE-AAC	44.1 kHz	40 kbps	Stereo
iPad	HLS	h264	960×540	1800 kbps	29.97	HE-AAC	44.1 kHz	40 kbps	Stereo
Connect Devices	Type	Format	Resolution	Vid BR	Frame Rate	Aud Codec	Sample Rate	Aud BR	Channels
OTT	HLS	h264	1024×576	1200 kbps	29.97	HE-AAC	44.1 kHz	96 kbps	Stereo
OTT	HLS	h264	1024×576	2500 kbps	29.97	HE-AAC	44.1 kHz	96 kbps	Stereo
OTT	HLS	h264	1280×720	3500 kbps	29.97	HE-AAC	44.1 kHz	96 kbps	Stereo

Table 14-1. Stream configurations for NBA League Pass in 2012 (bit.ly/TLP_ladder).

Certainly this approach is valid, and it's the one taken by most large organizations. The downside is that it involves producing and storing 14 streams, rather than seven or eight that could be distributed to all devices. However, using the same streams for all targets means that you might have to make some quality trade-offs, particularly at the low end. Let's look at the requirements of the individual target device categories and circle back to this question.

Computers and OTT Devices

Computers and OTT devices can all play all profiles and levels of H.264 encoded video, which means you can use the high profile throughout.

iOS Devices

Encoding for Apple devices changed dramatically in 2016. The status quo before August 2016 was that TN2224 directed encoding for iOS devices (bit.ly/appletn2224), while a new document called HLS Authoring Specifications for Apple TV, which I wrote about here (bit.ly/ATV_spec), directed encoding for Apple TV. Of course, since so many producers encode for iOS and Apple TV in a single set of streams, Apple had to merge the two.

Apple did so unceremoniously in August 2016, adding the following short note to TN2224, "Important: This document is concerned with practices and with the rationale behind them. For detailed requirements please refer to the HLS Authoring Specification for Apple Devices." Apple also changed the name of the Apple TV spec to the Apple Devices spec (A_Devices_Spec). To be honest, I didn't notice the change until my editor pointed out that Apple had changed the title of the latter document.

This switchover delivered several changes, not the least of which is a totally redesigned encoding ladder (Table 14-2). Two of the new rules in the Apple Devices spec state that, "Profile and Level MUST be less than or equal to High Profile, Level 4.2," and that you "SHOULD use High Profile in preference to Main or Baseline Profile." This is a pretty striking change from the older ladder, (which is available at bit.ly/tn2224_old), where Apple recommended encoding the lower-quality streams using the Baseline or Main profile. Those days are gone.

Video average bit rate (kb/s)	Resolution	Frame rate
145	416 x 234	≤ 30 fps
365	480 x 270	≤ 30 fps
730	640 x 360	≤ 30 fps
1100	768 x 432	≤ 30 fps
2000	960 x 540	same as source
3000	1280 x 720	same as source
4500	same as source	same as source
6000	same as source	same as source
7800	same as source	same as source

Table 14-2. The encoding ladder recommended by Apple in TN2224.

Regarding which HLS version to assume that your targets play, in TN2224, Apple says, "In practice you should expect that all devices will support HLS version 4 and most will support the latest version," though this isn't mentioned in the Apple Devices Spec. Interestingly, the major enhancement to HLS version 4 was the ability to use a single file with byte-range requests rather than individual segments. Obviously, the ability to use the High profile for all streams should improve the quality of the smaller streams as compared to files encoded using the Baseline profile, though we'll examine how much in a moment. In both documents, Apple also reduced the recommended key frame interval to two seconds, and mandated a six-second-segment size.

Obviously, you can continue to use the Baseline profile to ensure compatibility with older devices. To assist this decision, TN2224 provides the information shown in Table 14-3. To me, it looks like if you encode all the streams using the High profile, you exclude the oldest three devices shown. You can check your server logs to identify whether this is a significant chunk, but for most streaming producers, I'm guessing it's not.

Devices	Highest HLS version	Last OS update	Max. Profile & Level	Resolution & fps
iPhone	1	Feb 2010	Baseline 1.3	320x240 @30
iPod touch				
iPhone 3G	3	Nov 2010	Baseline 3.0	640x480 @30
iPod touch (2nd generation)				
iPad	4	May 2012	High 4.1	720p @30
iPod touch (3rd generation)			High 3.0	640x480 @30
iPhone 3GS	5	Feb 2014		
iPod touch (4th generation)			High 4.1	
iPhone 4	6	Jun 2014		720p @30
Apple TV (2nd generation)		Sep 2014	High 3.1	
iPad 2	7	Still current	High 4.1	
iPhone 4s				
All other iOS and tvOS devices			High 4.1 or greater	1080p @30 or greater

Table 14-3. Old iOS devices and their limitations.

The bottom line is that you can use the High profile for computers, OTT, and iOS devices. What about Android? Well, if you've been in the streaming space for a while, you know that Android is always the redheaded stepchild. Here's the story.

Android Woes Continue

The problem with Android is this. The Android operating system software only supports the H.264 Baseline profile. Most Android phones and tablets supplement this with hardware-based decode for the Main and High profiles, but Google doesn't publish this information, and there are simply too many devices out there to collect it. So the official recommendation presented in Android's "Supported Media Formats" includes three files, all encoded with the Baseline profile (bit.ly/androidvideospecs, Table 14-4).

Note the recommended settings page also states that, "In addition to these encoding parameter recommendations, a device's available video recording profiles can be used as a proxy for media playback capabilities. These profiles can be inspected using the CamcorderProfile class, which is available since API level 8." So you can interrogate the device and check its ability to play the Main and High profile, though I'm not aware of how common this is.

	SD (Low quality)	SD (High quality)	HD 720p (N/A on all devices)
Video resolution	176 x 144 px	480 x 360 px	1280 x 720 px
Video frame rate	12 fps	30 fps	30 fps
Video bitrate	56 Kbps	500 Kbps	2 Mbps
Audio codec	AAC-LC	AAC-LC	AAC-LC
Audio channels	1 (mono)	2 (stereo)	2 (stereo)
Audio bitrate	24 Kbps	128 Kbps	192 Kbps

Table 14-4. The recommended encoding settings for Android.

This raises the obvious question: should you choose the conservative route and encode at least some streams with the Baseline profile, or use the High profile and hope for the best? In every class I teach that touches on this issue, I poll the students. About half use the Baseline profile for compatibility with older devices and Android, while the other half use the High profile. So there is no right or wrong answer.

I can tell you that the qualitative difference between the High and Baseline profile is probably lower than you would think. Looking back at Table 10.1, we saw about a 1 dB difference in peak signal-to-noise ratio (PSNR) rating between the Baseline and High profiles in 720p tests, which would be unnoticeable. Table 14-5 shows the difference at several rungs in the TN2224 encoding ladder with the low-motion Talking Head clip on the left, and the higher-motion Haunted clip on the right. Note that I customized the data rates in the ladder for the content, and in both cases they were much lower than that specified by Apple. If you use the data rates recommended by Apple, the quality difference between the files will be even less.

Talking Head	Data Rate	Baseline	High	Delta		Haunted	Data Rate	Baseline	High	Delta
234p	145,000	33.79	34.20	1.22%		234p	145,000	30.46	31.56	3.61%
270p	350,000	35.72	35.99	0.75%		270p	365,000	33.14	33.73	1.79%
360p	600,000	38.16	38.37	0.54%		360p	900,000	35.99	36.38	1.10%
540p	1,000,000	40.04	40.33	0.71%		540p	1,500,000	38.09	38.62	1.38%
720p	1,500,000	40.78	41.32	1.34%		720p	2,500,000	39.28	39.84	1.42%
1080p	2,500,000	43.53	44.11	1.34%		1080p	6,000,000	41.31	41.86	1.32%
Average		38.67	39.05	0.98%		Average		36.38	37.00	1.77%

Table 14-5. Quality differences between Baseline and High profile at various TN2224 layers.

Obviously this is only important if you're attempting to create one ladder for all targets. In that case, I'm not recommending that you encode using the Baseline profile as much as pointing out that few viewers will notice if you do. Plus you enhance compatibility with older iOS and Android devices.

The other point of customizing your encodes for your target platform relates to bitrate control. When making the change from TN2224 to the Apple Devices Spec, Apple changed its maximum bitrate recommendation from 110 CVBR to 200% CVBR, which could cause problems under constrained delivery conditions. More on this later in the chapter.

Summing up, most of you will create a single ladder for all encodes, and package that as necessary for your various target platforms. When choosing both the number of streams and their configuration, here's my recommended approach. I'll work through the entire process, then circle back for some additional thoughts on resolutions and data rates.

Choose Mobile First

Start by choosing the number of mobile streams necessary to effectively reach your mobile viewers, as well as the data rate and resolution. To accomplish this, identify the lowest video bitrate that you'd like to support, reflecting your views about the lowest connection speed used by a relevant viewer group. For Apple in the Apple Devices Spec, (Table 14-2), that's 145 kbps—although I've had clients who produced video as low as 110 kbps.

	Clients		Dimensions for 16:9 aspect ratio	Dimensions for 4:3 aspect ratio	Frame rate	Video bit rate (average)	Video bit rate (peak)	Audio bit rate	Total bit rate
	CELL		416 x 234	400 x 300	12	145	200	64	264
	CELL	ATV	480 x 270	480 x 360	15	365	400	64	464
WiFi	CELL	ATV	640 x 360	640 x 480	29.97	730	800	64	864
WiFi	CELL	ATV	768 x 432	640 x 480	29.97	1100	1200	96	1296
WiFi		ATV	960 x 540	960 x 720	29.97 or source	2000	2200	96	2296

Table 14-6. Configure the lowest-quality streams for mobile.

Then identify the resolution/frame rate combination that delivers optimal quality at that video bitrate. If possible, try to choose a resolution that matches a window size used for browser-based playback on your website. You'll see when in the following section.

Then Browser-based Streams

Next, choose the configurations for streams to be played within your website, either by computer- or tablet-based viewers. Here your primary concern is producing at least one stream for every video window size on your website. You can see this in Table 14-7, which are the encoding parameters used by MTV for its web properties.

The two lowest-quality streams are for mobile and very-low-bandwidth connections, while the highlighted streams are for playback in a browser window. As you can see, MTV has a stream for each window size used on its websites.

What to do if you only have one window size within the browser, say 640x360, with the next jump to full screen? First choose the highest quality that you want deliver at the resolution, using the bits-per-pixel value. For example, at around 1.2 Mbps, the bits-per-pixel value would be around .174, which should be perfect for all but the hardest-to-encode video. Obviously, if the video looks perfect at 1.2 Mbps, there's no need to go any higher with a 640x360 stream.

Scenario	Format	Frame Size	Total Bitrate	Audio Bitrate	bits/pixel *frame @ 30 fps	bits/pixel *frame @ 24 fps
Mobile & constrained (low)	baseline, mono, 10 fps	448x252	150	48	0.09	0.09
Mobile & constrained (high)	baseline, mono	448x252	450	48	0.12	0.15
Sidebar placements	main profile, stereo	384x216	400	96	0.12	0.15
Small in-page	main profile, stereo	512x288	750	96	0.15	0.18
Medium in-page	main profile, stereo	640x360	1200	96	0.16	0.20
Large in-page	main profile, stereo	768x432	1700	96	0.16	0.20
Full size in-page	main profile, stereo	960x540	2200	96	0.14	0.17
HD 720p (full screen)	high profile, stereo	1280x720	3500	96	0.12	0.15

Table 14-7. Encoding configurations used by MTV.

After creating streams for all window sizes, choose a number of streams that provides good coverage from your highest-quality mobile stream to the stream you just configured. For example, if your highest-quality mobile stream was 640x360@640 kbps, and your largest window size is 640x360, another stream at 1.2 Mbps would be all that you need, since this would deliver a meaningful quality difference between the two streams.

Note that more streams are not necessarily better. More streams mean that the streams are closer together, minimizing the quality difference while increasing the frequency of stream switching, which can disrupt viewing. The ideal scenario is when the viewer quickly identifies the optimal stream and continues to watch that through the end of the video. For example, in his article "Live dynamic streaming with Flash Media Server 3.5" (adobe.ly/kapoorlivefms), Adobe's Abhinav Kapoor recommended:

> If your target viewer covers a broad spectrum of bandwidth capabilities, it is best to keep a wide range of stream bit rate encodings while keeping a large enough difference between successive bit rates. Too many bit rates too close to one another could result in too many stream switches, even with smaller bandwidth fluctuations. Besides the slight overhead in switching, the viewer's experience with too-frequent quality fluctuations may not be pleasant. Meanwhile, too few streams with a huge gap in bit rates would not provide the best quality or the most optimal stream for a particular bandwidth.

Here are some other factors to consider:

•   You'll need more streams for HD content than for SD. Most clients encoding SD video (often converted from DVD) used three or four streams, although I did have one client in the entertainment space with eight streams for SD content. Most clients producing HD content range from five to eight.

- You'll need more streams for subscription content than for free or advertising supported content. For example, the last time Major League Baseball shared its adaptive streaming schema, the service deployed 11 streams—and this was before 4K. I've seen the stats on other subscription services, and some use up to eight streams for their content. Note that the extra streams are usually at the high end, to really satisfy users watching in their living room on large flat-panel displays, either via an OTT device or computer.

OTT and Full-screen Playback Last

Once you've got mobile and computer streams set, configure the streams bound for OTT and full-screen playback on computers or mobile devices. In this regard, cost sets your maximum. For example, looking at Apple's highest-quality stream, at 8,728 kbps for 1080p video, an hour of video would consume around 4GB. According to a Dan Rayburn blog on Akamai (bit.ly/dr_cdn_2016), he's seeing prices well below $0.003 (three-tenths of a cent) per GB. Assuming you're paying $0.01/GB, that 4GB file costs you a whopping $0.04 (four cents) to deliver, which is a heck of a lot less than it used to.

Of course, bandwidth cost isn't the only reason not to adopt Apple's bandwidth model en mass. If you drop the 1080p stream from 7.8 to 6 Mbps, few viewers will notice the change. But you'll be able to deliver 1080p video rather than 720p video to viewers on slower connections, which improves their quality of experience.

When configuring your highest-quality stream, choose the highest data rate that you can afford, given your monetization strategy and cost structure. Since your top-quality stream has to look very good, you'll have to adjust video resolution accordingly. For example, if you can only afford 3 Mbps at the top end, encode at 720p, not 1080p.

Then, if you need to add a stream or two to bridge between the highest browser-based stream and the maximum OTT stream, add those in, using the same logic we just applied for the browser-based streams. For example, if your highest-quality stream were 720p@3 Mbps, a 2 Mbps stream at the same resolution would serve as a nice bridge from the 640x360@1200 kbps stream and the 720p@3 Mbps stream.

Other Considerations

Here are some other issues to consider when configuring your streams.

The Distance Between Streams

Apple provides the most guidance on this, recommending that "adjacent bit rates should be a factor of 1.5 to 2 apart." Obviously, if the streams are too close together, there's very little difference in terms of quality or deliverability. If too far apart, you could leave a viewer stranded at too low a data rate.

Table 14-8 shows us how well Apple heeds their own advice. Pretty well, actually, up until the last few rungs, which are too close together for my test. If Apple asked me, I would eliminate the 6 Mbps 720p stream, and boost the data rate of the current 4500 kbps 720p stream to 5 Mbps or so. Remember that you have to pay to encode and store each stream that you deploy, so fewer is certainly better as long as you provide good coverage for your viewers. I try to keep the layers in my encoding ladders between 1.5x and 2x apart.

Clients			Dimensions for 16:9 aspect ratio	Dimensions for 4:3 aspect ratio	Frame rate	Video bit rate (average)
	CELL		416 x 234	400 x 300	12	145
	CELL	ATV	480 x 270	480 x 360	15	365
WiFi	CELL	ATV	640 x 360	640 x 480	29.97	730
WiFi	CELL	ATV	768 x 432	640 x 480	29.97	1100
WiFi		ATV	960 x 540	960 x 720	29.97 or source	2000
WiFi		ATV	1280 x 720	960 x 720	29.97 or source	3000
WiFi		ATV	1280 x 720 or source	1280 x 960 or source	29.97 or source	4500
WiFi		ATV	1280 x 720 or source	1280 x 960 or source	29.97 or source	6000
WiFi		ATV	1920 x 1080	1920 x 1440	29.97 or source	7800

2.5x
2x
1.5x
1.8x
1.5x
1.5x
1.33x
1.3x

Table 14-8. Bitrate differences in the TN2224 encoding ladder.

Measure the Qualitative Difference

Beyond the rough measure of data rate, it's always useful to compute the objective quality of the streams, particularly when you have multiple streams at the high end of the encoding ladder. For example, a recent encoding client included three 1080p streams in its ladder, encoded at 3 Mbps, 4.5 Mbps, and 6.5 Mbps. Working with the most challenging clip in the test group, the qualitative difference proved insignificant (Table 14-9). Even encoding at 8.5 Mbps provided very little extra quality.

Resolution	Data Rate	Multiplier	SQM	Delta
1080p	8500	1.31	93.43	
1080p	6500	1.44	92.48	1.0%
1080p	4500	1.50	91.07	1.5%
1080p	3000		89.09	2.2%

Table 14-9. Streams above 4.5 Mbps probably won't deliver noticeable quality differences.

I argued that the client should drop both the 4.5 Mbps and 6 Mbps streams as unnecessary since even the sharpest golden-eye viewer would have trouble distinguishing the 3 Mbps and 6.5 Mbps streams. After reviewing these numbers, the client ultimately dropped the 6.5 Mbps stream, but kept the 4.5 Mbps stream to ensure high quality for particularly hard-to-encode clips (this was a one-size-fits-all scheme).

Have a High-Quality Stream at 3 Mbps or so

Netflix publishes a Speed Index that tracks the average delivery speed for Netflix content over all Internet service providers in the country. You can see the US index at bit.ly/nfispspeed. When I checked while writing this chapter, Verizon FIOS led with an average of 3.7 Mbps, and the top 10 all delivered 3.41 Mbps or higher. When I produce my encoding ladders, I want to reward these viewers with at least a 720p stream at 3 Mbps or so, and a 1080p stream if that's at all possible.

Go Slow not Low (res)

For low-bitrate files, I prefer to drop frame rate rather than resolution. You can read all about why in an article on my website titled "Configuring Low Data Rate Adaptive Streams" (bit.ly/configadaptive). Briefly, when producing at low bitrates, you have several options to preserve quality, including lowering the resolution, the frame rate or both. All options have some negatives. For example, lower resolutions preserve frame quality but can look pixelated when scaled for display. Higher resolutions avoid scaling artifacts, but frame quality can suffer. Dropping the frame rate preserves frame quality, but reduces smoothness.

Figure 14-5. Dropping resolution (on the right) results in an easier-to-encode file, but loss of detail throughout.

To help a client decide which strategy to pursue, I encoded files at the following configurations, all at 300 kbps and otherwise identical encoding parameters:
- 640x480@15 fps
- 640x480@30 fps
- 400x300@15 fps
- 320x240@15 fps
- 320x240@30 fps.

You can view all streams at bit.ly/configadaptive. Figure 14-5 shows a comparison of the 640x360@15 fps and 320x240@30 fps streams. Although the 30 fps stream was obviously smoother, this was offset by a persistent fuzziness and loss of detail. Ultimately, the client decided to encode all streams at 640x480 and adjust the frame rate downward rather than dropping the resolution and scaling upward for display.

More recently, I compared the encoding strategies of several online video platforms (OVPs). My client was encoding at a very low resolution and preserving the frame rate, while other services were encoding at higher resolutions and reducing the frame rate. When both videos were zoomed to full screen, the qualitative difference was striking, as you can see in Figure 14-6.

Figure 14-6. Higher-resolution, lower-frame-rate video on the left.

Obviously, these still images don't provide a feel for the differences in playback smoothness, but for talking head videos, the difference between 15 and 30 fps isn't that great. Interestingly, several of the OVPs had abandoned resolutions below 640x360 altogether. I explore this on my website in a posted titled "Encoding Brief: Phase Out Low Quality Streams in Your Encoding Ladder" (bit.ly/losesmallstreams). Read the comments, because there are some good ones on both sides of the issue. The bottom line is that I see no reason to go smaller than the 416x234 resolution Apple recommends in the Apple Devices spec, and for business-oriented websites, could see going no lower than 640x360@15 fps at, say, 400 kbps.

Cluster Streams at Target Resolutions

If you only have a few display resolutions, cluster your encoding targets at these resolutions. For example, in his white paper "Video encoding and transcoding recommendations for HTTP Dynamic Streaming on the Flash Platform," (adobe.ly/Levkovhttp), former Adobe technology evangelist Maxim Levkov pointed out that streams of identical resolution switch most smoothly and he recommends clustering streams at specific window sizes. Looking at Table 14-2, if my website had a 640x360 playback window, I would eschew the 768x432 stream in favor of a 640x360 stream at a slightly lower data rate. Similarly, if there were a 1280x720 window, I would convert the 960x540 stream to 1280x720 at a slightly higher data rate.

We discussed mod-16 in Chapter 2. As you may recall, mod-16 means that the height and width of the file are divisible by 16. This is important because H.264 divides videos into 16x16 blocks, and will artificially expand the video behind the scenes to fit this block structure if the resolution isn't mod-16. However, even at small resolutions like the 416x234 used by Apple, which isn't mod-16, the compression inefficiency this causes is minor. As an example, 640x360 is the most widely supported video resolution in use today. It's not mod-16, although it is mod-8, as 360/8 = 45. Try to keep your resolutions at mod-8 and above and you'll be fine.

Don't Encode at Resolutions Larger than Your Source

Scaling to higher resolutions for encoding doesn't add quality; you'll get a higher-quality result and save bandwidth by using the GPUs on your target playback device to scale the video.

More on Choosing Data Rate

Intuitively, for your lower-quality streams, deliverability is the key factor. That is, as we've discussed, you'll choose the lowest data rate you want to support and configure your video appropriately. At higher resolutions, maintaining quality is the most important consideration. For example, as you can see in Table 14-5, I deployed per-title values for the Talking Head and Haunted clips, which are very different in terms of encoding complexity. Still I used the same data rate for the 234p streams, which is why the Talking Head clip had a higher PSNR value—34.20 dB compared with 31.56. The data rates for the 270p streams are also very similar.

Beyond that, I started deploying a higher data rate for the Haunted clip to maintain overall visual quality. At 1080p, the Haunted clip had a data rate over twice that of the Talking Head, and even then, the PSNR value trailed 41.86 dB to 44.1. So, low-bitrate clips are about deliverability, higher-bitrate clips about quality.

To summarize, you want the data rates far enough apart to represent meaningful quality differences and to avoid too many stream switches. The ideal scenario is one where the viewer quickly identifies the optimal stream and continues to watch that through the end of the video.

> **Note:** *One analysis I've used before to create the optimal bitrate was inspired by Netflix's per-title encode optimization technique. I cover this in Chapter 16 in the text surrounding Table 16-1.*

Other Configuration Items

Beyond these basic stream configuration options, you'll need to make other adaptive streaming-specific configuration decisions. Among the most important is choosing the H.264 profile for your encoded files.

Choosing the H.264 Profile

By this point, you've already made the decision to either use one set of files for all targets, or customize your streams for each target. Here's a summary:

- If you're creating streams for computers and/or OTT, use the High profile without limitation.

- When encoding for iOS only, Apple advises to use High profile only.

- When encoding for Android, software compatibility requires Baseline only.

Haunted	Width	Height	Frame Rate	Video Bitrate	Multiple	Peak Bitrate	Buffer	Profile
234p	416	234	15	145,000		159,500	145,000	Baseline
270p	480	270	30	365,000	2.5	401,500	365,000	Baseline
360p_l	640	360	30	700,000	1.9	770,000	700,000	Baseline
360p_h	640	360	30	1,200,000	1.7	1,320,000	1,200,000	Main
720p_l	1,280	720	30	2,400,000	2.0	2,640,000	2,400,000	High
720p_h	1,280	720	30	3,100,000	1.3	3,410,000	3,100,000	High
1080p	1,920	1,080	30	5,200,000	1.7	5,720,000	5,200,000	High

Table 14-10. A single encoding ladder for all targets should include some low-end streams encoded using the Baseline profile.

If you're encoding one set of streams for all targets, I recommend using Baseline for two or three of your lowest-quality streams, including one 640x360 stream, to ensure that older Android and iOS devices can view at least some streams. This means an encoding ladder that looks something like that shown in Table 14-10. Note that this is a generic, one-size-fits all encoding ladder, not for any particular content type. My rationale is this. As shown in Table 14-5, the quality difference between files encoded with the Baseline and High profiles is minor. However, if you exclude a viewer, you lose them—possibly forever. Seems like encoding some streams with the Baseline profile is the best overall approach.

CBR or VBR

Back in Chapter 8, we discussed multiple approaches to controlling the bitrate of your videos. A reasonable summary of the chapter is this:

1. The overall qualitative difference between constant bitrate (CBR) and variable bitrate (VBR) is minor, although VBR delivers overall higher quality.

2. In addition, CBR can create transient quality issues that manifest as extremely ugly frames.

3. CBR produces the most deliverable stream, and 200 percent constrained VBR can reduce your viewer's quality of experience when delivering under limited bitrate conditions.

4. In most cases, 110 percent constrained VBR avoids CBR's transient quality problems.

5. Apple formerly directed that the maximum bit rate not exceed 110% of the average in TN2224, which they upped to 200% in the Apple Devices spec. Note that Apple isn't recommending that you encode using 200% constrained VBR, they're directing that your maximum data rate not exceed 200% of your average.

6. Most producers surveyed use 110 percent constrained VBR.

Given all this, I recommend that you encode with 110 percent constrained VBR with a one-second VBV buffer. Note that I recommend that you use this technique whether you're distributing to mobile, desktops or OTT. I know this varies with Apple's recommendations, but I proved back in Chapter 8 that 200 percent constrained VBR could cause quality-of-service issues.

> **Note:** *If you skipped Chapter 8, shame on you! But, you can get the skinny on my concerns about bitrate control and quality of experience by reading "Bitrate Control and QoE—CBR is Better" at* bit.ly/usecbr4qoe.

Key Frame Interval and Segment Size

As we talked about in Chapter 9, all stream switches in an adaptive streaming schema must occur on a key frame. This means that each segment or byte-range request must start with a key frame. To make this happen, your key frame interval must divide evenly into your segment size. For example, as noted above, Apple recommends a segment size of six seconds and a key frame interval of two seconds, which meets this requirement.

What do the researchers say? The best work I've seen was written by Stefan Lederer from Bitmovin, in an article titled "Optimal Streaming Formats MPEG-DASH & HLS Segment Length" (bit.ly/bestchunksize). I discussed his research on the Streaming Learning Center website at bit.ly/bestchunksize2, and I'm going to summarize from this article here.

First let's identify the stakes. Intuitively, shorter segment lengths allow ABR systems to change streams more quickly, which avoids stoppages when bandwidth goes down. While in the real world, the difference between four and 10 seconds is usually inconsequential, when you're in the middle of downloading a 10-second segment and your bandwidth plummets, it can seem like forever before the segment finishes downloading and the player can choose a lower-quality stream. Producers like shorter segments to minimize stoppages that bandwidth drops can cause.

On the other hand, shorter segments mean more communication between the server and the player. Since each segment requires the same communication load, dropping from 10 seconds to four seconds increases that load by 250 percent. In addition, if you deploy four-second segments, the longest key frame interval you can use is four seconds, while with a segment size of 10 seconds you can use a key frame interval of the same duration.

Let's talk about key frame interval first. As we learned back in Table 9-1, a key frame interval of 10 seconds delivers a PSNR value of 41.92. I didn't test for a key frame interval of 4, but if you average the values for three seconds (41.06) and five seconds (41.54) you get 41.3 dB—probably not a difference most viewers would notice. So I would ignore this issue for this discussion.

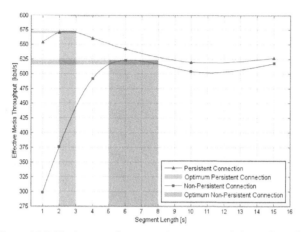

Figure 14-7. The impact of segment size on network throughput for persistent and non-persistent connection (from Bitmovin).

However, Lederer found that the communication issue was much more serious, and the optimum segment duration varied depending upon whether your server maintained a persistent or non-persistent connection with the player. Specifically, as you can see in Figure 14-7, if the connection was persistent, the optimum segment size was two to three seconds. If the connection was non-persistent, the communications associated with these smaller segments was very inefficient, and performance peaked at a segment length of six seconds.

Briefly, according to Wikipedia (bit.ly/per_con), a persistent connection uses "a single TCP connection to send and receive multiple HTTP requests/responses, as opposed to opening a new connection for every single request/response pair." Here's further explanation from Alex Martelli on stackoverflow, with minor edits to shorten (bit.ly/per_con2):

> Persistent means the server doesn't close the socket once it's finished pushing out the response, so the client can make other requests on the same socket. Reusing the socket can reduce overall latency compared to closing the original socket and opening new ones for all the follow-on requests.

Applying this impact to ABR streaming, Lederer continues:

> The influence of the network delay gets bigger when using smaller segment lengths. This especially affects the non-persistent/HTTP 1.0 connection results because in this case one round-trip-time (RTT) is needed for establishing the TCP connection to the server after each segment.

How do you know if your streaming server or CDN uses a persistent or non-persistent connection? Check documentation and settings. For example, this came from the Amazon CloudFront documentation (bit.ly/per_con3):

> When CloudFront gets a response from your origin, it tries to maintain the connection for several seconds in case another request arrives during that period. Maintaining a persistent connection saves the time that is required to re-establish the Transmission Control Protocol (TCP) connection and perform another Transport Layer Security (TLS) handshake for subsequent requests. To improve performance, we recommend that you configure your origin server to allow persistent connections.

Based upon this research, Lederer says:

> Bitmovin would recommend using DASH or HLS chunk sizes around 2 to 4 seconds, which is a good compromise between encoding efficiency and flexibility for stream adaptation to bandwidth changes. Furthermore, it is recommended to use Web servers and CDNs that enable persistent HTTP connections, as this is a easy and cheap way to increase streaming performance. Thus as presented, by doing so the effective media throughput and quality of service (QoS) can be increased without any changes to the client's implementation just by choosing the right segment length.

Obviously, if you're using a non-persistent connection for some reason, you should increase the segment duration to somewhere around six seconds.

> **Note:** *I've stayed away from live streaming in this book, but the article on the Streaming Learning Center (bit.ly/bestchunksize2) discusses the optimum segment size for live streaming as well.*

Quick Summary: Key Frame Interval and Segment Size

1. Make sure your key frame interval divides evenly into your segment size.

2. With a server with a persistent connection with the player, segment sizes of between two and four seconds deliver higher throughput and stream adaptation.

3. With a server with a non-persistent connection, a segment size of six seconds delivers the optimal throughput.

4. Apple recommends using a segment size of six second and a key frame interval of two seconds. It's unclear whether App Store approval is conditional upon using this configuration. This may be an issue for those who are distributing to iOS devices via apps.

5. Disable scene change detection unless you're sure the encoder will insert I-frames at the specified interval even if there's an intervening I-frame caused by a scene change.

6. In all cases, every I-frame should be an IDR frame.

Audio Parameters

Here, the major issue is whether to use the same audio parameters for all files, or whether to increase audio quality with the video quality. In the original TN2224 recommendations, Apple specified the same 64 kbps audio stream with all files, and in the early days of adaptive streaming, many pundits recommended using the same audio parameters in all files to avoid popping and other audible artifacts during stream switching.

As you can see in Table 14-2, Apple now scales audio parameters with the video—a tacit indication that this shouldn't cause a problem. Most of the ABR ladders that I've worked with over the past few years do the same, and my clients have experienced no audio artifacts.

I do recommend that you keep the sample rate the same for all audio files, usually 48 kHz because most source audio is 48 kHz and the sample rate conversion from 48 kHz to 44.1 kHz can cause issues. To make the jump from 64 kbps to 128 kbps, use 64 kbps mono for the lower-quality stream, and 128 kbps stereo for the higher-quality stream—both at 48 kHz. Unless you're working with very high-quality audio input, with a video where audio quality really matters, like a concert or ballet, I don't think there's any reason to go beyond 128 kbps.

This is especially true for talking-head video, which is almost always recorded using a monaural microphone or, at best, two stereo microphones too close together to make a difference. If you encode talking head audio as 64 kbps mono, your player decodes the stream and distributes the same signal over both channels. If you encode at 128 kbps stereo, the encoder duplicates the mono signal into both channels, and during playback your listeners hear the exact same thing. You haven't improved audio quality one bit, and you've doubled your audio bitrate. This is what you see in Figure 14-8, where the audio from a single microphone was encoded as stereo audio (at 44.1 kHz to boot).

Figure 14-7. Never encode mono audio as stereo.

If you do have a pristine recording of the London Symphony Orchestra, perhaps you could stray up to 192 kbps, but stay at 48 kHz. I'm guessing if you perform side-by-side testing of 128 kbps and 192 kbps streams on a set of wonderful speakers, you still wouldn't hear the difference.

Quick Summary: Audio Encoding for ABR Delivery

1. Most producers improve audio quality with video quality.

2. If you do this, use the same sample rate for all files. Usually 48 kHz is best, because that's the same rate for most source videos.

3. Consider encoding talking head audios as mono.

4. Unless audio quality is pristine and essential to the experience, going beyond 128 kbps probably delivers little, if any, noticeable improvement.

HLS Specific Recommendations

If you're encoding HLS, be aware of the following recommendations from Apple TN2224 (bit.ly/appletn2224) and the Apple Devices spec (A_Devices_Spec).

1. If you're seeking App Store approval, you have to supply at least one 192 kbps stream, which can be audio only, audio with a still image, or audio/video.

2. Audio sample rate should be 48 kHz, and stereo.

3. Key frame every two seconds with a segment size of six seconds. Note that TN2224 says, "We used to recommended a 10 second target duration. We aren't expecting you to suddenly re-segment all your content. But we do believe that, going forward, six seconds makes for a better trade-off." So don't feel like you need to repackage your entire library.

4. You can use the High profile for the entire ladder, although you will be excluding some older devices.

5. You should expect all target devices to be compatible with HLS version 4+, which means you can use a single file with byte-range requests rather than separate .ts fragments.

6. Bitrate variability should not exceed 200 percent of the target bitrate. This means you can use 200% constrained VBR, though I recommend 110% constrained VBR.

7. First stream in playlist for Wi-Fi playback is 2000 kbps stream. For cellular, the first stream should be the 730 kbps stream.

So now you know how to build your encoding ladder. Let's move on to actual encoding, shall we?

Chapter 15: Encoding and Packaging ABR Streams

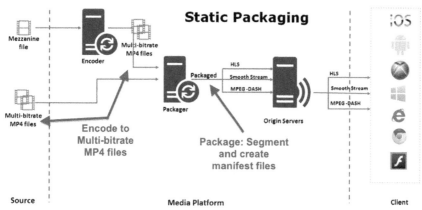

Figure 15-1. Encoding and packaging for HLS, Smooth Streaming, and DASH in Microsoft Azure.

In Chapter 13, you learned which adaptive bitrate (ABR) technology to use for which targets, and in Chapter 14, you built and configured your encoding ladder. In this chapter, you'll finally learn to produce your ABR streams. As suggested in Figure 15-1, this involves a two-step process. First you encode your mezzanine file into the multiple-bitrate MP4 files as per your encoding ladder. Step two is packaging, where you segment your media files and create the necessary manifest files. As with all things compression-related, there are more than one way to encode and package your ABR streams, and some techniques can save significant storage and encoding costs over others.

Specifically, in this chapter, you will learn:

- the difference between static and dynamic packaging, and the pros and cons of each

- how to produce ABR streams in typical desktop and enterprise encoding tools

- how to most efficiently produce multiple files with FFmpeg

- how to produce HTTP Live Streaming (HLS) packaging with FFmpeg

- how to create and check HLS presentations with Apple Media File Segmenter, Variant Playlist Creator, and Media Stream Validator

- how to produce Dynamic Adaptive Streaming over HTTP (DASH) packaging with MP4Box.

Encoding and Packaging

Figure 15-1 shows the two steps required to produce ABR-ready files. First, you encode your mezzanine file into the multiple files in your encoding ladder. Then you segment each input file and create the necessary manifest files. The encoding stage is the CPU-intensive, time-consuming stage, while packaging is simple and can be performed in real time or faster.

Traditionally, these two steps have been combined into one as shown in Figure 15-2. That is, in most cases, if you encode files to HLS output, you input the mezzanine file and the program produces multiple segments in the MPEG-2 transport stream container format (.ts) and the .m3u8 manifest files. You have what you need for HLS distribution, but if you need DASH and/or Smooth Streaming output, you have to repeat the entire time-consuming process.

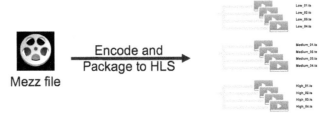

Figure 15-2. Single-step encoding/packaging.

If you're working with an encoder that outputs in a single step, supporting multiple output formats is overly time-consuming and limits your encoding capacity. If your cloud encoder can produce only a single set of ABR-ready output files from a single source, you'll be paying double for your HLS and DASH output. What's the alternative? Encoders that encode the mezzanine file to the multiple-bitrate MP4 files first, and then package as a second step. This is shown in Figure 15-3, where both HLS and DASH packages are produced from a single set of MP4 files.

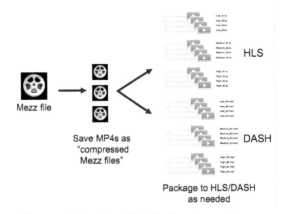

Figure 15-3. Encode to MP4 files first, then package.

Many higher-level encoders and some cloud encoders work this way. For example, Figure 15-4 shows a snippet from the interface of Elemental Cloud Encoder. In the first tab on the left, you choose your basic file parameters. Then you configure outputs for HLS, HTTP Dynamic Streaming (HDS), Smooth Streaming, and DASH in the tabs to the right. The encoder creates the MP4 files first, and then packages them, which the cloud encoder can perform almost instantaneously. Rather than encoding four times for HLS, HDS, Smooth, and DASH, you encode once and package for each output, cutting overall processing time by very close to 75 percent.

Figure 15-4. Elemental Cloud Encoder creates MP4 files first, and then packages them.

This two-step processing pays even more dividends when you add additional ABR formats to your distribution schema. Say you support HLS today and decide to add DASH support in six months. If you save the MP4 files encoded as the first step, you can simply package them for DASH in six months, rather than re-encoding. If you study Figure 15-1, you'll see that you can insert previously encoded multiple-bitrate MP4 files into the Microsoft Azure packager, illustrating this concept.

> **Note:** *Some cloud encoding platforms, like Amazon Elastic Transcoder, charge for each ABR output, so outputting for DASH, HLS, and Smooth would mean triple the charges. Others, like Zencoder and Telestream Cloud, have a discount for transmuxing. So you might pay 100 percent for the first streams, and then 25 percent for additional transmuxed streams. If you're outputting multiple ABR formats in the cloud, make sure you're not paying the full price for each output.*

Implementing Two-step Encoding/Packaging

Hopefully, I've convinced you that it's better to encode and package as two separate steps: first creating the multiple-bitrate MP4 files, then packaging those to the necessary formats. How do you do this?

Virtually all encoding tools—whether desktop, appliance, or cloud—can produce the required MP4 files, so that won't be a problem. The issue will be finding a tool that can input the MP4 files and package those as needed. Later in the chapter I'll demonstrate how you can create HLS packaging with FFmpeg, and DASH packaging with a free tool called MP4Box. What are your other options?

For DASH packaging, you can try the shaka-packager (bit.ly/Dash_pack1), Rebaca MPEG-DASH Segmenter (bit.ly/Dash_pack2), castLabs DASH.encrypt Packager (github.com/castlabs/dashencrypt) and Bento4 (bento4.com). For HLS, Apple offers Media Stream Segmenter (for segmenting MPEG-2 transport stream files) and Media File Segmenter (for segmenting MP4 files), which you can read more about in Apple's "HTTP Live Streaming Overview" (bit.ly/HLS_pack). For DASH, HLS, HDS, and Smooth Streaming tools, you can check out Unified Packager (bit.ly/Uni_pack), Elemental Delta (bit.ly/El_Del), and Harmonic ProMedia Package (bit.ly/harm_pack).

Static Packaging

Figures 15-1, 15-2, and 15-3 all illustrate what's called static packaging, which is best seen in Figure 15-2. That is, the encoder creates the necessary packaging, which is uploaded to an origin server for distribution to the various compatible clients. Although most packaging today is static, there are three problems with this workflow, all relating to supporting multiple output formats. First is storage space. That is, if you support HLS and DASH, you have to have two complete copies of your ABR packaging on your origin server, which is expensive.

The second problem is packaging latency. If you have a significant library of content, you have to create and upload the necessary packaging, which could take weeks or even months—particularly if you didn't have the multiple-bitrate MP4 files saved as compressed intermediate files. The third is cost, since you may have to pay a cloud service, or dedicate some of your own processing, to package the files.

What's the alternative? Dynamic packaging.

> **Note:** *Dynamic packaging is also called transmuxing. It refers to changing the container format of a file or files without re-encoding, and creating the manifest files necessary for the new ABR format.*

Dynamic Packaging

With dynamic packaging, you create the multiple-bitrate MP4 files and upload them to a streaming endpoint as shown in Figure 15-5, from the Microsoft Azure website. As different players request chunks or byte-range requests in the video, the server retrieves the MP4 file, dynamically creates the segments and manifest files required for the ABR format, and then sends them to the player. While the ABR chunks may be temporarily stored somewhere in the content delivery network's HTTP caching structure, they are never stored on the streaming server, so you're charged simply for storing the MP4 files. Since the server creates the ABR packaging dynamically, there's no encoding charge to produce that specific ABR format.

You can perform dynamic packaging even if you are applying digital rights management (DRM) to your video, or if you need to apply different caption formats for your target players. In most instances, there are few, if any, meaningful downsides.

There are multiple ways to support dynamic packaging, but let's start with Microsoft Azure, the service that supplied Figure 15-1 and 15-5. By way of background, Azure offers a media platform that can supply both encoding and file delivery services. Although the Azure cloud encoder was formerly able to produce static packaging, Microsoft is deprecating that capability as the company urges its customers to package dynamically, rather than statically.

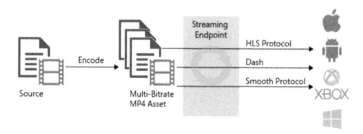

Figure 15-5. Dynamic packaging.

The cost for dynamic packaging? Basically, it's included in the cost of distribution. Specifically, with Azure, you can stream directly from the Azure origin server, or use the Azure content delivery network (CDN). The latter adds points of presence at the edge and caching, which should improve overall quality of experience of your viewers. Both services charge by the GB delivered. In each case, dynamic packaging—including captions and encryption—is included. Alternatively, you can send the packaged ABR videos from the origin server to a third-party CDN, in which case you'll pay for the transfer bandwidth to the CDN. Dynamic packaging is also included.

Microsoft offers the license-free Azure Media Player for live and video-on-demand (VOD) playback of HLS, DASH, or Smooth Streaming formats with fallback to Flash or Silverlight. Microsoft can supply license keys for PlayReady or Widevine at a small extra charge or provide access to a range of third-party providers of this service.

One case study on the Microsoft site describes how Japanese premium content platform Rakuten ShowTime used Azure to simplify its distribution workflow and cut costs (bit.ly/dpackage1). Briefly, at the time, Rakuten offered more than 120,000 videos for delivery to smart TVs, PCs, smartphones, tablets, and gaming platforms. Before moving to the Azure platform, the service created and stored separate iterations of each title in Smooth Streaming, HDS, HLS, and some others—often creating multiple iterations of these ABR formats for different DRM technologies.

In 2013, the number of discrete files managed exceeded 100 million, which was the limit of Rakuten's on-premises storage management system. This prompted a move to the cloud, and discussions with Microsoft Azure. Rakuten ultimately switched to dynamic packaging in 2015, and found three key benefits. First, Rakuten's storage costs were "reduced to 25 percent" of the previous amount. Second, the company was able to offer new titles faster because it no longer had to produce the multiple iterations. Third, since the number of output files was dramatically reduced, the company could more easily find and resolve file-related issues, which Rakuten stated cut management costs by "as much as 60 percent."

Dynamic Packaging with Wowza

One of the first (if not the first) to offer dynamic packaging capabilities was Wowza Media Systems, which offers the Wowza Streaming Engine for developers and the Wowza Streaming Cloud for those who want a managed service. Wowza pricing varies by the product, but you can start with a subscription for the Wowza Streaming Engine for $65/month. Wowza Streaming Cloud has plans ranging from single live events to 24/7 broadcasting, and both products can deploy using the new Wowza Player.

How much can dynamic packaging save? Well, in early 2016, I worked with a consulting client who was converting a large existing library over to ABR streaming, as well as producing significant hours of new videos. During the transition year, dynamic packaging reduced the encoding costs of the library transcode and ongoing encodes by close to $90,000, and cut storage costs by around $34,000. Add back the $20,000 or so it would cost to run Wowza Media Server (mostly cloud machine time), and total savings slightly exceeded $100,000.

Note that Wowza and Azure are not the only dynamic packaging solutions available. For example, CDNs Akamai and Limelight offer this service to their customers. Other media servers like Wowza include Nimble Streamer (bit.ly/pack_nimble), NGINX (nginx.com) with a plug-in from Kaltura (bit.ly/Kal_nginx), and MistServer (mistserver.org). In addition, Elemental Delta is a video delivery platform that can perform what the company calls "just-in-time video packaging," as well as many other features (bit.ly/El_Del).

Let's summarize up to this point.

> ***1.*** If you're currently encoding directly from a single mezzanine file to packaged ABR output, strongly consider a two-step workflow that will allow you to save the multiple-bitrate MP4 files as mezzanine files for later re-packaging.

> ***2.*** If you're distributing multiple ABR formats via static packaging, consider switching to a dynamic packaging workflow.

With all this as background, let's explore the actual encoding task. Through the middle chapters of this book, we learned much about the individual encoding parameters to apply to our files. Last chapter, we built our encoding ladder, which will look something like Table 15-1.

Ask 10 encoding professionals to create their ideal encoding ladder and you'll see 10 different ladders. Still, there's a lot to like about the ladder shown in Table 15-1 (if I do say so myself), which uses 110 percent constrained VBR (Chapter 8), a key frame interval of two seconds, B-frame interval of three, and 10 reference frames (Chapter 9).

	Width	Height	Frame Rate	Video Bitrate	Multiple	Peak Bitrate	Buffer	Profile	Audio Bitrate	Entropy	Key-frame	B-frame	Ref frame
234p	416	234	15	145,000		159,500	145,000	Baseline	64,000	CAVLC	2	NA	10
270p	480	270	30	365,000	2.5	401,500	365,000	Baseline	64,000	CAVLC	2	NA	10
360p_l	640	360	30	700,000	1.9	770,000	700,000	Baseline	64,000	CAVLC	2	NA	10
360p_h	640	360	30	1,200,000	1.7	1,320,000	1,200,000	Main	96,000	CAVLC	2	3	10
720p_l	1,280	720	30	2,400,000	2.0	2,640,000	2,400,000	High	128,000	CABAC	2	3	10
720p_h	1,280	720	30	3,100,000	1.3	3,410,000	3,100,000	High	128,000	CABAC	2	3	10
1080p	1,920	1,080	30	5,200,000	1.7	5,720,000	5,200,000	High	128,000	CABAC	2	3	10

Table 15-1. The generic encoding ladder applied in this chapter.

Although Apple says you can use the High profile for all streams, I'm being conservative with Baseline for the bottom three, and Main for the higher-quality 640x360 stream. Bitrate increments range from a little more than 2x to an average of about 1.9x (Chapter 14), with a 5.2 Mbps 1080p data rate that should be sufficient for all but the most demanding footage (Chapter 7). There's also a 3.1 Mbps 720p stream that should be sustainable by most viewers across the US. While I'd prefer to use per-title encoding, if I had to choose one encoding ladder for general-purpose content, it would look a lot like Table 15-1.

So now let's build that encoding ladder in an enterprise encoding application and FFmpeg.

Enterprise Encoders

Obviously, all encoders have different interfaces, so unless you're working with the Capella Systems Cambria encoder shown in Figure 15-6, what you see in your encoder is different than the figure. Still, whichever encoder you're using, the Single Rule That Must Be Obeyed is to configure key frames in an interval that divide evenly into your segment size. So the first controls you need to find relate to key frame interval and segment size.

As you can see in the figure, Capella makes it tough to break these rules. That is, you specify your group of pictures (GOP; shown as Maximum GOP on top) in either seconds or frames, and then your segment duration for MPEG-DASH as the number of GOPs. With a GOP setting of two seconds, the segment duration of two GOPs equals four seconds—right in line with the recommendations for DASH in the Chapter 14.

Not all programs make these selections so idiot proof, and with FFmpeg, you're obviously in charge. Again, you can get away with errors in almost all other configurations, but if GOP size doesn't divide evenly into segment size, you could have noticeable jumps in your videos at every data rate switch—or a host of other problems, like crashing or out and out stoppages.

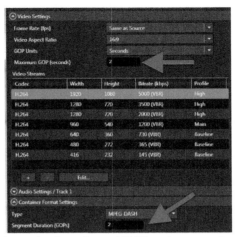

Figure 15-6. Setting key frame interval (GOP) and segment size of two GOPs.

Multiple-file Encoding in FFmpeg

OK, let's learn how to do all this in FFmpeg. Back in Chapter 8, you learned about two-pass encoding with FFmpeg, so let's start there. The text below shows a simple two-pass argument, with explanations for the syntax

```
ffmpeg -y -i TOS.mp4 -c:v libx264 -b:v 5200k -pass 1 -f mp4 NUL && \
ffmpeg -i TOS.mp4 -c:v libx264 -b:v 5200k -pass 2 TOS_1080p.mp4
```

Here's an explanation of the commands used.

Line 1:

`-y` overwrites previous log file.

`-i` defines the input file.

`-c:v libx264` sets the video codec to x264.

`-b:v 5200k` sets the bitrate at 5200 kbps.

`-pass 1` defines the first pass.

`-f mp4` says the output format will be mp4.

`NUL` creates the log file.

`&& \` says to run second pass if the first pass is successful.

Line 2:

-i defines the input file.

-c:v libx264 sets the video codec to x264.

-b:v 5200k sets the bitrate at 5200 kbps.

-pass 2 defines the second pass.

TOS_2P.mp4 sets the output file name.

As we've discussed, during the first pass, the encoder gathers information about the complexity of the file, which is used to control the data rate during the second pass. All the options in the first pass must be included in the second, although you can add more options during the second pass.

While the first pass is usually faster than the second pass, it can be time consuming. If you're encoding multiple files, using the same pass for multiple outputs can save lots of time. This leads to three questions.

1. When can you use the first pass more than once?

In building your encoding ladder, you'll be changing resolution, video bitrate values, H.264 profile, key frame interval, and audio values. You can use the same argument when changing video resolution and all video bitrate values, but not frame rate, key frame interval, or H.264 profile. If you try to change these options in the second pass, you'll see the error message shown in Figure 15-7.

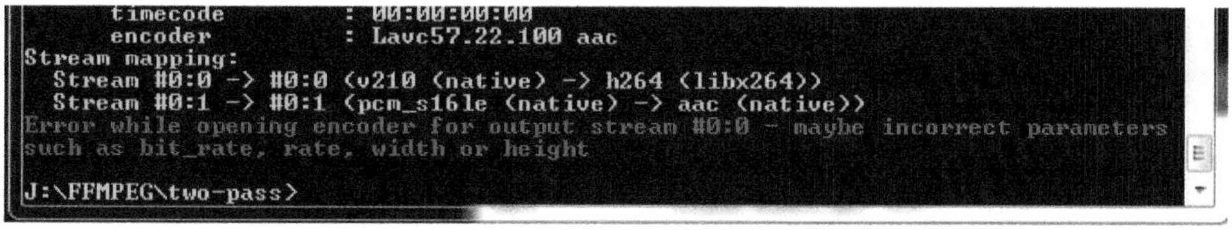

Figure 15-7. This is what you see if your second pass conflicts with your first pass.

Accordingly, for the seven files in the encoding ladder in Figure 15-1, you would need four first passes, as follows.

- **First Pass 1.** 1080p, 720p_h, 720p_l

- **Second Pass 1.** 360p_h (different profile from first three)

- **Third Pass 1.** 360p_l and 270p (different profile)

- **Fourth Pass 1.** 232p (different frame rate)

Since the files with the longest encoding time will be the top three, you'll get the most bang for your buck there.

Obviously, if you use the High profile for all streams, as Apple recommends, you can use the same first pass for all files except for the lowest-quality stream. Going beyond the configurations typically adjusted in an ABR group, note that you also can't use the same first pass when changing B-frame or reference frame values in the second pass.

2. Which parameters need to be in the first and second pass?

I'm sure someone knows, but I don't. I just know what has worked and hasn't worked.

Typically, I include x264 preset; target bitrate (but not maximum or bufsize); and B-frame, reference frame and key frame settings. I do not typically include video resolution or audio settings, although some sources say audio settings are essential so I'm including them in the command lines that follow. I do not include H.264 profile unless I'm encoding to the Main or Baseline profile; it has not been necessary for encoding to the High profile. That is, if your output file will be Main or Baseline, you need to include that in both the first and second passes.

3. Which parameters do you include in the first pass?

Our encoding ladder has seven rungs—which configuration do you use for the first pass? The knee-jerk reaction is to use the highest-quality pass, although most experts recommend a stream somewhere in the middle of the ladder. I created a simple encoding ladder to test this theory, and encoded three ways, as shown in Figure 15-8. The first used the 1080p parameters in the first pass, the second the 720p parameters, and the third the 360p parameters. The encoding parameters in the second three passes were identical in all test cases.

Pass 1: 1080p params	Pass 1: 720p params	Pass 1: 360p params
Pass 2: 1080p	Pass 2: 1080p	Pass 2: 1080p
Pass 2: 720p	Pass 2: 720p	Pass 2: 720p
Pass 2: 360p	Pass 2: 360p	Pass 2: 360p

Figure 15-8. Identifying the optimal encoding parameters for the first pass.

Which configuration delivered the best quality? Table 15-2 tells the tale, and shows that on average, the 360p first pass configuration delivered the best overall quality. Note that the overall quality delta is very small, and it's only one test, so if I were starting a massive transcode of my content, I'd probably test with a few more streams before finalizing my strategy.

TOS	1080p First Pass	720p First Pass	360p First Pass	Delta
1080p	34.99	35.14	35.09	0.41%
720p	33.36	33.24	33.46	0.65%
360p	32.93	33.00	32.97	0.20%
Average	33.76	33.79	33.84	0.42%

Table 15-2. The 360p pass delivered the best quality by a hair.

In the ABR group shown in Table 15-2, I would likely use the parameters in the 720p_h file for the first pass for the three top-quality files, then the 270p configuration for the 270p and 360p files.

Extracting Audio or Video

Sometimes you'll need to create an audio-only or video-only stream. For example, you'll need an audio-only stream for DASH and perhaps HLS. You can add an audio only stream as the last argument in your FFmpeg batch, and specify audio only via the –vn argument. I'll duplicate the same first pass argument from above for simplicity, and add the second pass.

```
ffmpeg -y -i TOS.mp4 -c:v libx264 -b:v 5200k -pass 1 -f mp4 NUL && \

ffmpeg -i TOS.mp4 -vn -c:a aac -b:a 128k -ac 2 -ar 48000 -pass 2
no_vid.mp4
```

In the second pass, the –vn says skip the video (video? no!), while the other parameters identify the audio codec and set encoding parameters. Note that the audio-only file could have the .mp4 or .aac extension. As you'll see, MP4Box uses the .mp4 extension, which is why I used that there.

What about excluding audio from the .mp4 file? Here I would add the –an argument (audio? no!) to produce the video-only .mp4 file.

```
ffmpeg -y -i TOS.mp4 -c:v libx264 -an -b:v 5200k -pass 2 no_audio.mp4
```

Again, I could have produced this file as a .h264 file that would be video only, but MP4Box prefers working with mp4 files.

Putting it All Together

Here's the command line argument for the first three files and the audio file.

```
ffmpeg -y -i TOS.mp4 -c:v libx264 -s 1280x720 -preset medium -g 48
-keyint_min 48 -sc_threshold 0 -bf 3 -b_strategy 2 -refs 5
-b:v 3100k -c:a aac -b:a 128k -ac 2 -ar 48000 -pass 1 -f mp4 NUL && \

ffmpeg -i TOS.mp4 -c:v libx264 -preset medium -g 48 -keyint_min 48
-sc_threshold 0 -bf 3 -b_strategy 2 -refs 5 -b:v 5200k -maxrate 5720k
-bufsize 5200k -c:a aac -b:a 128k -ac 2 -ar 48000 -pass 2
TOS_1080p.mp4

ffmpeg -i TOS.mp4. -c:v libx264 -s 1280x720 -preset medium -g 48
-keyint_min 48 -sc_threshold 0 -bf 3 -b_strategy 2 -refs 5 -b:v 3100k
-maxrate 3410k -bufsize 3100k -c:a aac -b:a 128k -ac 2 -ar 48000
-pass 2 TOS_720p_h.mp4
```

```
ffmpeg -i TOS.mp4 -c:v libx264 -s 1280x720 -preset medium -g 48
-keyint_min 48 -sc_threshold 0 -bf 3 -b_strategy 2 -refs 5
-b:v 2400k -maxrate 2640k -bufsize 2400k -c:a aac -b:a 128k -ac 2
-ar 48000 -pass 2 TOS_720p_l.mp4

ffmpeg -i TOS.mp4 -vn -c:a aac -b:a 128k -ac 2 -ar 48000 -pass 2
TOS_audio.mp4
```

Packaging HLS Files

Packaging HLS files involves three steps—two that FFmpeg can do, one that it can't. These are:

1. Produce a .ts file or file segments. FFmpeg can do this.

2. Produce a .m3u8 playlist file for each file. FFmpeg can do this.

3. Create a master .m3u8 file for the entire presentation. FFmpeg can't do this, at least as of December 2016. There is an Apple tool, Variant Playlist Creator that can, and I detail how that works below.

In this section, you'll learn how to package HLS content from existing MP4 files, which is the workflow I recommend. You'll also learn how to create HLS output from a single mezzanine file, which I don't recommend for reasons discussed earlier. Then I'll describe how to create a master .m3u8 file.

Packaging Existing MP4 Files

Using the command line arguments shown earlier, we just created four MP4 files: the top three files in our encoding ladder (TOS.mp4, TOS_720p_h.mp4, TOS_720p_l.mp4) and an audio-only file (TOS_audio.mp4). To package these files, we need to create output in the required MPEG-2 transport stream container format, as well as the necessary manifest files. Here are the FFmpeg commands to make that happen.

```
ffmpeg -i TOS_1080p.mp4 -bsf:v h264_mp4toannexb -codec copy -f hls
-hls_time 6 -hls_list_size 0 -hls_flags single_file TOS_1080p.m3u8

ffmpeg -i TOS_720p_h.mp4 -bsf:v h264_mp4toannexb -codec copy -f hls
-hls_time 6 -hls_list_size 0 -hls_flags single_file TOS_720p_h.m3u8

ffmpeg -i TOS_720p_l.mp4 -bsf:v h264_mp4toannexb -codec copy -f hls
-hls_time 6 -hls_list_size 0 -hls_flags single_file TOS_720p_l.m3u8

ffmpeg -i TOS_audio.mp4 -codec copy -f hls -hls_time 6
-hls_list_size 0 -hls_flags single_file TOS_audio.m3u8
```

Here's an explanation of the new commands used.

`-bsf:v h264_mp4toannexb` is necessary when converting from MP4 to .ts. Otherwise, you'll see a "bitstream malformed" error.

`-codec copy` tells FFmpeg to copy the encoded streams, rather than transcoding them.

`-f hls` sets output as HLS.

`-hls_time 6` sets a segment size of six seconds.

`-hls_list_size 0` ensures that FFmpeg includes all segments in the .m3u8 file. If not included, the .m3u8 file will contain only the first five segments.

`-hls_flags single_file` creates a single output file and a playlist that specifies byte-range requests rather than separate segments (Figure 15-9, on the right). If excluded, FFmpeg will create separate segments and a manifest file that points to those segments (Figure 15-9, on the left). Note that you need clients compatible with HLS version 4.0 and above to use a single file with byte-range requests.

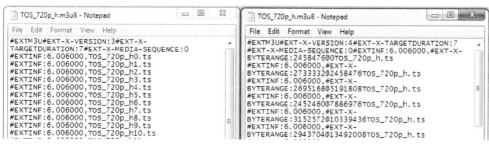

Figure 15-9. A manifest file calling individual fragments on the left, byte-range requests on the right.

Note: *There are many more HLS options, which you can find documented at bit.ly/FF_HLS.*

Creating HLS Output from Scratch

I don't recommend creating HLS output from scratch because you'll be unable to reuse the MP4 files that FFmpeg has to encode before packaging into an MPEG-2 transport stream. If your workflow absolutely requires this conversion, here's how to do it.

Basically, it's a combination of the "Putting it All Together" and the "Packaging Existing MP4 Files" command lines from earlier. That is, you simply add all the HLS specific arguments after `-f` in the "Packaging" arguments to the "Putting it all Together" arguments, and change the output file extension. Here are the arguments to create the top three files in the encoding ladder, as well as the audio file.

```
ffmpeg -y -i TOS.mp4 -c:v libx264 -s 1280x720 -g 48 -keyint_min 48
-sc_threshold 0 -bf 3 -b_strategy 2 -refs 5 -b:v 3100k -c:a aac
-b:a 128k -ac 2 -ar 48000 -pass 1 -f HLS -hls_time 6 -hls_list_size 0
-hls_flags single_file NUL && \
```

```
ffmpeg -i TOS.mp4 -c:v libx264 -g 48 -keyint_min 48 -sc_threshold 0
-bf 3 -b_strategy 2 -refs 5 -b:v 5200k -maxrate 5720k -bufsize 5200k
-c:a aac -b:a 128k -ac 2 -ar 48000 -pass 2 -f hls -hls_time 6
-hls_list_size 0 -hls_flags single_file TOS_1080p.m3u8

ffmpeg -i TOS.mp4 -c:v libx264 -s 1280x720 -g 48 -keyint_min 48
-sc_threshold 0 -bf 3 -b_strategy 2 -refs 5 -b:v 3100k -maxrate 3410k
-bufsize 3100k -c:a aac -b:a 128k -ac 2 -ar 48000 -pass 2 -f hls
-hls_time 6 -hls_list_size 0 -hls_flags single_file TOS_720p_h.m3u8

ffmpeg -i TOS.mp4 -c:v libx264 -s 1280x720 -g 48 -keyint_min 48
-sc_threshold 0 -bf 3 -b_strategy 2 -refs 5 -b:v 2400k
-maxrate 2640k -bufsize 2400k -c:a aac -b:a 128k -ac 2 -ar 48000
-pass 2 -f hls -hls_time 6 -hls_list_size 0 -hls_flags single_file
TOS_720p_l.m3u8

ffmpeg -i TOS.mp4 -vn -c:a aac -b:a 128k -ac 2 -ar 48000 -pass 2
-f hls -hls_time 6 -hls_list_size 0 -hls_flags single_file TOS_audio.m3u8
```

You can refer to the sections earlier for descriptions of the various commands.

Creating the Master Playlist File

HLS requires two types of playlist files: a media playlist for each stream of content, and a master playlist that refers to all the playlist files. The media playlist points to the segments or byte-range requests in the file (Figure 15-9) and it's what we created with FFmpeg earlier. The master manifest is what we're examining now, and it has several jobs.

- First, it lists the encoding characteristics of the available streams so the player can identify which it can play and which it can't.

- Second, it identifies the location of the playlists for those streams so the player knows where to find the streams.

- Finally, it tells the player which layer to retrieve and start playing first.

Figure 15-10 shows a master .m3u8 manifest file produced by Sorenson Squeeze, along with a screenshot from FileZilla (a free FTP utility) showing the files uploaded to the Doceo website. If you navigate to bit.ly/test_hls in Safari on the Mac or in Microsoft Edge, you can play the HLS files uploaded there. Note that this won't work in Chrome or Firefox, since neither supports HLS natively.

As highlighted in the figure, there are folders for each stream with a master playlist (ZOOLANDER_1080p.m3u8) at the root. Each folder contains the media files for that stream and a media playlist file like that shown on the left in Figure 15-9. The master playlist points to the media playlist files (called index.m3u8) in the individual folders. Sorenson Squeeze output the files in the structure shown. As long as you upload the files to your web server without changing the structure or the folder or file names, it should work just fine.

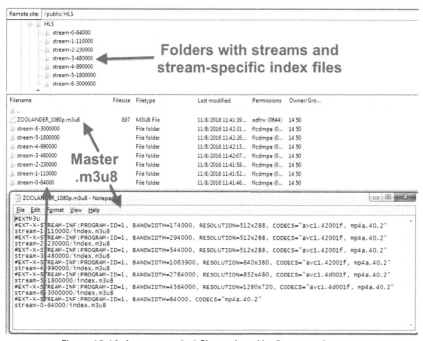

Figure 15-10. A master .m3u8 file produced by Sorenson Squeeze.

The master .m3u8 file is open in Notepad on the bottom of the figure. The structure of each `#EXT-X-STREAM-INF:` entry is <attribute list><URI>, or Uniform Resource Identifier, which is the location of the index file for that stream. For example, on the bottom of Figure 15-10, in the last line of Notepad, you see a 64,000 bps audio-only stream where the bottom line is `stream-0-64000/index.m3u8`. As the arrow shows, this points to that folder on the web server. It's basically saying, "Hey, if you want to play this stream, grab this index file."

At the start of playback, the player scans through this master playlist from the top down to identify the first compatible stream. It then finds the location of the stream-specific media playlist and downloads it. Then it finds the location of the first available media file (or byte-range), which it retrieves and starts playing. When it's time to switch streams up or down, the player checks back with the master .m3u8 to identify other available streams, and their location.

What information must be in the master .m3u8 files? This is dictated by the HLS Specification that Apple submitted to the Internet Engineering Task Force (IETF) back in 2009, which is now up to version 20 (bit.ly/HLS_spec). If you scroll to page 27 of the spec, you'll see that there are multiple attributes that can be listed in the .m3u8 file. The spec distinguishes which descriptors must be included, which should be included, and which are optional. Table 15-3 contains a summary of the most common attributes, plus their status and description.

Variant	Status	Description
BANDWIDTH	Required	Peak bitrate in bits per second
AVERAGE-BANDWIDTH	Optional	Average bitrate in bits per second
CODECS	Should Include	Codecs in the stream (see Table 15-4)
RESOLUTION	Recommended for Videos	Pixel resolution
FRAME-RATE	Recommended for Videos	Maximum frame rate rounded to 3 decimal places. Should be included for videos with frame rates in excess of 30 fps

Table 15-3. The most common variants in HLS streams.

From my perspective, you should include the first four in every master .m3u8 playlist, and FRAME-RATE when your frame rates exceed 30 fps. To assist your efforts, Table 15-4 contains a list of the audio/video codec codes, which is from Apple's "HTTP Live Streaming Overview" (bit.ly/HLS_oview).

AAC-LC	"mp4a.40.2"
HE-AAC	"mp4a.40.5"
MP3	"mp4a.40.34"
H.264 Baseline Profile level 3.0	"avc1.42001e" or "avc1.66.30" Note: Use "avc1.66.30" for compatibility with iOS versions 3.0 to 3.1.2.
H.264 Baseline Profile level 3.1	"avc1.42001f"
H.264 Main Profile level 3.0	"avc1.4d001e" or "avc1.77.30" Note: Use "avc1.77.30" for compatibility with iOS versions 3.0 to 3.12.
H.264 Main Profile level 3.1	"avc1.4d001f"
H.264 Main Profile level 4.0	"avc1.4d0028"
H.264 High Profile level 3.1	"avc1.64001f"
H.264 High Profile level 4.0	"avc1.640028"
H.264 High Profile level 4.1	"avc1.640029"

Table 15-4. Audio/video codec codes for your master .m3u8 file.

If you're creating your own master .m3u8 file, the Apple overview answers questions like how to specify an audio only stream, or how to add a still image to an audio stream. Check with the IETF spec for details on other optional components—like High-bandwidth Digital Content Protection (HDCP) level, subtitles and closed captions. For basic operation, you should be able to build your own .m3u8 file by duplicating the structure and attribute list in the Squeeze file shown in Figure 15-10, and substituting in your own attribute list and location information.

Working with Apple Tools

Apple has three HLS-related command-line tools that are very useful if you have access to a Mac. These are:

- **Media File Segmenter.** Can segment an existing H.264 encoded MP4/MOV file and create the media playlist.

- **Variant Playlist Creator.** Can create a master playlist file if you've created the media playlists with mediafilesegmenter.

- **Media Stream Validator.** Can verify that all the links that you've uploaded to the web are working, and that the file segments all meet the recommended specifications.

All three tools are available for free at developer.apple.com/streaming under "Downloads," once you sign in with your developer ID. Once you install the utilities using the Apple-supplied installation routine, they should be available from any folder on the Mac. Let's take a brief look at all three tools.

Media File Segmenter

Again, the inputs for Media File Segmenter are media files—specifically H.264 encoded files in either .mov or .mp4 format, as well as audio files encoded as .aac or even Dolby encoded audio.

The operational syntax is simple and shown below.

```
#! /bin/bash
mediafilesegmenter -I -t6 -f /Users/janozer/TOS/360p
/Users/janozer/TOS/TOS_360p.mp4
mediafilesegmenter -I -t6 -f /Users/janozer/TOS/720p
/Users/janozer/TOS/TOS_720p.mp4
mediafilesegmenter -I -t6 -f /Users/janozer/TOS/1080p
/Users/janozer/TOS/TOS_1080p.mp4
mediafilesegmenter -I -t6 -f /Users/janozer/TOS/audio
/Users/janozer/TOS/TOS_audio.mp4
```

Here's an explanation of the command structure in the batch files I created. Note that there are many more switches available, particularly for encryption and related functions.

`mediafilesegmenter` calls the application.

`-I` creates the property list file (.plist) which identifies important file characteristics.

`-t6` sets the segment duration at six seconds.

`-f /Users/janozer/TOS/360p` sets the output location Note that you have to create these folders beforehand; Media File Segmenter won't create these folders for you.

`/Users/janozer/TOS/TOS_360p.mp4` identifies the input file.

I'm not expert in Mac batch file creation, but to make the utility work I had to include the full path to both the target folder and source file. Figure 15-11 shows the files created after running the batch file.

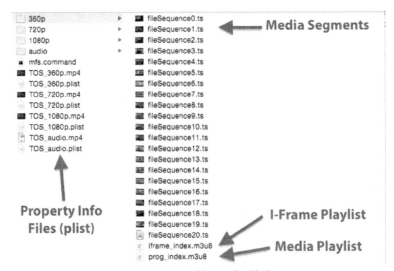

Figure 15-11. Files created by Media File Segmenter.

Here's a brief explanation of the various outputs. You know what the media segments and media playlists are. The I-frame playlist is a playlist used to add Trick Play, fast forward, and rewind to the HLS presentation, which is beyond the scope of what I'll cover here.

Note the four .plist files, one for each media file processed. This file contains basic information about the processed file including resolution, bandwidth, average bandwidth, codecs used, and the like. If you create your master playlist using Variant Playlist Creator, you'll input the .plist file and the utility will create a wholly formed master playlist. If you create your playlists manually, you can get all necessary information about each media playlist from the .plist file.

Variant Playlist Creator

Variant Playlist Creator inputs the media playlist and .plist files, and outputs the master playlist. The syntax is as follows:

```
variantplaylistcreator -o master.m3u8
/Users/janozer/TOS/720p/prog_index.m3u8
/Users/janozer/TOS/TOS_720p.plist
/Users/janozer/TOS/1080p/prog_index.m3u8
/Users/janozer/TOS/TOS_1080p.plist
/Users/janozer/TOS/360p/prog_index.m3u8
/Users/janozer/TOS/TOS_360p.plist
/Users/janozer/TOS/audio/prog_index.m3u8
/Users/janozer/TOS/TOS_audio.plist
```

Here's an explanation of the command structure.

`variantplaylistcreator` runs the utility.

`-o master.m3u8` identifies the output file name.

`/Users/janozer/TOS/720p/prog_index.m3u8` identifies the media playlist URL. Repeat for each stream included in master.

`/Users/janozer/TOS/TOS_720p.plist` identifies the .plist file URL. Repeat for each stream included in master.

Then you repeat the structure for each of the media playlists included. You can also include `-iframe-url` to identify the URL of the I-frame playlist, if desired.

The command line includes the 720p file first, since this is the stream that most viewers should be able to maintain (see the following section), then 1080p, then 360p, then audio only. This created the master playlist shown in Figure 15-12. Note that I manually removed the references to `/Users/janozer` in the master playlist to match the navigation the presentation would have once I uploaded it to the web. I also removed any mention of closed captions.

```
#EXTM3U
#EXT-X-STREAM-INF:AVERAGE-BANDWIDTH=1659547,BANDWIDTH=1931856,CODECS="mp4a.40.2,
avc1.64001f",RESOLUTION=1280x720,FRAME-RATE=23.976
720p/prog_index.m3u8

#EXT-X-STREAM-INF:AVERAGE-BANDWIDTH=3180204,BANDWIDTH=3586075,CODECS="mp4a.40.2,
avc1.640028",RESOLUTION=1920x1080,FRAME-RATE=23.976
1080p/prog_index.m3u8

#EXT-X-STREAM-INF:AVERAGE-BANDWIDTH=1160684,BANDWIDTH=1363470,CODECS="mp4a.40.2,
avc1.64001e",RESOLUTION=640x360,FRAME-RATE=23.976
360p/prog_index.m3u8

#EXT-X-STREAM-INF:AVERAGE-BANDWIDTH=132693,BANDWIDTH=134396,CODECS="mp4a.40.2"
audio/prog_index.m3u8
```

Figure 15-12. The master playlist.

Media Stream Validator

This utility checks all the links in the presentation and then certain file details you can read about in Apple Technical Note TN2235: Media Stream Validator Tool Results Explained (bit.ly/tn2235). Running the program is simple, although it only works on files already uploaded to the web. Here's the command syntax:

```
mediastreamvalidator http://www.doceopub.com/TOS/master.m3u8
```

Yup, utility name and then the URL of the master playlist file. You can see the preliminary results in Figure 15-13, which shows that all the files are present and accounted for.

```
Jan-Mac-Pro:TOS janozer$ mediastreamvalidator http://www.doceopub.com/TOS/master.m3u8
mediastreamvalidator: Version 1.2(160525)

[/TOS/master.m3u8] Started root playlist download
[audio/prog_index.m3u8] Started media playlist download
[720p/prog_index.m3u8] Started media playlist download
[1080p/prog_index.m3u8] Started media playlist download
[360p/prog_index.m3u8] Started media playlist download
[audio/prog_index.m3u8] All media files delivered and have end tag, stopping
[720p/prog_index.m3u8] All media files delivered and have end tag, stopping
[360p/prog_index.m3u8] All media files delivered and have end tag, stopping
[1080p/prog_index.m3u8] All media files delivered and have end tag, stopping
```

Figure 15-13. All the files are present and accounted for—a good start.

Beyond this, Media Stream Validator presents a range of other information that's particularly important when you're seeking App Store approval for an app that will play your videos. You should run this utility for all HLS presentations you upload, particularly when you're first starting out.

OK, now that we know how to produce the master playlist file, let's take a look at which file you should place first.

Which Stream First?

As mentioned earlier, the stream listed first in the .m3u8 file is the stream played first by the HLS player. Which stream should you deploy first? In Tech Note TN2224, Apple says, "Therefore, the first bit rate in the playlist should be the one that most clients can sustain." In the Apple Devices spec, Apple gets even more directive, saying, "For WiFi delivery, the default video variant(s) SHOULD be the 2000 kb/s variant. For cellular delivery, the default video variant(s) SHOULD be the 730 kb/s variant." (bit.ly/A_Devices_Spec). How important is this issue? Tests performed in mid 2016 indicate that the choice of first stream can seriously impact early quality of experience.

You read a bit about these tests back in Chapter 8 when I discussed bitrate control and quality of experience (QoE). Or, you can see the original article on my website at bit.ly/cbr_qoe. The high-level objective was to test how CBR and VBR encoding impacted QoE. To test this, I created an eight-minute test file that alternated 30 seconds of talking head with 30 seconds of ballet. Then I encoded the file using CBR, 200 percent constrained VBR and 110 percent constrained VBR.

To measure QoE, I restricted the bandwidth of the playback station using a tool called Charles Web Debugging Proxy (bit.ly/Chas_proxy, Chapter 3), and used the same tool to identify the bitrate of the segments retrieved by the player in each test. The bottom line: the stream encoded using 200 percent constrained VBR delivered the lowest QoE as measured by the number of stream switches during playback and the average bitrate of the segments actually viewed.

During the tests, at some settings, stream switching oscillated noticeably at the start. To see if this related to which stream the player retrieved first, I created two .m3u8 files as follows:

- The first listed the highest-quality file (1080p@4500 kbps) first.

- The second listed the third-highest-quality file (720p@2100) first.

Then I set an artificial throttle of 3200 kbps with Charles and played both M3U8 streams in Safari until the first eight segments were downloaded. Again, it's the same encoded files; the only difference is which stream was listed first in the .m3u8 file.

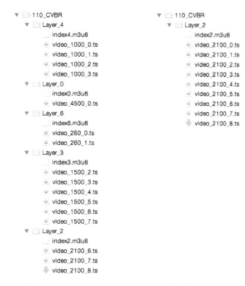

Figure 15-14. Playback with 4500 kbps stream called first on the left, and 2100 kbps stream called first on the right.

Figure 15-14 shows the results. On the left, the initial file was the 4500 kbps file. Safari immediately sensed a problem, and started retrieving layers as low as layer 6 to address it. The viewer sees a quick panoply of multiple quality levels, finally settling in at layer 2 about 36 seconds in. During this scramble, Safari retrieved 16 segments to play the first eight, which obviously wastes bandwidth. Safari retrieved segments from five categories, indicating at least four stream switches.

On the right, the initial stream was the 2100 kbps file. Safari immediately settled into smooth playback, downloading eight segments to play eight segments. Since Safari only downloaded segments from one category, there was no stream switching. So the player viewed a higher overall quality level of packets without the stream switching and obviously slower quality segments. Obviously, the QoE with the 2100 kbps played first was much better.

Of course, if the bandwidth hadn't been constricted, the QoE with the 4500 kbps file listed first would have been superior. However, the reason we use ABR is to handle constricted bandwidth—not just during playback, but at the start as well. So it's best to factor this into your decision as to which file you list first.

Note that I prepared all files and packages for this test with the Capella Systems Cambria encoder. Like most encoders, Cambria lists files in the master .m3u8 file based upon the order of layers in the encoding preset. If you build your encoding ladder from the top down, like I did, the highest-quality file is listed first. If you build from the bottom up, the lowest-quality stream is listed first. Seldom, if ever, is either of these choices the correct one. For these tests, I simply switched stream location in Notepad to change which stream Safari retrieved first.

Target Specific Master Manifest Files

When a device hits your website, your player should be able to determine some basic specs of the playback device, like whether it's a computer or OTT device, or a smartphone or tablet. You can create different .m3u8 files for each class of devices.

For desktop or OTT playback, the initial stream should be a reasonably high-quality stream—say around 3 Mbps or so, but no higher, since few ISPs can sustain bandwidths higher than this. That way, quality starts at a good level, and will improve for higher-quality connections. If you're concerned about startup time, consider starting with a lower-quality stream that will take less time to retrieve. For short-form content, a faster startup time is usually more important than it is for long-form content.

For mobile, the initial stream should be lower-quality—perhaps a 360p stream, which will look good for most viewers, and again will improve for those with high-bandwidth connections. What you want to avoid in both cases is a high-bitrate stream that will push the player into panic mode, resulting in the low QoE and inefficient playback shown on the left in Figure 15-11.

> **Tip:** *I recently observed the data rates retrieved by Amazon and Netflix during the first few minutes of video playback. In both cases, when testing playback on a very high-speed network, the services started with a mid-range quality stream, which they retrieved for two to three minutes before starting to retrieve higher-quality streams. Both services used this as a buffer against later bandwidth reductions or even out and out stoppages, which worked very well in my tests. I know nothing about the player side of implementing this strategy, but if you're delivering long-form content it's worth looking into.*

Packaging for DASH with MP4Box

Packaging DASH output involves the same basic steps as HLS, although FFmpeg can't perform any of them. Instead, I'll demonstrate with an open-source tool called MP4Box.

MP4Box is one of multiple open-source utilities created by GPAC, which includes the Osmo4 player, MP4Box, and multiple server tools. You can download the complete set of utilities at bit.ly/dlMP4box, and click through the site to read more about the tools and organization.

To package your files with MP4Box, you need to ensure that your key frame interval divides evenly into your segment size, which I'll show you how to set below. I'll be working with the same four output files creating earlier in the section titled "Putting It All Together," which I encoded using a key frame interval of 48 frames, or two seconds.

As mentioned earlier, MP4Box can only perform this DASHing process with MP4 inputs (hence the name), which is why I produced the audio/video and audio-only files in MP4 format. Note that most DASH players want separate audio video streams, rather than interleaved or muxed audio/video streams as with HLS and standard MP4 files. Rather than create a set of video only MP4 files, I'll use the `#video` option in the command line to tell MP4Box to only insert video from the MP4 files into the MPD file.

Here's the command line.

```
mp4box.exe -dash 4000 -rap -dash-profile dashavc264:onDemand
-bs-switching no TOS_720p_l.mp4#video TOS_720p_h.mp4#video
TOS_1080p.mp4#video TOS_audio.mp4
```

Here's an explanation of the switches shown.

`mp4box.exe` runs the program.

`-dash 4000` sets the segment length (in milliseconds), so this is four seconds..

`-rap` forces segments to begin at random access points.

`-dash-profile dashavc264:onDemand` makes sure a single file accessed via byte-range requests is output, rather than separate segments.

`TOS_720p_l.mp4#video TOS_720p_h.mp4#video TOS_1080p.mp4#video TOS_audio.mp4` defines the input files, using the #video to insert only the video into the fragmented MP4 file.

The output from this function are the files shown in Figure 15-15, which you upload to your web server to make available to your viewers, linking to the .mpd file. The four .mp4 files are each elementary streams, meaning that they contain only audio or video, but not both. The .mpd file directs the player which streams to retrieve and how to mux them for playback. In this case, the player is retrieving a byte-range request within each file, since we chose this approach rather than producing separate segments.

Name	Date modified	Type	Size
TOS_1080p_dash.mpd	11/8/2016 4:53 PM	MPD File	3 KB
TOS_720p_h_track1_dashinit.mp4	11/8/2016 4:53 PM	VLC media file (.m...	51,267 KB
TOS_720p_l_track1_dashinit.mp4	11/8/2016 4:53 PM	VLC media file (.m...	29,427 KB
TOS_1080p_track1_dashinit.mp4	11/8/2016 4:53 PM	VLC media file (.m...	73,087 KB
TOS_audio_track1_dashinit.mp4	11/8/2016 4:53 PM	VLC media file (.m...	1,932 KB

Figure 15-15. The output from DASHing the input files.

MP4Box contains many more useful options, which you can read about at bit.ly/mp4boxdash. You can read up on DASH in general at bit.ly/mp4boxdash2. French company Streamroot has done a nice job posting several articles on encoding and packaging for DASH, which you can read at bit.ly/srdashing. I think I've done a good job incorporating Streamroot's direction into this chapter, but if it's 2017 or beyond or you're looking for more advanced tutorials, go there.

> **Tip:** *MP4Box can also encode the files for you if that's your preference.*

So, we're good for encoding and packaging your ABR streams. Look at you, and how much progress you've made! Next chapter we explore different ways to customize your output via per-title encoding.

> **Author's note:** *I would like to thank Streamroot's Erica Beavers and Nikolay Rodionov for their tech read of this chapter, and many helpful suggestions. Streamroot is a leading provider of innovative OTT video optimization technologies for content publishers, network service providers, and enterprise customers. You can read more about Streamroot at streamroot.io.*

Chapter 16: Per-title Encoding

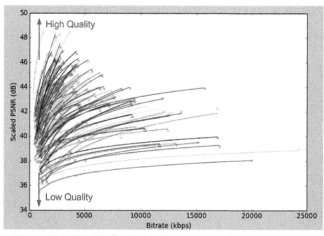

Figure 16-1. Why Netflix decided per-title encoding was essential.

In Chapter 7, you learned how to use constant rate factor (CRF) values to choose the bitrate for a file. This is a form of per-title encoding. In this chapter, you'll learn about more formal techniques being used to compute the ideal bitrate for individual files or categories of files. In my own practice, I've looked at per-title encoding for two clients. As you'll learn, both times it worked out well—just in completely different ways.

In this chapter, you will learn about:

- Netflix's and YouTube's approaches to per-title encoding

- the approach used by Cappella Systems in its Cambria encoder

- how to use capped CRF encoding to encode individual files.

Netflix and Per-title Encoding

Netflix announced its per-title encoding technique via a blog post titled "Per-Title Encode Optimization" published on December 14, 2015 (bit.ly/nf_pt). It's a pretty technical discussion that I summarized with input from Netflix for Streaming Media in an article titled "How Netflix Pioneered Per-Title Video Encoding Optimization" (bit.ly/nf_pt2).

Netflix's rationale for per-title encoding is best summarized in Figure 16-1, which Netflix created by encoding multiple files at four different quantization parameter (QP) levels. Like CRF encoding, which we discussed back in Chapter 7, QP encoding delivers a certain quality level by adjusting the encoding data rate up or down. What Figure 16-1 shows is that some files achieved a very high quality level at a very low bitrate, like the files represented by the nearly vertical plot lines on the upper left. Conversely, other files, represented by nearly horizontal plot lines on the lower right, never achieved high quality, even at very high bitrates.

Figure 16-1 pretty much shouts, "All files are different, and you shouldn't use the same encoding ladder for them all." True that, although Netflix's technique for computing the optimal encoding ladder for each file is probably beyond most readers technically and economically.

Creating the Encoding Ladder

After establishing that all files need different encoding ladders, the post describes how Netflix produces its ladder. At a high level, Netflix runs a number of test encodes at different resolutions and QP values to plot the peak signal-to-noise (PSNR) quality at each bitrate/resolution pair, and uses that to identify the optimum encoding ladder.

One observation made in the post is that while increasing the bitrate at the same resolution consistently increases stream quality, these quality increases flatten out once the bitrate goes above a certain threshold. You can see this for the low-, mid-, and high-resolution plots in Figure 16-2. If you plot a line that includes the peak quality/bitrate efficiency points from all resolutions, you get a "convex hull," a term describing the shape that most efficiently bounds all data points.

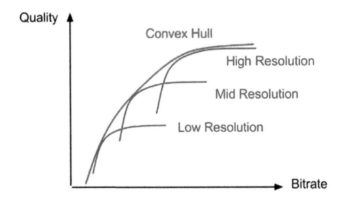

Figure 16-2. Plotting the convex hull, where each resolution delivers maximum quality.

As part of its article, Netflix shared the before and after encoding ladder for an animated movie, which are both shown in Table 16-1. On the left is the now obsolete default ladder, which would have encoded the file at up to 5800 kbps—a bitrate potentially necessary to ensure top quality for *Mission Impossible X*, but not for a simple animation. This compares to a top rate of 3840 kbps in the per-title ladder, a savings of about 34 percent from 5800 kbps.

Resolutions	Default bitrate ladder	Per-title bitrate ladder
320x240	235	150
384x288	375	200
512x384	560	290
512x384	750	
640x480	1050	
720x480	1750	440
720x480		590
1280x720	2350	830
1280x720	3000	1150
1920x1080	4300	1470
1920x1080	5800	2150
1920x1080		3840

Table 16-1. Netflix's encoding ladders, before and after.

Looking at the lower bitrates, Netflix was able to distribute a 720p file at 1150 kbps, where using the obsolete ladder, the resolution would have been 640x480 for 1050 kbps. Particularly for animated films, with artificially sharp edges, this increased resolution would make a huge difference in perceived quality. Clearly, per-title encoding saved Netflix bandwidth costs and improved the quality of experience of its viewers.

Just to be clear, Netflix uses this technique to identify the optimal encoding ladder and encodes for final output using two-pass constrained VBR encoding, with the level of constraint unknown.

> **Note:** *In June 2016, Netflix switched its per-title analysis from PSNR to a new metric called Video Multimethod Assessment Fusion (VMAF). You can read about that metric at bit.ly/nf_vmaf.*

Applying the Netflix Technique

Soon after the Netflix post, I attempted to duplicate Netflix's work via a slightly different technique. Rather than encoding to QP values, I encoded at various resolutions and data rates, and used PSNR to identify the highest-quality resolution at each data rate. You can see this in Table 16-2, where the green background identifies the highest-quality file at each bitrate. Once I chose the data rate values on my encoding ladder, I used this data to choose the best resolution at each data rate.

PSNR	1080p	720p	540p	360p	270p	180p
4900	44.94					
4600	44.73					
4300	44.50					
4000	44.24					
3700	43.96					
3400	43.65	42.80				
3100	43.30	42.59				
2800	42.89	42.35				
2500	42.42	42.07	41.39			
2200	41.85	41.71	41.15			
1900	41.16	41.27	40.84	38.65		
1600	40.30	40.69	40.43	38.47		
1300	39.20	39.91	39.87	38.20		
1000	37.70	38.75	39.00	37.76	35.35	
900		38.27	38.60	37.55	35.25	
800		37.69	38.12	37.29	35.13	
700		37.01	37.54	36.95	34.97	
600			36.85	36.52	34.74	31.57
500			35.97	35.93	34.43	31.47
400				35.14	33.97	31.30
300					33.24	31.02
200					31.97	30.44

Table 16-2. PSNR values at various bitrates and resolutions.

My version of the convex hull is shown in Figure 16-3, which visually reveals several key data points. First, the 180p and 270p streams never produced the highest-quality video at any resolution, meaning that they can be dropped. Second, at all data rates beyond 2200, the 1080p file produced the highest-quality output. Third, as with Netflix's convex hull, increasing the data rate at all resolutions produced diminishing returns beyond a certain point.

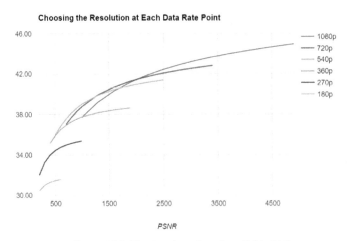

Figure 16-3. Plotting the values from Table 16-2.

The problem with this, and the Netflix approach, is the number of calculations necessary to support it. I count 63 outputs in Table 16-2, and this is with a short two-minute test file. Netflix applies an even more extensive grid on the complete TV show or movie.

Interestingly, in a cloud encoding environment, if you own your own encoding system, as Netflix does, this analysis would be neither cost- nor time-prohibitive. I recently wrote a white paper where I learned that the machine time involved in encoding a one-hour file to 10 iterations in both DASH and HLS was about $1.24 (bit.ly/hybrik_cost). This encode process involved 20 encodes at various resolutions (10 layers times two ABR outputs). If you own your own encoding software, the 63-point analysis shown in Table 16-2 would cost roughly three times as much, or just less than $4.00.

In terms of time, the 20-output tests performed for the white paper took about 10 hours, but we limited usage to 10 cloud machines. Netflix can access hundreds or even thousands to accelerate this process for a single file, or can run multiple files in parallel, so time wouldn't be an issue. Given that a single encoded Netflix file is distributed millions of times, this investment in time and cost makes perfect sense.

On the other hand, if you were paying Amazon for this, the cost would be about $90 (three times $28.56, the Amazon cost computed in the white paper), and the time would be glacial. Even if you owned your own encoders, most encoding shops can't take the time to encode each file 60 or more times to derive the optimal encoding ladder.

What about with my client? I was using this technique to identify the optimal encoding ladder for movie-based, real-life content—as opposed to animation. I was also trying to create the optimum encoding ladder for animated and (ahem) adult content. The problem was that the complexity within each group, as measured via CRF, was too significant to create a meaningful per-category encoding ladder. Fortunately, the client was using the Capella Systems Cambria encoder, which offers its own per-title feature that I'll describe shortly.

OK, that's Netflix. Let's take a really brief look at how YouTube performs per-title encoding.

YouTube and Per-title Encoding

I wrote about YouTube's approach to per-title encoding in a Streaming Media article titled "Conference Research Tests Adaptive Video and Quality Benchmarks" (bit.ly/yt_pt). In the article, I described a presentation at a quality conference I attended in San Francisco, as well as the associated paper authored by Google researchers.

YouTube's solution involves creating, deploying, and educating a neural network, which is probably more than you signed up for when you started reading this chapter. Since describing the approach further won't advance any previous or future discussion, and to save some trees that otherwise would be consumed to print this material, I'll refer you to the online article for a more complete description.

Per-title Encoding with Capella Systems Cambria

I reviewed Capella Systems Cambria FTC encoder for Streaming Media in a review you can read at bit.ly/cambria_pt. I first encountered the program working with the client mentioned in the Netflix section, and was pleasantly surprised to learn that it had a per-title option.

The official name for Cambria's feature is source-adaptive bitrate ladder (SABL). The starting point for every encode is the encoding ladder at the heart of each preset, like the one shown in the last chapter in Figure 15-6. When SABL is enabled via a script, like that shown in Figure 16-4, Cambria runs a fast CRF encode of the file to gauge encoding complexity. As we've covered several times, CRF is an encoding technique available with x264 and several other codecs that lets you select the desired quality level rather than a data rate. While encoding with CRF, x264 produces a file with the selected CRF quality level, adjusting the data rate as necessary to deliver that quality.

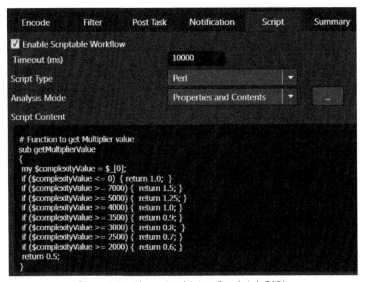

Figure 16-4. The script driving Cambria's SABL.

In this fashion, the data rate produced during the CRF encode is a measure of encoding complexity. For example, Table 16-3 shows the files I used to test SABL, and the results of the complexity measurements from the 1080p CRF encode, where all figures show the kbps output. The 30 Sec Peak value shows the highest averaged data rate for any 30-second chunk of the movie, while the 10 Sec Peak shows the highest average data rate for any 10-second chunk. The Average Complexity shows the average rate for the entire movie.

To reflect, like Figure 16-1, Table 16-3 shows exactly why a fixed-bitrate ladder is so suboptimal. Consider the 4300 kbps target data rate for the 1080p stream shown in Figure 16-2. Applied to the *Zoolander* movie, it would be too low, resulting in a poor-quality file. Applied to almost all other files in the test, it would be too high—especially for synthetic files such as the Screencam or Tutorial files. These files would be encoded at too high a data rate, wasting bandwidth and limiting their reach on slower-bandwidth connections.

Back on point, you control which measure that encoder uses to adjust the encoding ladder. A conservative approach might use 10 seconds as the measure, pushing the data rate up even though it might only benefit one highly complex region in the file. This would generally result in files with few encoding artifacts, but with some bandwidth wasted in other areas.

Alternatively, you could base the decision on the 30-second peak, which would result in a lower overall data rate, but perhaps some artifacts in some shorter regions. You could also set it for any arbitrary length.

Title	Description	30 Sec Peak	10 Sec Peak	Average Complexity
Elektra Movie (2 min clip)	Fight scene in movie	3,677	4,530	2,380
El Ultimo Movie (5 min)	Cartoon	1,458	1,865	1,183
Freedom	Music Video	5,162	5,849	3,651
Iron Man Cartoon (2 min)	Cartoon	2,996	3,298	2,744
New Clip	Test clip	3,558	7,009	2,120
Screencam	Camtasia-based footage	730	1,056	541
Talking Head	Simple Talking Head	1,893	2,338	1,488
Tutorial	PowerPoint and talking head	398	452	364
Zoolander movie (2 min)	Awful movie	6,973	7,978	6,422
Tears of Steel	2-minute segment	3,884	5,473	3,110

Table 16-3. Results from SABL computations.

Once this value is returned, the script shown in Figure 16-4 manages the adjustment. That is, if the encoding complexity was more than 7000 kbps, the encoder would adjust the data rate of all streams in the adaptive group by 1.5, boosting the target data rate by 50 percent. If the complexity value was 2000 kbps or less, the encoder would adjust the date by 0.6, dropping the data rate of all streams by 40 percent.

All these adjustments are totally configurable. For example, a conservative encoding shop could adjust the data rate upward for complex clips but never adjust the data rate downward for simple clips, maintaining a very high quality level. Or, you could adjust the data rates for some, but not all, of the streams. Of course, you select both the encoding thresholds and the percentage adjustments to each level.

How Did SABL Perform?

Intuitively, the goal of any per-title optimization technique would be to boost the data rate and quality of a file when necessary, but only when the improvement would be noticeable to the viewer. Otherwise, bandwidth would be wasted. Conversely, you would want the encoder to drop the bitrate and quality when possible, but only when it wouldn't result in visible artifacts that would degrade the viewer's quality of experience.

How do we measure these concepts? As detailed in other chapters, in the "Per-Title Encode Optimization" blog post, Netflix made several general observations about the peak signal-to-noise ratio (PSNR) metric that originally powered its analysis. First, Netflix stated that PSNR values in excess of 45 are seldom noticeable by the viewer. ("For encodes with PSNR 45 dB or above, the distortion is perceptually unnoticeable.") At the other end of the quality spectrum, the researchers also stated that PSNR values below 35 are often accompanied by visible artifacts. ("35 dB will show encoding artifacts.") Let's agree that these are very rough metrics, but they're a useful yardstick for assessing Cambria's SABL-related performance.

Title	SABL Data Rate	Bandwidth Reduction	PSNR Original	PSNR - SABL	Quality Reduction
Elektra Movie (2 min clip)	3,870	-10.00%	42.10	41.96	-0.34%
El Ultimo Movie (5 min)	2,150	-50.00%	47.10	45.23	-3.98%
Freedom	5,375	25.00%	40.42	41.29	2.15%
Iron Man Cartoon (2 min)	3,010	-30.00%	44.78	42.45	-5.19%
New Clip	3,870	-10.00%	41.63	41.31	-0.78%
Screencam	2,150	-50.00%	52.70	47.52	-9.84%
Talking Head	2,150	-50.00%	44.69	43.45	-2.78%
Tutorial	2,150	-50.00%	53.78	50.73	-5.67%
Zoolander movie (2 min)	5,375	25.00%	37.58	38.42	2.23%
Tears of Steel	3,870	-10.00%	40.66	40.21	-1.12%

Table 16-4. Analyzing the effectiveness of Cambria's SABL.

Table 16-4 shows the results of my tests for the 1080p stream. The SABL data rate is the rate after the analysis; the original rate was 4300 kbps. The bandwidth reduction is the percentage reduction between the original and SABL rate, with the PSNR values calculated for both the original and SABL streams.

In these 10 tests, the results are all positive (in some cases, extremely positive). For example, with the cartoon El Ultimo, Cambria dropped the bitrate by 50 percent while keeping the PSNR at 45.24 dB. This is quite a significant data rate drop with a quality delta that should be imperceptible to viewers. We see similar results in the Screencam and Tutorial clips, where 50 percent data rate reductions still left the SABL PSNR well above 45 dB. At no point did bitrate reduction push the PSNR value anywhere close to 35 dB. In the two clips where Cambria increased the data rate, the music video "Freedom" and the short *Zoolander* clip, the increase was clearly beneficial and not wasteful (i.e., it didn't push the data rate above 45 dB).

Let me reiterate that virtually all the parameters used in these tests are configurable. If I wanted to create another level at the bottom that dropped the data rate by 60 percent, I could. I could also create another level at the top, or push the data rate for existing levels higher for complex videos. You control all basic parameters so you can dial in the desired level of risk and reward.

What's the takeaway? There are several. If you're buying a new encoding tool, you should ask whether it has a similar feature, and you should consider Cambria in your selection. Second, if you have a home-grown system, you can probably programmatically duplicate what Capella Systems has done in a couple of man-days of scripting. Capella's genius wasn't in discovering a new technique, but rather deploying a known technique in a different way.

What you don't get with the Capella approach is the resolution adjustments that Netflix's approach delivers. That is, it doesn't tell you which resolution delivers the best quality at a particular data rate, which would be different for different types of content. So it wouldn't push animated content towards higher resolutions in the same way as the Netflix scheme; it would just lower the data rate at each existing resolution. Still very valuable in my opinion, and a whole lot easier to implement—just not as sophisticated and far reaching.

Category-specific Encoding

Category-specific encoding is a technique I've tried to apply twice with consulting clients. Both attempts evolved around an analysis like that shown in Table 16-5, which you saw first as Table 7-1. Basically, you take three to five samples of content from each category, and encode using a CRF value like 23. If the data rates for all samples in the content are fairly uniform, you should be able to derive a category-specific encoding ladder, either informally, like we discussed in Chapter 14, or using the workflow discussed above around Table 16-2.

CRF23	Frame Rate	Description	Data Rate	SQM	Overall PSNR	Low PSNR
Tears of Steel	24	Movie	4,485	94.28	41.71	36.96
Sintel	24	Complex animation	5,002	94.45	41.53	34.36
Big Buck Bunny	30	Simpler animation	3,375	95.91	43.64	32.62
Screencam	30	Camtasia	1,200	98.83	46.85	36.06
Tutorial	30	PowerPoint and talking head	690	97.93	47.28	41.49
Talking Head	30	Simple talking head	2,638	93.24	44.09	40.58
Freedom	30	Concert	5,467	91.56	41.87	38.63
Haunted	30	DSLR movie-like production	6,064	92.05	42.23	36.74

Table 16-5. Data rate and quality values at CRF 23 encoding.

In my experience, it's tough coming up with meaningful per-category ladders unless the content is very, very disparate. For example, the one time I successfully applied it was when the client was deploying talking-head videos, as well as screencams and PowerPoint-based videos with and without talking heads. In Table 16-5, you see the data rate of the Talking Head video was about 2.6 Mbps—still pretty efficient, but much higher than the Camtasia (1200 kbps) and PowerPoint videos (690 kbps). As long as your real-world content were limited to simple talking heads (rather than a broad range of low- and high-motion content) you likely would be able to create three different categories with very meaningful differences in the encoding ladder.

For example, with many Camtasia-based videos, you can get excellent quality at configurations like 720p@200 kbps, which are way too low for real-world videos. Ditto for PowerPoint-based videos, which have sharp edges that noticeably degrade at lower resolutions. Not only would you want different data rate maximums, but significantly different resolutions at each step in the encoding ladder.

Again, where per-category didn't work was where I was trying to create categories for animations, movies, and adult content. You can see this in Table 16-5, where one animation, Big Buck Bunny, encoded at 3375 kbps, while another, Sintel, encoded at 5002 kbps at roughly the same quality level. While some romantic comedies or dramas might encode just fine at a maximum of 3500 kbps or so, action movies might need up to 6 Mbps or even higher for similar quality. Sure you can expend the last of categories, but then the solution starts to get ungainly.

Ad Hoc Per-title Encoding

Of course, you could easily combine the CRF approach with the encoding ladder approach deployed by Capella Systems. Basically, you would create a generic encoding ladder like that discussed in Chapters 14 and 15, perhaps much like that shown in Table 15-1.

Then come up with your own adjustment method that operates similarly to how Cambria performs. For example, in the script shown in Figure 16-4, the encoder adjusts the existing encoding ladder according to the following formula. Again, in the Cambria system, these numbers are totally configurable; these numbers are simply the ones that I used for testing. A simpler way to apply this is would be to create several encoding ladders, and then slot each video into the respective ladder based upon the results of your CRF encode.

Compared with Cambria, this approach doesn't isolate the impact on difficult-to-encode sections of the video, so high-motion areas might suffer. Of course, you can assess this in the Moscow State University Video Quality Measurement Tool (VQMT) by identifying and viewing the lowest-quality frames in the video.

Data Rate	Adjustment
Over 7000	1.5
From 5000 to 6999	1.25
From 4000 to 4999	1
From 3500 to 3999	0.9
From 3000 to 3499	0.8
From 2500 to 2999	0.7
From 2000 to 2499	0.6
Below 2000	0.5

Table 16-6. Adjustments for ad hoc per-title encoding.

Here the workflow would be:

1. Create your encoding ladder.

2. For each video, run a CRF encode at a value of 19 (high quality) to 23 (very good quality) to assess the encoding complexity of each video.

3. Adjust the encoding ladder as shown in Table 16-6, or by slotting it into one of several pre-existing encoding ladders.

4. Encode the video using your normal techniques, and then run the output through VQMT to identify the average PSNR value, and to view the lowest-quality frames. If the average PSNR is over 40, and there are no particularly ugly frames, you're good to go.

5. If either overall or lowest-quality frames don't pass muster, re-encode at a higher level and re-evaluate.

To implement this, you're encoding at least twice, and analyzing each output file, which is time-consuming. However, particularly if you're dealing with repetitive types of content, I'm sure patterns will become obvious and you should be able to reduce the amount of analysis without sacrificing the quality of your files.

Capped CRF Encoding

Capped CRF encoding is a bitrate control method you can use with x264, x265, and VP9. We covered it briefly in Chapter 12. Basically, capped CRF works the way it sounds. You set a CRF level to control target quality, but also a cap to make sure that the data rate doesn't exceed a specified level. In this fashion, every encode is a per-title encode, because the data rate automatically adjusts to the content.

For example, I used the following command line argument to encode the test file discussed at the end of Chapter 8, where we looked at the impact of CBR and VBR on file deliverability. To recount, the test file is eight minutes long and contains two alternating 30-second clips: one a talking head shot, the other a ballet sequence.

```
ffmpeg -i Test_1080p.mp4 -vcodec libx264 -crf 23 -g 60 -keyint_min 60
-sc_threshold 0 -refs 5 -bf 3 -b_strategy 2 -maxrate 4500k -bufsize
4500k Test_1080p_CCRF19_final.mp4
```

Here's an explanation for the components relevant to capped CRF.

-crf 23 sets the CRF level.

-maxrate 4500k sets the maximum rate for the file.

-bufsize 4500k sets the buffer size.

Just for comparison purposes, I encoded the same file using this two-pass script which deploys most of the lessons and encoding decisions learned in this book, including 110 percent constrained VBR.

```
ffmpeg -y -i Test_1080p.mp4 -c:v libx264 -g 60 -keyint_min 60
-sc_threshold 0 -refs 5 -bf 3 -b_strategy 2 -b:v 4500k -pass 1
-f mp4 NUL && \

ffmpeg -i Test_1080p.mp4 -c:v libx264 -g 60 -keyint_min 60
-sc_threshold 0 -refs 5 -bf 3 -b_strategy 2 -b:v 4500k
-maxrate 4950k -bufsize 4500k -pass 2 Test_1080p_110pCVBR_f.mp4
```

Let's look at both files in Bitrate Viewer. Figure 16-5 shows the capped CRF file, and Figure 16-6 shows the 110 percent constrained VBR file.

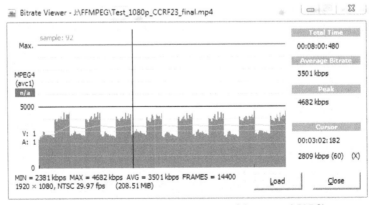

Figure 16-5. Note the irregular data rate of the capped CRF file.

As you can see in Figure 16-5, the data rate follows the encoding complexity of the file, with the talking-head sequences around 2.5 Mbps, and the ballet sections peaking at about the desired 4.5 Mbps. The average data rate of the capped CRF file is 3501 kbps, a savings of about 1 Mbps over the file shown in Figure 16-6. Despite this data rate savings, the capped CRF file trailed by only half a dB in PSNR tests, scoring 40.50 compared to 40.96 for the constrained VBR file.

However, as we learned back in Chapter 8, data rate irregularities can degrade file deliverability of the file, and you can see that the data rate of the 110 percent constrained VBR file is much smoother (Figure 16-6). Of course, the irregularities in the capped CRF file will be offset to some degree by the generally lower data rate. That is, video with an average data rate of 3501 kbps is easier to deliver than video with a data rate of 4481 kbps. In addition, keep in mind that the test file shown in the two figures is a worst-case file; most files show much less variability in encoding complexity.

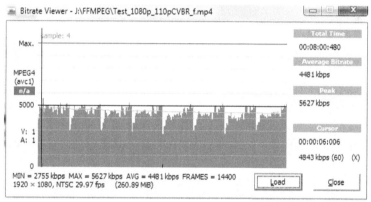

Figure 16-6. The data rate for 110 percent constrained VBR is much smoother, but it's also about 1 Mbps higher on average.

Note that JW Player uses capped CRF for its online video platform for both VP9 and x264. This is a technically savvy group that wouldn't use this encoding technique if it seriously degraded delivery performance. In some applications, like video delivered internally on corporate networks, capped CRF is a natural, since it reduces overall bandwidth in an environment where data spikes aren't an issue. Capped CRF also works well with videos that have generally low data rates anyway, like talking-head videos, or synthetic videos created from screencams or PowerPoint.

If you use capped CRF, remember that you still need to include the normal key frame, B-frame, and reference frame configurations. For some strange reason, capped CRF seems to go haywire if you don't. For example, Figure 16-7 shows two files encoded with capped CRF. The blue file was encoded using CRF 19, but without regular key frames or B-frames. The red file was encoded using CRF 23, with the argument shown earlier.

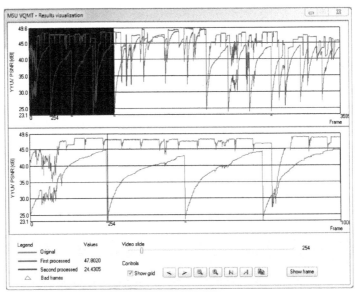

Figure 16-7. Capped CRF without regular key frames seems to go crazy.

The results visualization screen shows PSNR comparisons. Remember that lower CRF values supposedly delivery higher PSNR values, so it's strange that red (CRF 23) is generally higher than blue (CRF 19). What's even worse is how crazy low the blue numbers get at various points in the video file. While the red results drop some as well, it's nowhere near as often, and nowhere near as low.

Quick Summary: Capped CRF

1. Capped CRF encodes at a specific quality level, but also caps the data rate.

2. A CRF value of 21 to 23 is a good starting point.

3. When encoding with capped CRF, you still need the normal frame controls for key frames, B-frames, and reference frames.

4. The biggest concern with capped CRF is the irregular data rate that it produces, which may cause deliverability issues with some files.

So that's it—all the video encoding knowledge in my head, now in yours. Good luck with all this and drop me a line at <u>streaminglearningcenter.com</u> to let me know how you get along.

Index

CPSIA information can be obtained
at www.ICGtesting.com
Printed in the USA
BVOW10s0031120117
473169BV00003BB/3/P

9 780998 453002